HERITAGE FROM MENDEL

edited by R. ALEXANDER BRINK,
with the assistance of E. DEREK STYLES

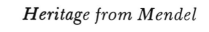

Heritage from Mendel

Proceedings of the
Mendel Centennial Symposium
Sponsored by the
Genetics Society of America

1965

Heritage from Mendel

Edited by

R. ALEXANDER BRINK

with the assistance of

E. DEREK STYLES

The University of Wisconsin Press

Madison, Milwaukee, and London, 1967

Published by

THE UNIVERSITY OF WISCONSIN PRESS

Madison, Milwaukee, and London

U.S.A.: Box 1379, Madison, Wisconsin 53701

U.K.: 26–28 Hallam Street, London, W. I

Copyright © 1967 by the

Regents of the University of Wisconsin

Printed in the United States of America

by the George Banta Company, Inc., Menasha, Wisconsin

Library of Congress Catalog Card Number 67–11059

Contributors

Charlotte Auerbach
Institute of Animal Genetics, Edinburgh, Scotland

George W. Beadle
President, University of Chicago, Chicago, Illinois

W. Beermann
Max-Planck-Institut für Biologie, Tübingen, Germany

Gérard Buttin
Service de Genetique microbienne, Institut Pasteur, Paris, France

Hampton L. Carson
Department of Zoology, Washington University, St. Louis, Missouri

L. L. Cavalli-Sforza
International Laboratory of Genetics and Biophysics, Pavia Section, Instituto di Genetica, Universita di Pavia, Pavia, Italy

James F. Crow
Genetics Laboratory, University of Wisconsin, Madison, Wisconsin

M. Delbrück
Division of Biology, California Institute of Technology, Pasadena, California

M. Demerec (*deceased*)
Division of Biology, Brookhaven National Laboratory, Upton, New York

J. B. Gurdon
Department of Zoology, Oxford University, Oxford, England

Ernst Hadorn
Zoologisches Institut, Universität-Zürich, Zürich, Switzerland

Gesa Heller
Max-Planck-Institut für Experimentelle Medizin, Göttingen, Germany

François Jacob
Service de Genetique microbienne, Institut Pasteur, Paris, France

H. Kihara
National Institute of Genetics, Misima, Sizuoka-ken, Japan

Horst Kleinkauf
Botanisches Institut der Technischen Hochschule, Braunschweig, Germany

E. B. Lewis
Division of Biology, California Institute of Technology, Pasadena, California

Heinrich Matthaei
Max-Planck-Institut für Experimentelle Medizin, Göttingen, Germany

Helga Matthaei
Max-Planck-Institut für Experimentelle Medizin, Göttingen, Germany

Matthew Meselson
The Biological Laboratories, Harvard University, Cambridge, Massachusetts

Jacques Monod
Service de Biochemie cellulaire, Institut Pasteur, Paris, France

H. J. Muller
Distinguished Service Professor of Zoology, Emeritus, Indiana University, Bloomington, Indiana; Visiting Professor, University of Wisconsin, Madison, Wisconsin

C. P. Oliver
Department of Zoology, University of Texas, Austin, Texas

Alan Robertson
Institute of Animal Genetics, Edinburgh, Scotland

T. M. Sonneborn
Department of Zoology, Indiana University, Bloomington, Indiana

A. H. Sturtevant
Division of Biology, California Institute of Technology, Pasadena, California

K. Tsunewaki
National Institute of Genetics, Misima, Sizuoka-ken, Japan

Hans-Peter Voigt
Max-Planck-Institut für Experimentelle Medizin, Göttingen, Germany

Sewall Wright
Genetics Laboratory, University of Wisconsin, Madison, Wisconsin

Foreword

The Mendel Centennial Symposium was held in conjunction with the annual meeting of the Genetics Society of America at the Colorado State University, Fort Collins, from September 7 to 11, 1965. The local arrangements were made by a committee composed of David Pettus (Chairman), G. H. Fechner, R. L. Foskett, J. E. Ogg, T. McN. Sutherland, C. E. Townsend, J. S. Williams, and D. R. Wood. We are indebted to this committee and to the Colorado State University for making the centennial, and hence this volume, possible by providing excellent physical facilities, the assistance of many people, and a fine atmosphere of congeniality and cordiality.

The idea of holding a Mendel Centennial in 1965 was initiated in 1962 by a group of geneticists, led by David Pettus, at the Colorado State University. In response to their request that the Genetics Society of America sponsor a centennial meeting, R. D. Owen, then President of the society, appointed a committee consisting of R. A. Brink, David Pettus, M. M. Rhoades, Jack Schultz, A. H. Sturtevant, and R. P. Wagner. This committee, under the chairmanship of Professor Brink, organized the Mendel Centennial Symposium program. The Executive Committee of the Genetics Society made application to the National Science Foundation for the funds necessary to pay the expenses of speakers coming from abroad and for assistance in editing the manuscripts constituting these proceedings. The application was approved, and we wish to express our appreciation to the National Science Foundation for this assistance.

We would also like to thank the presiding officers of the evening sessions of the Mendel Centennial observance, W. L. Russell (then President of the Genetics Society of America), G. F. Sprague, G. L. Stebbins, and A. G. Steinberg.

The Editor has asked that acknowledgment also be made to Dr. Nancy Ziebur for assistance with the page proof and the index.

ROBERT P. WAGNER
Secretary, Genetics Society of America

Preface

We can now perceive, after one hundred years, the full impact on biology of Mendel's experiments on heredity in peas. The central concept around which genetics has developed is the gene. It embodies the key principle Mendel first discovered, namely, that the hereditary substance is discrete and particulate, and can be symbolized algebraically. This incisive generalization, and the widely applicable experimental procedures used in establishing it, were Mendel's primary contributions to science. They mark the beginning of hereditary analysis, and represent an inflection point in the development of biology.

Only as genetics progressed toward maturity and became integrated with related fields, however, did the magnitude of our debt to Mendel become apparent. The gene theory was extensively elaborated and refined during the half century following the rediscovery of Mendel's findings. A turning point was reached when effective contact was made with biochemistry. The science broke through its original boundaries and moved into areas that permitted much higher resolution of the genetic material. Its parameters multiplied accordingly. A climax was reached with a description of the gene in molecular terms. This revolutionary advancement provided the basis for an evolving new biology, and has made genetics an extraordinarily instructive form of inquiry, penetrating to the core of life itself.

The diversity of subjects treated in this book reflects the wide range spanned by genetics. The chapters illustrate the progress made in several, but not all, the principal branches of the field. Omission of some important topics and the varying treatments by the several authors of the subjects presented may partially obscure the image of genetics as a coherent body of biological doctrine. Yet genetics has evolved in a unified way. The remarkable degree to which the now highly developed science is based on Mendel's theory of hereditary units is evident in all the chapters in which history of the topic is recounted. Continuity with basic earlier ideas is apparent even with such a radical concept as the Watson and Crick model of the gene. The gene, as the counterpart of Mendel's segregating factor, is still the functional unit in heredity. Molecular genetics has not altered the focus of the science, but has greatly increased the magnification, as it were, at which the gene can be studied.

It is appropriate that we remind ourselves of Mendel's unique place in genetics amid the welter of new developments from our burgeoning science. The essays in this volume are presented in commemoration of the hundreth anniversary of Mendel's announcement to the Brünn Natural History Society in 1865 of his studies on inheritance in the pea.

R. A. BRINK

Madison, Wisconsin
December, 1965

Contents

1

Resolution of the Genetic Material

1

Dogma and the Early Development of Genetics

C. P. Oliver

Mendel gave biologists the first critical experimental method for the study of heredity, yet his work remained almost unknown for a generation. The clash of new ideas with existing dogma delayed acceptance of theories now widely recognized as valid. The same tendency to follow dogma that prevailed then has occurred since, and will occur again. I propose in this opening chapter to review briefly some of the controversial issues, the resolution of which determined the pace at which genetics developed in its early years.

Studies of Heredity before 1900

When Mendel reported his results, biology had not developed to the extent that scientists could correctly appraise his conclusions. The adequacy of Mendel's experimental method, developed with the garden pea, was subsequently confirmed by similar results with beans. Mendel's data on the hawkweed, however, did not agree with his other findings. It was not learned until many years later that nonconformity in this case was the result of apomictic reproduction. Mendel was largely unknown among both professional biologists and plant hybridizers. The latter had their dogmas, methods, and procedures, and were convinced that they had the correct approach to the study of heredity. Before the rediscovery of Mendel's laws, heredity appeared to many biologists to be fortuitous and to defy accurate analysis. Darwin was among those who felt acutely the lack of knowledge in this area. His theory of pangenesis was a provisional attempt at an explanation of heredity and was one of several that were discarded later.

Mendel's Law of Segregation

Three botanists, de Vries, Correns, and Tschermak, working independently, conducted experiments that led them, in 1900, to conclusions identical with those of Mendel, to whom credit was given for his earlier discoveries. Mendel's most significant conclusion was that during germ cell formation in a hybrid the discrete and unmodified members of a pair of hereditary factors segregate from each other.

Early Mendelists supposed that there was regularly a one-to-one relationship between genetic factors and their associated characters. Each character was considered to be unitary in inheritance. A pair of alternative characters was thought to be determined by a corresponding pair of genes. This conclusion developed into a dogma, which had to be abandoned later because it was found not to be consistent with breeding data. Bateson and Punnett, for example, observed that rose comb in the fowl behaved as an alternative to single comb. Furthermore, pea comb also acted as an alternative to single. Yet rose did not behave as an alternative to pea; a different phenotype, termed walnut, characterized this heterozygote. An interpretation (see Punnett 1911) eventually was brought forward that reconciled Mendel's concept of alternative factors with the breeding evidence. All fowls were considered to carry the gene S for single comb. Rose comb individuals also carried R, a dominant factor replacing the r of single comb birds. Thus the formulas arrived at were $R\ R\ P\ P\ S\ S$ for walnut, $R\ R\ p\ p\ S\ S$ for rose, $r\ r\ P\ P\ S\ S$ for pea, and $r\ r\ p\ p\ S\ S$ for single comb. However, with the demonstration that the ordinary dihybrid ratio could be modified to 9:7 in the case of flower color in certain plants and that laboratory mammals heterozygous for two pairs of factors could give offspring in the ratio of 9 agouti, 3 black, and 4 albino, it became apparent that phenotypes frequently resulted from gene interactions. Another prevailing dogma of the time was Bateson's presence-absence theory, according to which, for example, all colored mammals were assumed to carry the gene B, for black. The expression of B was supposed to depend upon the presence or absence in the genome of various modifying genes. The presence-absence theory was an extraordinarily persistent idea. The discovery of gene interactions was one of the early developments that demonstrated its inadequacy.

Genes and Chromosomes

The foundations of nuclear cytology were laid in the quarter century prior to 1900. By 1904 investigators, including Boveri (1904) and Sutton (1903), began to call attention to the parallelism between chromosome behavior and gene segregation. Bateson, however, opposed the idea that chromosome reduction in meiosis was associated directly with gene segregation. Proof of the chromosome theory of heredity awaited experiments by Bridges (1916) on nondisjunction of the X chromosome in *Drosophila melanogaster*. Meanwhile the fact that organisms had more pairs of alternative characters than they had chromosomes appeared to be in direct conflict with the accepted law of independent assortment.

Independent Assortment and Linkage

Independent assortment of genes, a postulate that Mendel first set forth, became so strongly entrenched in the thinking of early geneticists that there was reluctance to give it up in the face of later evidence showing that more than one gene is carried by a chromosome and that exchange of material takes place between chromosomes. Bateson and Punnett described the first well-documented exception to independent assortment. They found a higher than expected proportion of offspring which showed the parental forms and a lower than expected proportion of recombinants within a population of sweet peas segregating for two pairs of factors. According to their theory of coupling and repulsion, genes might attract or repel each other preferentially during germ cell formation, thus distorting the gametic ratio. Bateson (1909) later referred to the difficulty of accounting for the phenomenon in terms of a system of strictly symmetrical cell division. He suggested that, following the assortment of linked alleles in the dihybrid case, two of the resulting classes of germ cells multiplied more rapidly than the two complementary classes.

A simpler explanation of linkage was proposed by Morgan (1911) who had described the "sex-limited" inheritance of white eye in *Drosophila melanogaster* a year earlier. On the basis of studies with a number of sex-linked mutants, Morgan offered the explanation that genes are linked as a result of being carried by the same chromosome, and that genes lying close together in a chromosome would be coupled more frequently than those more distant from each other. Recognition that chiasmata are formed during the synapsis of homologous chromosomes and that they could be associated with the exchange of chromosome parts gave support to this idea. Sturtevant (1913) argued that if Morgan's explanation was correct, it should be possible to map the genes in linear order using recombination frequency as an index of relative position in the chromosome. He verified the prediction by the construction of a chromosome map of the sex-linked genes then known in *D. melanogaster*.

Stern (1931) and Creighton and McClintock (1931) presented convincing evidence that genic crossing over is associated with interchange between homologous chromosomes. Later, Painter (1933, 1934*a,b*) described another method of studying gene order in *Drosophila*, using the giant chromosomes in larval salivary gland nuclei, and mapped the position of various genes and inversions in the X chromosome. This method came to be widely used in studies of the relations between genes and chromosomes.

Integrity of the Gene

Forty years ago most geneticists believed the gene was the smallest unit of heredity and indivisible. Little was then known, however, about the gene. Series of multiple alleles, usually having similar, but not identical, effects on the organism had been observed in several species. A satisfactory explanation was not at hand. According to a commonly held view, expressed in a textbook by Babcock and Clausen (1927) in use at that time, allelomorphic factors occupied identical positions in homologous chromosomes and could not be obtained together in the same chromosome.

The peculiar behavior in mutation of the bar-eyed character in *D. melanogaster* proved significant in the study of gene integrity. Zeleny (1921) reported that bar mutated to wild type with high frequency and also with a lower frequency to ultrabar, an extreme reduction in eye size. Sturtevant (1925), using marker genes on each side of the bar locus, showed that mutations of bar to normal and to double bar were associated with crossing over. He postulated that the crossing over was unequal, with the result that one chromosome gained, and the other lost, genetic material. Bridges (1936) later verified this interpretation by the use of salivary gland chromosomes. Bar-eye flies were found to possess a particular set of bands in duplicate, as compared with normal individuals, whereas three sets of bands in tandem were present in double-bar flies.

Two conclusions drawn by Sturtevant were of special importance for the development of genetic theory. The first was that crossing over between homologous chromosomes does not always involve exchange of equal amounts of genetic material. Of still greater influence on the subsequent thinking of geneticists was Sturtevant's demonstration that two bar genes positioned in sequence on one chromosome of a pair $(BB/+)$ have a different phenotypic effect from that of two bar genes carried on homologous chromosomes (B/B). The action of this gene, therefore, is a function of both constitution and position relative to other genes.

Oliver (1940) then showed that crossing over can occur between genes conventionally considered to be multiple alleles. Spectacle eye (lz^s) and glossy eye (lz^g) are alleles of lozenge. Both are recessive to wild type. The phenotype is mutant in lz^s/lz^g heterozygotes, as expected for most multiple allelic series. Oliver used a stock carrying identical inversions, so that regular crossing over could be studied. Among the progeny of

lz^s/lz^g heterozygotes carrying marker genes bracketing the lz region, reversions to wild-type flies occurred with a frequency of about 0.2 per cent. Such reversions were regularly associated with recombination between the marker genes. Each reversion to wild type, with one exception, was shown to have received the right portion of the chromosome which had carried the glossy allele and the left end of the spectacle-bearing chromosome. The complementary crossover type did not appear. Oliver (1941) and later Oliver and Green (1944) concluded that crossing over between two alleles had been demonstrated. Salivary gland chromosome studies gave no evidence that the crossing over associated with the wild-type reversions was irregular. In accordance with prevailing opinions about the relationship between alleles, however, the possibility in this instance of unequal crossing over, as discovered by Sturtevant (1925), or of "repeats," as reported by Bridges (1938), was kept in mind. Subsequently Green and Green (1949) reported crossing over between other lozenge alleles and determined the relative positions of these alleles in the cluster. In a heterozygote carrying a chromosome of wild-type origin and its two recessive alleles on the homologous chromosome, the phenotype is normal. Lewis (1942, 1945) obtained similar results with the star and asteroid mutants in *D. melanogaster*. Later Lewis (1951) reported the position effects associated with several series of multiple alleles and discussed the functional relationship of gene clusters.

Many examples of this phenomenon are now known in higher organisms. Similar relationships have been described more recently in bacteriophage. Benzer (1955) showed that a particular class of mutants, termed rII, in T4 bacteriophage was located in a small portion of the phage linkage map. The mutants were separable into two functionally distinguishable groups, located in adjoining segments. Benzer related his results on genetic fine structure to the DNA nature of the hereditary substance. These findings can, of course, be interpreted in the light of modern genetic dogma, but consideration of current concepts is beyond the scope of this chapter.

Artificial Induction of Mutations

For a long period the only materials available for the study of genetic variability were the results of spontaneously occurring mutations. New variations were difficult to acquire because the natural rate of mutation is very low. The opinion was expressed that, because of this limitation, genetics had reached a plateau and might even become a dying science. It was recognized that a method was needed to increase the frequency of mutations by artificial means. Experiments were made with irradiations, temperature shocks, and various other external agents. Probably some mutations were induced by these procedures, but the genetic techniques applied were inadequate to prove it. Either the results were unconvincing statistically or proper allowance was not made for possible mutants pre-existing in the stocks used.

Using special genetic procedures, Muller (1927a,b) proved that mutations could be induced in *D. melanogaster* at a frequency many times higher than the spontaneous rate. The new mutants included morphological variants, lethals which killed the fly before sexual maturity, and also chromosomal rearrangements. Some of the artificially induced mutations were indistinguishable from variants already known. Others yielded new phenotypes but behaved genetically like spontaneous mutations. The simple, but ingenious experimental techniques used were an important factor in Muller's success. Similar procedures have been used extensively in studies of the effect of irradiational dosage, treatment distribution, and the like, on mutation frequency.

Stadler (1928), working with plants, corroborated Muller's findings with *Drosophila* that X-rays are mutagenic. In later studies he gave special attention to the comparability (or lack of it in the case of maize: Stadler 1941) of spontaneous and induced mutations. Other investigators have subsequently shown that certain other irradiations are mutagenic, as are numerous chemicals also.

Artificial mutagenesis has become a valuable tool. Procedures for increasing mutation frequency have been developed for all the classes of organisms used in genetic investigations. By the use of induced mutations in *Neurospora* Beadle and Tatum (1941) showed that genes function primarily in the production of enzymes. Their studies marked the beginning of a vast expansion in biochemical genetics, from which have developed methods for the molecular analysis of genetic phenomena. The artificial induction of mutations as an experimental technique has stood the test of time. Only the nature of the induced changes continues to be the subject of controversy.

No attempt has been made in this brief discussion to consider the early work on developmental genetics, of which Wright's (1917) pioneer study on the determination of coat color in mammals is an example. We have much to learn about the relationship between genes and the control of developmental processes and about genes in relation to chromosome organization, as Stadler (1954) emphasized over a decade ago. Cellular differentiation within the individual still defies a satisfying analysis. We are awaiting an effective experimental method for its study, just as biologists at the turn of the last century were awaiting an appropriate method for the study of heredity. Eventually the right man will choose a suitable organism and an appropriate technique and, regardless of prevailing dogma, will open the narrow pathway to new insights.

Literature Cited

BABCOCK, E. B., AND R. E. CLAUSEN, 1927. *Genetics in Relation to Agriculture,* 2nd ed. McGraw-Hill Co., New York.

BATESON, W., 1909. *Mendel's Principles of Heredity.* Cambridge Univ. Press, London.

BEADLE, G. W., AND E. L. TATUM, 1941. Genetic control of biochemical reactions in *Neurospora.* Proc. Nat. Acad. Sci. U.S. 27: 499–506.

BENZER, S., 1955. Fine structure of a genetic region in bacteriophage. Proc. Nat. Acad. Sci. U.S. 41: 344–354.

BOVERI, T., 1904. *Ergebnisse über die Konstitution der chromatischen Kernsubstanz.* Fischer, Jena.

BRIDGES, C. B., 1916. Non-disjunction as proof of the chromosome theory of heredity. I. Genetics 1: 1–52; II. Genetics 1: 107–163.

———, 1936. The bar "gene," a duplication. Science 83: 210–211.

———, 1938. A revised map of the salivary gland X-chromosome of *Drosophila melanogaster.* J. Hered. 29: 11–13.

CREIGHTON, H. B., AND B. McCLINTOCK, 1931. A correlation of cytological and genetical crossing-over in *Zea mays.* Proc. Nat. Acad. Sci. U.S. 17: 492–497.

GREEN, M. M., AND K. C. GREEN, 1949. Crossing-over between alleles at the lozenge locus in *Drosophila melanogaster.* Proc. Nat. Acad. Sci. U.S. 35: 586–591.

LEWIS, E. B., 1942. The star and asteroid loci in *Drosophila melanogaster.* Genetics 27: 153–154.

———, 1945. The relation of repeats to position effects in *Drosophila melanogaster.* Genetics 30: 137–166.

———, 1951. Pseudoallelism and gene evolution. Cold Spring Harbor Symp. Quant. Biol. 16: 159–174.

MORGAN, T. H., 1911. Random segregation versus coupling in Mendelian inheritance. Science 34: 384.

MULLER, H. J., 1927a. Artificial transmutation of the gene. Science 66: 84–87.

———, 1927b. The problem of genic modification. Verhandl. V Int. Kongr. Vererbungswiss.: 234–260.

OLIVER, C. P., 1940. A reversion to wild-type associated with crossing-over in *Drosophila melanogaster.* Proc. Nat. Acad. Sci. U.S. 26: 452–454.

———, 1941. Crossing over between two alleles of lozenge in *Drosophila melanogaster.* Genetics 26: 163.

OLIVER, C. P., AND M. M. GREEN, 1944. Heterosis in compounds of lozenge alleles in *Drosophila melanogaster.* Genetics 29: 331–347.

PAINTER, T. S., 1933. A new method for the study of chromosome rearrangements and plotting of chromosome maps. Science 78: 585–586.

———, 1934a. A new method for the study of chromosome aberrations and the plotting of chromosome maps in *Drosophila melanogaster*. Genetics **19**: 175–188.

———, 1934b. The morphology of the X-chromosome in salivary glands of *Drosophila melanogaster* and a new type of chromosome map for this element. Genetics **19**: 448–469.

PUNNETT, R. C., 1911. *Mendelism*. 3rd ed. Macmillan Co., New York.

STADLER, L. J., 1928. Mutations in barley induced by X-rays and radium. Science **68**: 186.

———, 1941. The comparison of ultraviolet and X-ray effects on mutation. Cold Spring Harbor Symp. Quant. Biol. **9**: 168–177.

———, 1954. The gene. Science **120**: 811–819.

STERN, C., 1931. Zytologisch-genetische Untersuchungen als Beweise für die Morgansche Theorie des Faktorenaustausches. Biol. Zentralbl. **51**: 547–587.

STURTEVANT, A. H., 1913. The linear arrangement of six sex-linked factors in *Drosophila*, as shown by their mode of association. J. Exp. Zool. **14**: 43–59.

———, 1925. The effects of unequal crossing-over at the bar locus in *Drosophila*. Genetics **10**: 117–147.

SUTTON, W. S., 1903. The chromosomes in heredity. Biol. Bull. **4**: 231–251.

WRIGHT, S., 1917. Color inheritance in mammals. J. Hered. **8**: 224–235.

ZELENY, C., 1921. The direction and frequency of mutation in the bar-eye series of multiple allelomorphs of *Drosophila*. J. Exp. Zool. **34**: 203–233.

2

Mendel and the Gene Theory

A. H. Sturtevant

The quantitative, experimental, analytical approach to the study of heredity was new in Mendel's time, although it already existed in physiology—after all, Helmholtz was a contemporary. It is interesting that Mendel was born in the same year as Pasteur and Galton, of whom the former was an experimentalist and reached a particulate interpretation of infectious diseases, while the latter applied quantitative methods to the study of heredity and also (Galton 1889) expressed a particulate interpretation of the nature of the hereditary material.

Mendel's own combination of methods may be attributed in part to his training at Vienna. He studied physics under Doppler and Ettinghausen, and presumably derived from them his quantitative and experimental point of view. He studied botany under Unger, from whom he evidently came to an understanding of the essential facts of fertilization which was in advance of the views of his contemporary, Darwin, and was part of the necessary background for his theoretical developments. Finally, he studied chemistry under Redtenbacher, who was apparently a student of Liebig. There is at least one joint paper by Liebig and Redtenbacher. One may surmise that this was a source of Mendel's particulate interpretation, for he must have been exposed not only to the atomic interpretation of matter but also to Liebig's ideas about organic radicals as semi-permanent substitutable building-blocks.

It had long been known that the characters of organisms can be shuffled and recombined—even casual observations of human hair color, eye color, stature, etc., make this obvious—and several of the earlier plant hybridizers had emphasized the point in discussions of hybrids. Some of them had also understood that increased variability and recombination of characters appears first in the F_2 generation. However, this was thought of as recombination of characters, not of discrete germinal elements.

The usual interpretation of heredity involved some form of the idea of a mixing of fluids at fertilization, as supposed, for example, by Aristotle and by Kölreuter. On that theory the contributions from remote ancestors were gradually and regularly diluted in successive generations, but could still come to expression in occasional individuals. Such belated expression, under the name of "reversion," was what was usually emphasized in discussing cases that we should now attribute to segregation and recombination—as will be apparent if one reads the discussions by Darwin or his predecessors and immediate followers.

Mendel usually used the word "Merkmal" ("character") in referring both to the phenotypes of his plants and to the composition of their gametes. I have found no clear distinction in his paper between the character as such and the hereditary element responsible for it. Nevertheless, a distinction is strongly implied by the formulae used, by his insistence on the essential phenotypic identity of the homozygous dominant and the heterozygote, and by the discussion of independent assortment. Especially to be noted is his suggestion that the presence of color in the flowers of his *Phaseolus* hybrids might be due to *either* of two independently segregating dominant genes. Here he was clearly thinking in terms of separable elements, rather than of visible characters—a point of view that was not widely understood until several years after 1900.

Darwin's (1868) "provisional hypothesis" of pangenesis involved particles ("gemmules") that were the hereditary agents. This hypothesis, never widely accepted, was the forerunner of the particulate theories of Weismann, Galton, de Vries, and others that were developed before 1900.

The development of knowledge about the chromosomes in the 1880's provided an observational basis for particulate theories of heredity. The most widely known and discussed scheme of the period was that of Weismann (1891–92). Weismann made very real and important contributions, but in his speculations about chromosomes he went wrong. He concluded that each chromosome is essentially like every other one in the same organism, and that each carries all the essential hereditary material for producing a whole organism. Following Roux (1883), he supposed that each chromosome was made up of a linear series of diverse hereditary elements (the cytologically visible chromomeres). He also supposed that each chromosome was a unit, transmitted unchanged from generation to generation. Since the different chromosomes of an individual might come ultimately from numerous different ancestors, they might differ somewhat among themselves in the nature of the contained elements. On this basis he built up an elaborate theory of development and inheritance, which involved a complicated hierarchy of imagined hereditary units and subunits of several degrees.

One of the most remarkable discussions of the particulate interpretation in this period is that of Francis Galton (1889). Here is a very explicit statement that inheritance depends on a multitude of discrete units which are capable of separate transmission, and that the number transmitted by an egg or a sperm must, on the average, be half of that possessed by the individual that produced it. This conclusion was applied to characters that appear to blend (which Galton thought of as intimate mosaics) as well as to alternative characters such as eye color. One must regret that Galton at this period was not familiar with Mendel's paper, for his statistical type of mind, combined with these views, would surely have led him to appreciate it.

In the same year appeared de Vries' (1889) *Intracelluläre Pangenesis*. As pointed out by Heimans (1962), this small book contains the first clear statement of the view that the hereditary elements ("pangenes") remain in the nucleus and only indirectly condition the characters of the individual. The older views had at least implied that these units somehow developed directly into the characters. It was in this respect that the theories of de Vries at this time differed most markedly from those of Weismann and of Galton, but the difference was important, for it led to theories about differentiation and recombination that were much more in accord with present knowledge. It was no accident that de Vries was one of the men to understand and appreciate Mendel's paper in 1900.

The supposed essential equivalence of the separate chromosomes was called into question by Montgomery (1901) and Sutton (1902) when they demonstrated that, in some animals, the chromosomes occur in definite pairs that are distinguishable by their sizes and shapes. The final proof of their essential diversity came from the classic work of Boveri (1902) on dispermic sea-urchin eggs.

With this work the way was opened for a chromosomal interpretation of Mendelian heredity, as was suggested in 1902 by Correns, Boveri, Guyer, Cannon, and Sutton, and clearly developed by Sutton in 1903. But there was a difficulty, as recognized by Sutton and by de Vries: There must be supposed to be more Mendelian genes than there are chromosomes, and the separate pairs of genes were supposed to segregate independently. So long as a chromosome was thought to be a permanent entity, this was a fatal objection.

The view that exchange of materials between homologous chromosomes may occur was suggested by Correns in 1902 and by de Vries in 1903 but was not well received. In 1906 Lock followed this with the suggestion that such recombination might occur only occasionally and that this might be the basis for the newly discovered phenomenon of incomplete linkage. There followed the cytological work of Janssens (1909), in which he described chiasmata in the salamander *Batrachoseps* and interpreted them as arising from exchanges between paired homologous chromosomes. Not all cytologists were convinced by this evidence, but in 1910 Morgan presented convincing genetic evidence that such exchanges do occur. In 1911 Morgan discovered linkage between sex-linked genes and then utilized the ideas of Lock and of Janssens to lay down the essence of the modern chromosome theory of inheritance.

The further advances in gene theory for the next ten to fifteen years are so well known to all geneticists that their description here would be superfluous. Those that came still later will be discussed by other contributors to this volume.   . .

In summary, the development of the modern gene theory may be said to have begun with the publication of Mendel's paper a hundred years ago, in the year of the birth of T. H. Morgan.

Literature Cited

BOVERI, T., 1902. Ueber mehrpolige Mitosen als Mittel zur Analyse des Zellkerns. Verhandl. deut. Physiol. Med. Ges. zur Würzburg N.F. **35**: 67–90.

CANNON, W. A., 1902. A cytological basis for the Mendelian laws. Bull. Torrey Bot. Club **29**: 657–661.

CORRENS, C., 1902. Ueber den Modus und den Zeitpunkt der Spaltung der Anlagen bei den Bastarden vom Erbsen-Typus. Bot. Z. **60**: 66–82.

DARWIN, C., 1868. *The Variation of Animals and Plants under Domestication.* John Murray, London.

GALTON, F., 1889. *Natural Inheritance.* Macmillan and Co., London.

GUYER, M. F., 1902. Hybridism and the germ-cell. Bull. Univ. Cincinnati No. 21.

HEIMANS, J., 1962. Hugo deVries and the gene concept. Amer. Natur. **96**: 93–104.

JANSSENS, F. A., 1909. La théorie de la chiasmatypie. La Cellule **25**: 389–411.

LOCK, R. H., 1906. *Recent Progress in the Study of Variation, Heredity and Evolution.* Dutton and Co., New York.

MONTGOMERY, T. H., JR., 1901. A study of the chromosomes of the germ-cells of Metazoa. Trans. Amer. Phil. Soc. **20**: 154–236.

MORGAN, T. H., 1910. The method of inheritance of two sex-limited characters in the same animal. Proc. Soc. Exp. Biol. Med. **8**: 17–19.

———, 1911. An attempt to analyze the constitution of the chromosomes on the basis of sex-limited inheritance in *Drosophila.* J. Exp. Zool. **11**: 365–412.

ROUX, W., 1883. *Ueber die Bedeutung der Kerntheilungsfiguren.* Engelmann, Leipzig.

SUTTON, W. S., 1902. On the morphology of the chromosome group in *Brachy-stola magna*. Biol. Bull. 4: 24–39.

———, 1903. The chromosomes in heredity. Biol. Bull. 4: 231–251.

VRIES, H. DE, 1889. *Intracellulāre Pangenesis*. Fischer, Jena.

———, 1903. *Befruchtung und Bastardierung*. Veit and Co., Leipzig.

WEISMANN, A., 1891–92. *Essays on Heredity*. Translated by A. E. Shipley, S. Schönland, and others. Oxford University Press, London.

3

Genes and Gene Complexes

E. B. Lewis

This work was supported in part by a grant from the U.S. Atomic Energy Commission [AT(04-3)-41].

Mendel was ahead of his time, but he was not so far ahead that he could not arrive at the first great generalizations of genetics—his first and second laws. How fortunate that Mendel did not discover linkage, for he might then have failed to deduce the second law. How fortunate, too, that Mendel, by having chosen to work on peas, failed to discover "gene conversion," not to mention "meiotic drive," for he might then have failed to deduce even the first law.

Mendel left it for others to study the role played by the hereditary factors in development, but he did make an observation in this area that turns out to be another sound generalization not without exception. It will be recalled that five of his seven pairs of factors were functionally interrelated, in the sense of affecting the color or form of the seeds or seed pods; nevertheless, these five pairs, as well as the other two, are known to assort independently. This observation that the hereditary factors or genes are distributed throughout the genome in a more or less random fashion with respect to their function in development remains valid for many of the known genes of higher organisms. It might well be called Mendel's third law. How fortunate for Mendel that his five functionally related genes did not happen to reside in an operon!

I would like to turn now to certain exceptions to this "third law"—namely, cases in which two or more functionally related genes do lie close together in the chromosome, forming a pseudoallelic series; or, to introduce a simpler term, a "gene complex" (Brink 1932).* The term "gene cluster" is also in common use for such cases.

* The "gene complexes" of *Oenothera* have now come to be called "Renner complexes" or simply "complexes"; therefore, no confusion between this usage of the term and the present one should arise.

Gene complexes seem to be scattered here and there throughout the genome of higher organisms, and in bacteria and phages the genes may often be arranged in an almost continuous succession of such complexes. It now seems likely that the study of gene complexes will have much to tell us not only about the way in which genes control and regulate biosynthetic and developmental pathways but also about the way in which new genes arise from old ones. The existence of gene complexes, however, has added to the difficulty of developing operational criteria for defining the gene. Therefore, it may first be useful to review the present status of the gene concept.

The Gene Concept

The first operational definition of a hereditary unit was provided by Mendel's concept of a factor which assorts independently of other factors. For many years it was a satisfactory approximation to treat the gene as if it were at once a unit of mutation, a unit within which crossing over or other forms of chromosomal breakage and reunion did not occur, and a unit of function determining the production of a specific protein. The work of Benzer (1955) and of others (especially Yanofsky 1963) has shown that certain kinds of mutational and recombinational tests can resolve the gene into smaller units—the "muton" and "recon" (Benzer 1957), respectively. These smaller units not only coincide with one another but almost certainly correspond to the individual base pairs of the DNA molecule.

It still seems best to reserve "gene" for the larger functional unit. That unit is now thought of as the portion of the genetic code that carries the information needed to specify the production of a single polypeptide. This unit is sometimes called the "code-message," while "code-word" or "codon" denotes the triplet of base pairs coding for a single amino acid.

In most cases the code-message unit is thought to "transcribe," or code for the production of, an intermediate ribonucleic acid (RNA) template which is then "translated" into a polypeptide. This is the concept of the "structural gene" (Jacob and Monod 1961). Evidently, some code-message units code for RNA molecules that do not function as templates, such as the transfer RNA's. Such units have quite properly also been considered genes. In the Jacob-Monod terminology, they would constitute one type of "regulatory gene."

The relationship among some of the terms currently in use for the genetic units is summarized in Figure 3.1. The gene, or code-message unit, occupies a "locus," consists of a linear array of mutons, and exists in a number of alternative forms or "alleles." A gene complex, sometimes called a "pseudoallelic series," occupies a "region," and

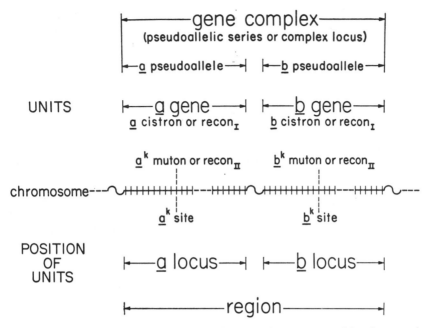

Fig. 3.1.—Diagram of some of the terms that have been proposed for the genetic units and for their location in the chromosome.

consists of a linear array of genes or "pseudoalleles." At least some of the gene complexes of microorganisms form "operons" (Jacob and Monod 1961); that is, in addition to a cluster of linked structural genes, the gene complex contains a region, or "operator," which controls the coordinate repression or de-repression of all the genes of the operon. The operator, which may be a separate region or a part of one of the structural genes, seems to be the point at which transcription of the genetic message of the operon is initiated.

We need operational methods of defining a unit that is approximately equivalent to the structural gene. Functional, recombinational, mutational, and rearrangement tests have all been used to help define such a unit. In the discussion which follows, these four tests are examined separately; however, it should be kept in mind that they are closely interrelated and no one test is likely to prove adequate for distinguishing between a gene, on the one hand, and a gene complex, on the other.

Functional tests

The cis-trans test provides a purely genetic method of defining a unit of function—the "cistron" (Benzer 1957). The cis-trans test involves comparing the phenotypes of the two possible forms of the heterozygote for two linked mutants, a and b. If the cis $(a\,b/+\,+)$ and the trans $(a\,+/+\,b)$ forms are both wild type in phenotype, then a and b fall in different cistrons, and a and b are said to "complement" each other; conversely, if the cis and trans forms differ (the trans being mutant and the cis, wild type), then a and b fall in the same cistron, or are said to fail to complement.

In many situations, the cis-trans test works well. At one extreme if a and b tend to be far apart on the genetic map and to complement, they probably are mutant alleles of two different structural genes. Or, at the other extreme, if a and b are so close that no genetic recombination is observed in many trials and if they fail to complement as well, they probably are mutant alleles of the same structural gene. A logical difficulty arises in the latter case, however, since there might in fact be two structural genes so closely linked and functionally interrelated that they behave like one. In practice such cases of gene complexes are known to occur. For an understanding of the ramifications of the cis-trans test it becomes necessary to consider the four possible relationships which can arise for the trans-heterozygote, depending upon whether there are two closely linked structural genes or only one structural gene and depending upon whether the mutants complement or not. Actually, examples of all four possible relationships have been found, and a biochemical basis for each relationship can be inferred from the known examples of its type (Fig. 3.2). For simplicity, it is assumed that in all four cases the mutants a and b complement in the cis arrangement. Often, as in all of the examples shown in Figure 3.2, the double mutant type has not yet been identified. In such cases, the cis-trans test is made without the cis-heterozygote, which is then assumed to have a wild-type phenotype.

The first type of trans-heterozygote shown in Figure 3.2 involves noncomplementing alleles (NCA). This is the classical case of multiple allelism. An example, well understood at the polypeptide level, is the trans-heterozygote for the mutant genes which determine the abnormal human hemoglobins, S and E. Blood samples from two such heterozygotes were shown by Acksoy and Lehmann (1957) to lack the normal beta chain of hemoglobin A and to contain only the S and E types of beta chains. The latter chains are known to differ from the normal beta chains in having single amino acid substitutions in the sixth and twenty-sixth positions, respectively (Hunt and Ingram 1959). Pedigree data support, but are not sufficient to establish, allelism of the mutant genes determining the S and E beta chains (Acksoy and Lehmann 1957). The requisite genetic information to construct a normal beta

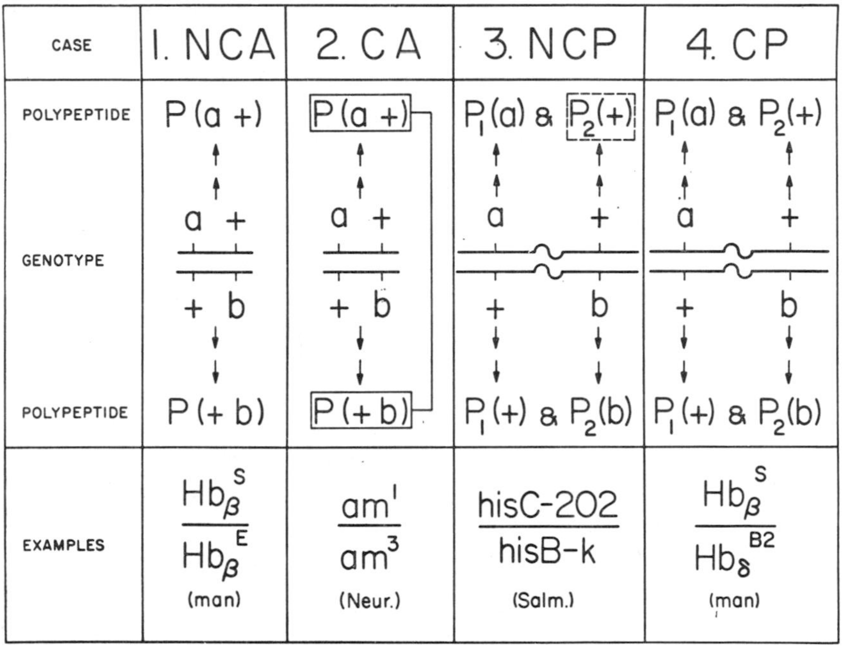

Fig. 3.2.—Diagram of four possible kinds of trans-heterozygotes for two closely linked genes, *a* and *b*, depending upon whether the genes are (1) noncomplementing alleles (*NCA*), (2) complementing alleles (*CA*), (3) noncomplementing pseudoalleles (*NCP*), or (4) complementing pseudoalleles (*CP*). The arrows signify the steps of transcription and translation which intervene between the gene and its polypeptide (*P*).

chain is available in the trans-heterozygote in the form of the wild-type, or "+," sites corresponding to the S and E mutant sites; yet in human somatic cells such + sites seem to be unable to cooperate at the DNA, RNA, or protein levels to produce normal beta chains. In this case the unit defined by the cis-trans test probably coincides with the structural gene.

The two mutants of a trans-heterozygote for complementing pseudo-alleles (*CP*) by definition occupy separate but closely linked and functionally related loci (case 4 of Fig. 3.2). Again, an example taken from the genetics of human hemoglobins well illustrates the biochemical basis of this case. A number of trans-heterozygotes have been found which have a mutant allele, usually the $Hb_\beta{}^S$ allele, of the gene determining the beta chain of the normal major hemoglobin component A_1, and a mutant allele, $Hb_\delta{}^{B2}$, of the gene determining the delta chain of the normal minor component A_2 (Ceppellini 1959; Horton and Huisman

1963; Boyer *et al.* 1963). The trans-heterozygote in this case produces four kinds of hemoglobin (A_1, A_2, S, and B_2) corresponding to the four polypeptides derived from the mutant and wild-type alleles of the two genes. In 41 opportunities no recombinants between the two loci were observed (Boyer *et al.* 1963). This result is consistent with the close linkage that would be expected between pseudoallelic genes. That the genes for the beta and delta chains form a gene complex (i.e., are functionally closely related to one another, as well as being closely linked) is made clear from amino acid sequence determinations of the corresponding polypeptides (Ingram and Stretton 1961; Baglioni 1963). Thus, the beta and delta chains are each composed of 146 amino acid residues and are identical in sequence except for about nine single amino acid differences.

The cis-trans test leads to ambiguous results in the remaining two types of trans-heterozygotes. At one extreme, in the case of complementing alleles (*CA,* case 2 of Fig. 3.2), the cistron seems to be a smaller unit than the structural gene. The basis of this once-puzzling phenomenon of intra-allelic complementation (Fincham and Pateman 1957; Giles, Partridge, and Nelson 1957; review by Catcheside and Overton 1958) has now been clarified. The structurally abnormal polypeptides produced by each allele are known to aggregate even *in vitro* and to produce a polymeric product with some wild-type activity (Woodward 1959). For example, in *Neurospora* a series of amination-deficient (*am*) mutants are known which have structural defects in the enzyme glutamate dehydrogenase (GDH). Fincham and Coddington (1963) have shown that the proteins determined by heteroallelic mutant genes, such as *am*[1] and *am*[3], react *in vitro* under suitable conditions to form active GDH. The enzyme is known in this case to be a polymer composed of possibly eight identical subunits (Barratt 1961). Evidently the active enzyme formed in the complementation reaction results from mixed aggregations of the protein subunits produced by the two complementing mutants. The CA case is exceptional in that only a protein with polymeric subunits, and not every such protein, shows the phenomenon of intra-allelic complementation.

At the other extreme, in the case of noncomplementing pseudoalleles (*NCP,* case 3 of Fig. 3.2), the cistron seems to be larger than the unit coding for a single polypeptide. This phenomenon of "position pseudoallelism" (Lewis 1955) may have more than one biochemical basis, but the one now favored for examples in phage and bacteria is based on the finding that in some gene complexes a mutant gene at one locus in the complex is able to reduce the rate of synthesis of proteins which would normally be produced by wild-type alleles of the genes lying beyond it in the same complex. Such "polarity" mutants (Jacob and Monod 1961) are believed to be of at least two kinds: (1) reading-frame shift mutants (Crick *et al.* 1961), in which the insertion or deletion of a base pair disturbs the reading of the code-message from that point on; or (2) mutants with a base-pair substitution which results in a different or "modulating" codon that is then read with reduced efficiency (Itano, cited by Ames and Hartman 1963). In either case the polarity mutant is assumed to exert its effect during translation of the RNA message into protein.

An example of the NCP case is taken from the work of Hartman, Hartman, and Šerman (1960). Mutant *hisC-202* is a point mutant of the *C* gene of the histidine operon of *Salmonella*. This polarity mutant only poorly complements mutants at the adjoining *B* locus, symbolized in Figure 3.2 as *hisB-k*. In fact, *hisC-202* only poorly complements mutants at any of the six loci (*E, I, F, A, H,* and *B*) of the *his* operon that lie to the left of *C*. Enzymatic assay of the strain with mutant *hisC-202* by Martin, Whitfield, and Ames (personal communication 1965) shows that it has only about 15 per cent of the normal amounts of the enzymes made by the *B* gene and the other genes to the left, while it has normal amounts of the enzymes made by the two genes (*D* and *G*) to the right. Failure of complementation between certain mutants at two different loci of a gene complex may therefore have its biochemical basis in the coordinate and polarized synthesis of polypeptides which possibly takes place on a single polycistronic messenger RNA.

Recombinational tests

A genetic criterion of first importance in arriving at a definition for a hereditary unit is the extent of divisibility of that unit by recombination. Mendel, of course, discovered one form of genetic recombination —independent assortment. If two factors assort independently, there is little doubt that they belong in separate units; in most such instances, they probably will even be in different chromosomes. The discovery of linkage and crossing over led to a working definition of the gene as a unit within which crossing over does not take place. The discovery of an intragenic recombinational process (Mitchell 1955), or "gene conversion," has tended to confuse the picture. As already noted, the occurrence of gene conversion has permitted resolution of the gene presumably into its ultimate subunits, the DNA base pairs. Even though intragenic recombination and crossing over may be different aspects of the same phenomenon of hybrid DNA formation followed by enzymatic excision and repair of the hybrid region, along the lines visualized by Whitehouse (1963), Holliday (1964), and Whitehouse and Hastings (1965), nevertheless these two types of recombination are operationally distinguishable to some extent.

Crossing over is characterized by reciprocality (that is, production of wild-type and double mutant recombinants simultaneously in the same tetrad from a trans-heterozygote) and by positive interference. On the other hand, intragenic recombination is characterized by nonreciprocality (recovery of either wild-type or double mutant recombinants but usually not both from the same tetrad) and by negative interference. In view of these circumstances, it seems best to proceed on the basis that there may be two types of units of recombination, $recon_I$, the smallest unit recognizable by the test of crossing over, and $recon_{II}$, the smallest unit recognized by the test of intragenic recombination. The former unit may (in higher organisms) correspond to the structural gene; the latter unit, as has already been noted, seems to correspond to the muton.

Operationally, interference may turn out to be the more useful property for distinguishing between $recon_I$ and $recon_{II}$. A critical test would involve studying the pattern of recombinational events in a heterozygote that has, ideally, several mutant alleles at each of two (or more) adjacent loci—for example, a heterozygote of the type, $a + b + / + a^2 + b^2$, where a and a^2 are mutant alleles of one gene and b and b^2 are mutant alleles of an adjacent gene. (Of course, such a heterozygote must also carry closely linked, outside-marker mutants.) Stadler, Towe, and Murray (1965) have analyzed this type of heterozygote in *Neurospora* except that they have used only one mutant allele at each of the two loci. That is, they have studied recombination in a trans-heterozygote for *cys-1* and *cys-2*, which are mutants of two different but closely linked cistrons concerned with cysteine synthesis. In this case, the observed pattern of recombination events supports the hypothesis that intragenic recombination involving one of the genes strongly interferes with intragenic recombination at the other. It may therefore turn out that interference between units of the $recon_{II}$ type will be strongly negative, whereas interference between units of the $recon_I$ type will be strongly positive.

The remarkable discovery of polarization of intragenic recombination events in *Ascobolus* has led Rizet, Lissouba, and Mousseau (1960) to postulate the existence of the "polaron," a unit within which there is polarized nonreciprocal recombination. Reciprocal recombination, by this concept, is believed to occur at the linkage structure which unites two polarons. Polarized nonreciprocal recombination has been reported in other fungi (Murray 1963; Stadler and Towe 1963). It is possible that the polaron will turn out to be equivalent to one of the larger units of the genetic code, perhaps to the gene or the gene complex.

Mutation tests

It was implicit in the preceding discussion that the mutants which are employed in cis-trans or recombinational tests represent point mutations, in the sense of their having arisen from wild type by single base-pair substitutions. Operational means of recognizing such point mutations therefore become an essential part of the analysis of the fine structure of genes.

Yanofsky and co-workers (review by Yanofsky 1963) have been remarkably successful in showing that in *Escherichia coli* certain mutant alleles of the structural gene for tryptophane synthetase cause single amino acid replacements to appear in the protein of the mutant strain. From knowledge of the genetic code (e.g., Nirenberg *et al.* 1965) it has been possible in many instances to infer that the mutant alleles responsible for such replacements probably differ from wild type by single base-pair substitutions.

In principle, certain analogs of the DNA base pairs and certain other chemical mutagens, such as nitrous acid, may be used to induce mutants which have specific kinds of single base-pair substitutions. "Forward" mutants induced in this way can be further characterized by re-treatment with chemical mutagens to induce "reverse" mutations. From the pattern of response to such mutagens, the nature of the base-pair substitution is then inferred. Although this approach has had some success with certain phages and other viruses (review by Freese 1963), much remains to be done before gene mutations in higher organisms can be induced at will and in a specified manner.

A surprising kind of operational test for characterizing at least certain kinds of base-pair substitutions has recently become available in microorganisms and may have general applicability to higher forms as well. This is the test of susceptibility of specific classes of mutant alleles of a gene to phenotypic reversal by certain suppressor genes. Such suppressor genes, which are allele-specific but not locus-specific, seem to act at the level of translation of the RNA message into protein. The best example is a suppressor strain of *E. coli* which can suppress, at least partially, the phenotype of "nonsense" mutants (Benzer and Champe 1962). Nonsense mutants are believed to result from base-pair substitution in a "sense" codon (one coding for a particular amino acid) to form a nonsense codon (one which fails to code for any amino acid). In an especially favorable case involving nonsense or "amber" mutants for the head protein of phage T4, Stretton and Brenner (1965) showed that, in strains of *E. coli* without the suppressor, the amber mutant causes synthesis of the polypeptide chains of head protein to be terminated prematurely at the point of the nonsense codon. In a strain of *E. coli* with a specific suppressor gene (*Su-1*), the amber mutant is able to make functional head protein. However, at the point where the nonsense codon of the amber mutant would normally have occurred and where the wild-type head protein carries the amino acid glutamine, the head protein of the suppressed mutant strain now carries the amino acid serine. Other examples of correction of the nonsense triplet in a suppressor strain of *E. coli* to yield serine, or other amino acids depending upon the nature of the original nonsense codon, have been reported independently by Notani *et al.* (1965) and by Weigert and Garen (1965) for mutants of bacterial enzymes. Brody and Yanofsky (1963) have described a suppressor which appears to correct the reading of a missense codon (a codon for the wrong amino acid).

It may be envisaged that the above types of suppressor mutants will be increasingly used to characterize mutant alleles of structural genes in terms of the probable kind of altered codon involved. Examples of such suppressors are known in yeast (Hawthorne and Mortimer 1960) as well as in bacteria and phage. A possible example in *Drosophila* is discussed below.

Rearrangement tests

A powerful and elegant method of resolving the genetic material involves the manipulation of chromosomal rearrangements to synthesize deficiencies and duplications for minute regions of the chromosome. This method, which is due to Muller (1935), may not permit so high a degree of resolution as do the recombinational methods already discussed; nevertheless, rearrangements can help to specify the limits of a gene or especially of a gene complex. (Indeed, Raffel and Muller [1940] employed the method to try to resolve the scute gene in *Drosophila*; whether they were successful or not is still unclear since the rearrangements they used are now known to have variegated-type position effects extending over the achaete-scute gene complex.)

In spite of the position effects which often accompany chromosomal rearrangements, there are many instances in which chromosomal breakage and reunion do not lead to detectable changes in gene action. Evidently there is some kind of punctuation between the code-message units which allows the reading of the message to be interrupted and then restarted without difficulty. That is, in addition to the main portion of the code-message unit which must be concerned with specifying an RNA molecule (be it messenger, transfer, or ribosomal RNA), and in addition to prefixes and suffixes which presumably are needed for starting and ending the reading of the message (discussed by Stretton and Brenner 1965), the chromosomes may, as many have suggested, contain "linkers" (composed perhaps of protein) which separate individual DNA molecules. Such linkers might undergo breakage and new unions without causing a disruption in the reading and translation of the essential part of the code-message unit.

In a prophetic paper, Brink (1932) proposed that the position effects which are known to accompany certain rearrangements might be explained as breakages within gene complexes:

It might be assumed that the chromosome in its essential make-up consists not of genes which are entirely distinct from each other in function but of aggregates of groups of genes which are physiologically interdependent. On this hypothesis it is supposed that propinquity of the genes within a group is essential to normal gene action. On this view translocations involving breaks between groups of genes would not alter the genotype.... If, however, the chromosome is broken in such a way as to separate the members of a gene group more or less profound changes in the physiological properties of the complex would follow.

There is an increasing amount of evidence that rearrangement processes go on within the gene and produce alterations comparable in type to some of the familiar kinds of gross rearrangements which have been detected cytologically. Evidence for intragenic rearrangements comes from a number of sources: for example, the deletion (and addition) mutants of phage genes (Benzer 1955; Crick *et al.* 1961); and the presumed translocation of a portion of one of the histidine genes of *Salmonella* to another part of the genome, accompanied by a breakdown of the histidine operon (Ames, Hartman, and Jacob 1963).

Tandem duplications either of the direct or reverse type form a class of rearrangements that have special relevance to the present discussion. Such duplications may involve groups of genes, single genes, or portions of a gene, and may arise by rare, nonhomologous exchange between sister or nonsister chromatids. The Bar duplication in *Drosophila* (Sturtevant 1925; Bridges 1936; Muller *et al.* 1936) is a typical example of the tandem direct type. Such a duplication is known to be unstable in the sense that unequal crossing over (the occurrence of homologous crossing over within unequally paired segments of the duplication) generates the original unduplicated state or the complementary triplicated state.

Peterson and Laughnan (1963) have shown that certain rare exceptional types which arise from the Bar duplication and which have lost or gained segments of that duplication are most readily interpretable as arising from intrachromosomal (sister strand) unequal crossing over. Such exceptional types are nonrecombinant with respect to end markers, and hence they mimic the multiple exchange events associated with intragenic recombination.

It seems likely that gene complexes may often represent instances in which tandem gene duplications or higher repetitions have become established in a species and then have become differentiated by mutation into clusters of functionally similar but no longer identical genes. Examples of gene complexes that have been interpreted in this way will be discussed below.

Examples and Properties of Gene Complexes

The remainder of this paper will be devoted to the properties of gene complexes as revealed by specific examples. The cases chosen by no means exhaust the list of possible examples (for additional ones see reviews by Stephens 1951; Lewis 1951; Carlson 1959b; and Green 1963, 1965).

Bacteria

In bacteria the genes which control sequential reactions in a particular biosynthetic pathway seem usually to be organized into a single operon. The most thoroughly studied case is the operon for the histidine pathway in *Salmonella,* already cited above. The genes controlling the arginine pathway in *E. coli* constitute an exception; although not organized as an operon, these genes may nevertheless have once been part of an operon (discussion and references in Horowitz and Metzenberg 1965).

Ames and Martin (1964) have reviewed the numerous examples of operons in bacteria and have further elaborated the theory of the operon as first put forward by Jacob and Monod (1961). This theory or model states that the functioning of the genes of an operon is regulated by means of repressor substances which act on the operator region and which are the product of regulatory genes. However, the manner in which the regulation is carried out at the biochemical level has not yet been elucidated. In a few cases, there is evidence that the operon is transcribed into a single polycistronic messenger RNA which is apparently then translated as a unit by the ribosomes. Nevertheless, different enzymes of the same operon are known in some cases to be synthesized in respectively different amounts. In order to account for the latter finding, as well as for the behavior of polarity mutants, Ames and Martin (1964) have proposed a "modulation" model for the reading of the operonic messenger RNA. Their model states that each of the possible codons for a given amino acid determines a different rate of enzyme synthesis through assumed differences in the relative amounts of the corresponding species of transfer RNA's. For example, when a gene contains a "modulating" codon corresponding to one of the less abundant species of transfer RNA, the reading of the messenger RNA slows down, presumably because the ribosomes tend to fall off the messenger at that point. The model can thus explain the differential rate of synthesis of different enzymes of the same operon. As expressed by Ames and Martin (1964), "the relative molar quantities of each enzyme made would be determined by the spacing of modulating triplets. The sequence of genes in the operon (which need not correspond to the sequence of enzymes in the pathway, as appeared at first) would be related to the number of molecules (in terms of the fundamental subunits) of each enzyme made. Thus, there would have been an evolutionary selection so that the order of genes is from the least efficient enzymes (of which more molecules are needed) to the most efficient."

Polarity mutants, by this model, would represent changes of the original codon to nonsense, missense, or modulating codons. Such changes would either interrupt or slow down the reading of the messenger—hence accounting for the observed coordinate repression of enzymes controlled by the gene containing the polarity mutant and by all genes distal to it in the operon.

Not all of the regulatory phenomena associated with gene complexes in bacteria have been satisfactorily explained by the operon theory (review by Horowitz and Metzenberg 1965). However, the utility of this theory as a working hypothesis is unquestioned. The way in which operons may have originated is discussed below in the section on fungi.

Bacteriophage

Whereas a bacterium is estimated to have in the neighborhood of 2000 different gene functions, a bacteriophage such as phage T4D may have only on the order of 100 (Edgar and Epstein 1965). With the aid of conditional lethal mutants, Edgar and Epstein and their collaborators have mapped perhaps one-half of the genome of this phage. When gene order is correlated with gene function, a striking result emerges. That part of the genome which has been mapped appears to be made up to a large extent of clusters of genes with similar phenotypic effects (Epstein *et al.* 1963). Although these clusters bear a resemblance to the operons of bacteria, it is not known whether a true parallel exists since neither polarity mutants nor mutants of regulatory genes or operator regions have been detected.

Fungi

In spite of the large number of biosynthetic pathways that have been genetically analyzed in *Neurospora* and yeast, only a few cases have been found in which genes with related functions are clustered. Although most of the genes corresponding to those in the histidine operon of *Salmonella* have been identified in *Neurospora,* only the genes controlling steps 2, 3, and 6 of the histidine pathway form an operon in *Neurospora* (Ahmed, Case, and Giles 1964). Giles, Case, and Partridge (1965) have recently found in *Neurospora* a group of polyaromatic auxotrophic mutants which form a "supragenic functional unit" having many of the characteristics of a bacterial operon. The genes of this "aromatic" (*arom*) operon control the activities of five enzymes in a pathway composed of at least seven steps. Four of the genes of the *arom* operon have been identified by a combination of complementation, recombinational, and enzymatic studies.

Operons may also be rare in yeast. For example, although most of the genes corresponding to the galactose operon of *E. coli* (review by Ames and Martin 1964) have been identified in yeast, only three of these are closely linked in yeast (Douglas and Hawthorne 1964); furthermore it is not clear whether these three form a typical operon.

The possible basis for the scarcity of operons in fungi relative to the number in bacteria has been discussed by Horowitz (1965). He postulates that operons have often arisen by a process of repeated tandem gene duplications accompanied by gradual functional differentiation of the daughter genes. He further postulates that operons which are concerned with biochemical functions of great antiquity have tended to remain intact in bacteria but have become fragmented in higher forms such as *Neurospora.* He suggests, as one possibility, that such fragmentation may have occurred because of the demands imposed by the greatly increased gene number in *Neurospora* and the associated development of a complement of seven pairs of chromosomes compared to the single bacterial "chromosome." It remains possible that operons associated with pathways which have evolved after the separation of the fungi from the bacteria will still tend to remain intact in *Neurospora.* Few such pathways have been studied thus far in *Neurospora,* since the analysis has been restricted largely to those pathways which must have antedated the evolution of fungi from bacteria.

Higher plants

In maize a number of mutant series have long been known to exhibit considerable functional complexity. Examples which seem likely to represent gene complexes are (1) mutants of the "*R*" series, which determine absence of anthocyanin pigmentation in the aleurone or the plant or both (Stadler and Nuffer 1953; Stadler 1954; Stadler and Emmerling 1956), and (2) mutants of the "*A*" series, which affect the distribution of anthocyanin pigmentation in the plant and pericarp. In recent years Laughnan has found genetic evidence that the *A* series is associated with a tandem gene duplication which has become established in at least some strains of maize and which undergoes unequal crossing over (review by Laughnan 1961).

Stephens (1951) has reviewed other possible examples of gene complexes in higher plants.

That intragenic recombination occurs in higher plants is suggested by Nelson's (1962) discovery that the waxy gene in maize can be mapped as a linear array of sites on the basis of the frequency with which wild-type recombinants arise from heterozygotes for different mutant alleles of this gene. Presumably, in this case, only a single enzymatic function is involved (Nelson and Tsai 1964); however, it is not clear whether waxy is the structural gene or a regulatory gene for this function.

Mammals

The most thoroughly understood example of a gene complex, from the standpoint of biochemical characterization of the associated polypeptides, is the cluster of two closely linked genes, already referred to above, which determines the beta and delta polypeptide chains of normal adult human hemoglobins A_1 and A_2, respectively. This gene complex may also include the gene which determines the gamma chain of fetal or F hemoglobin. The sequence of amino acids in the gamma chain has been determined by Schroeder *et al.* (1963). The close similarity among the amino acid sequences exhibited by the beta, delta, and gamma chains suggests that the three genes may have arisen from a single ancestral gene by a process of repeated gene duplication (Ingram 1961). However, proof that the gene for the gamma chain is linked to the other two genes is lacking. Evidence that the genes for the beta and delta chains are adjacent and to some extent homologous comes from the discovery of an abnormal hemoglobin, Hb-Lepore. This hemoglobin variant has arisen independently on at least two occasions and is remarkable in that it contains a new type of polypeptide chain in which the left (C-terminal) portion seems to correspond to the left portion of a beta chain while the right (N-terminal) portion seems to correspond to the right end of a delta chain. Since the amino acid sequences in the central regions of the beta and delta chains are virtually identical with one another over long stretches, Baglioni (1962) has postulated that the requisite unequal crossover event probably took place at a time when the central region of a beta-chain gene was unequally paired with the central region of a delta-chain gene. Smithies (1964) has discussed in detail the probable regions within which a crossover must have occurred to produce the two known kinds of Hb-Lepore.

Smithies, Connell, and Dixon (1962) have found that one of the human haptoglobin variant genes (Hp^2) produces an alpha chain that is almost twice as large as the alpha chains resulting from the two common haptoglobin genes, Hp^{1F} and Hp^{1S}. On the basis of preliminary peptide studies, these investigators speculate that Hp^2 arose by nonhomologous crossing over in a heterozygote for Hp^{1F} and Hp^{1S}. Hp^2 might therefore be an incipient gene complex that has not yet become established in the species.

According to Herzenberg (1964), the heavy chains of mouse gamma globulins may be under the control of two closely linked genes in a manner analogous to that described for the beta and delta chains of human hemoglobin; however, sequence data are lacking.

The extensive series of tailless mutants found in mice was one of the first known examples of clustering of genes with similar effects (Dunn and Caspari 1945). When studied in paired combinations, the three dominant mutants of this series, Fused, Kinky, and Tailless, were found to be separated by several map units. This relatively high frequency of recombination suggests not only that three separate loci are involved (rather than three sites within a single gene) but also that the loci may not be contiguous. The dominant mutants are in turn closely linked to a series of recessive tailless mutants which Dunn and his collaborators have isolated from wild populations (review by Dunn 1956). But the precise nature of the linkage is obscure, since many of the recessive mutants are apparently associated with chromosomal rearrangements which suppress crossing over throughout the cluster.

Drosophila

Only a few of the numerous examples of gene complexes in *Drosophila* will be reviewed in this chapter. Mention should first be made of two examples of allelic diversity in *Drosophila* that seem most simply interpretable on the basis of a single gene rather than a gene complex. These are the rosy and garnet series of eye-color mutants.

Biochemical genetic analyses of the rosy series suggest that rosy is the structural gene for the enzyme xanthine dehydrogenase or for a polypeptide component of that enzyme (Forrest, Glassman, and Mitchell 1956). By the cis-trans test, all of the available rosy mutants fall into a single cistron. Recombinational analysis of the rosy mutants by ingenious selective techniques (Chovnick *et al.* 1964) indicates that many recombinationally separable sites may exist within the rosy cistron. These sites, moreover, can be linearly ordered with reference to the behavior of outside marker genes. Although the analysis of this series has not progressed to the point of determining whether recombination is of the crossing-over or the intragenic type, it seems likely that Chovnick and his collaborators have succeeded in producing a linear map of a single gene quite comparable to the gene maps of phages, bacteria, and fungi.

The mutants of the garnet series also fall into a single cistron by the cis-trans test. In this case, half-tetrad analyses by Hexter (1958) and Chovnick (1961) suggest that recombination within this series of mutants may be of the intragenic type since both nonreciprocal recombination and high negative interference are found. Although biochemical data are lacking and very few sites have been identified, the garnet mutants, like the rosy mutants, seem to form a single allelic series rather than a pseudoallelic one.

In a number of other mutant series in *Drosophila,* there is morphological evidence for functional diversity which would suggest that gene complexes are involved, but a firm conclusion cannot yet be drawn in most instances. A brief account will be given of only a few extensively studied examples—namely, the white, lozenge, Notch, and dumpy series.

The white series of mutants, located at 1.3 map units in the X chromosome of *Drosophila,* form a single cistron by the cis-trans test. There is, however, evidence for functional diversity within the series. One group of mutants is characterized by producing a generally lighter color in the male than in the female (that is, males fail to show the normal dosage compensation of sex-linked mutants of this organism) and by acting as suppressors of the zeste (z) mutant (Gans 1953; Green 1959); this group, to which the original white mutant belongs, is called the "white" group. To the left of this group, there is another group of mutants which is characterized by usually causing a darker color in the male than in the female (that is, the gene dosage is overcompensated) and by failing to act as suppressors of zeste (Green 1959). This is the "apricot" group. A third group of mutants is characterized by a variegated eye-color phenotype. This is the "spotted white" group of mutants (Lewis 1956; Green 1959). Mutants in this group partially complement all mutants of the apricot or white groups (that is, the trans-heterozygote has a nearly normal eye color). This is not a case of additive dominant effects since the cis-heterozygote exhibits a wild-type eye color. Half-tetrad analysis of trans-heterozygotes for the white and apricot mutants indicates that the mutants are separable by recombinational events of the classical crossing-over type, and hence at least two loci, white and apricot, can be identified by this test (Lewis 1952). Many of the mutants of the white series were first ordered into two groups corresponding to the apricot and white loci by MacKendrick and Pontecorvo (1952). The spotted white group seems to occupy a separate locus very near and to the right of the white locus (Lewis 1956; Green 1963).

Judd (1959) and Green (1959) have found evidence for further subdivision of the apricot group into either two sites or two loci. The occurrence of unequal intragenic recombination, involving certain mutants of the apricot group, has tended, however, to obscure the picture (Green 1965; Judd 1964). At the present time the most likely interpretation of the entire series of mutants is that it represents a gene complex composed of three or four pseudoallelic genes. Moreover, there is cytological evidence in this case that the series is associated with at least two or three bands, two of which (3C1-2) form a "doublet"—a structure that has been interpreted as a tandem single-band duplication probably of the reverse type ($ABBA$) (Bridges 1935).

The lozenge series of roughened eye mutants has been studied extensively (Oliver 1940; Green and Green 1949, 1956). The vast majority of mutants in this series fail to complement one another. Although half-tetrad analyses have not been made, recombination seems to be of the classical crossing-over type (that is, interference seems to be strongly positive within this series). Although many mutants are known, only four loci or sites have thus far been demonstrated. In contrast with the white series, the loci of the lozenge series are not obviously functionally differentiated from one another. This does not preclude, however, the existence of separate pseudoallelic genes. For example, the known lozenge mutants may be mostly of the polarity type; if so, the diversity of morphological effects (on the eye, leg, antenna, and female reproductive tract) may be pleiotropic effects exerted by the most distal gene of the series.

The Notch series of sex-linked wing mutants form a functionally diverse series, which has been examined in detail by Welshons (1958) and Welshons and von Halle (1962). Mutants of this series exhibit more or less independently varying morphological effects on eyes, wings, and bristles. Recombinational analysis provides some evidence that exchange between mutant genes of this series is not always accompanied by end-marker recombination—that is, interference is sometimes negative—suggesting that intragenic recombination occurs. However, half-tetrad analysis has not been undertaken. Eleven sites have already been identified, and these are linearly ordered. Scattered throughout the locus or region are extreme, dominant, Notch mutants which act as recessive lethals. These fail to complement either each other or the recessive viable mutants of the series. Cytological studies have suggested that perhaps only one band is associated with the Notch region. This does not, however, preclude the existence of many cistrons (Rudkin 1965). The Notch series, in spite of its functional complexity at the morphological level, may well represent either a single allelic series or a gene complex involving only a few pseudoallelic genes.

Mutants of the dumpy series in the second chromosome of *Drosophila* produce more or less independently varying alterations in wing shape, thoracic structure, and viability. Historically, this was the first example found in *Drosophila* of an apparently allelic series in which some members of the series complement one another (Muller 1922).

In recent years Carlson and his collaborators have studied the dumpy series extensively. The series can be divided into two groups of mutants: a "vortex" group, in which the mutants produce whorls of hairs or vortices on the thorax, and an "oblique" group, in which the mutants produce truncated wing effects which may or may not be combined with vortex effects and with recessive lethal effects. Carlson (1959 *a*) finds that members of the vortex group lie consistently to the right of members of the oblique group, the recombination distance being about 0.04 map unit. Southin and Carlson (1962) find that the oblique group can be further subdivided by recombination into eight more sites or loci, as the case may be. When recombination was measured in heterozygotes that had two morphologically distinct types of dumpy mutants, interference was generally strongly positive and there was no difficulty in ordering the mutants. In heterozygotes that had morphologically similar types of mutants of independent origin, either no recombination between the mutants was observed or, in one case, a possible gene conversion or revertant was found. The dumpy series is associated with section *25A* of the salivary gland chromosomes (Bridges and Brehme 1944), a region which contains a four-banded repeat structure (Bridges 1935).

Although the dumpy series may involve only a single locus, it seems more likely that the series is a gene complex composed of at least two closely linked and functionally somewhat distinct genes. The complex may owe its origin to repeated gene duplication in tandem but further cytogenetic studies are needed to clarify this point.

The bithorax (*bx*) pseudoallelic series is a possible example of an operonic type of gene complex (Lewis 1951, 1955, 1963, 1964) and appears especially favorable for the study of genetic control of developmental pathways. It is made up of five groups of mutants, each group having characteristic phenotypic effects that are readily distinguishable from those of the other groups. Recombination studies have identified five loci which have a one-to-one correspondence with the five phenotypic classes. The five loci will be symbolized here simply by the letters *a, B, C, d,* and *e.* Mutants at the *a* and *e* loci cause the anterior and posterior portions, respectively, of the metathorax segment of the fly to change developmental courses such that the metathorax becomes a wing-bearing instead of a halter-bearing segment. Mutants at the *d* locus cause a transformation of the first abdominal segment toward a thoracic state and at the same time have effects characteristic of the *e* mutant. Mutants at the *C* locus are dominant and, except for one case, are lethal when homozygous; they seem from mosaic studies (Lewis 1963) to combine the properties of the *a, d,* and *e* loci. A single mutant is known at the *B* locus. It transforms the wing-bearing segment in the direction of the halter-bearing segment, the inverse of the transformation controlled by the *a* and *e* genes. In some respects the *B* mutant formally resembles the operator-constitutive, or o^c, type of mutant of the bacterial operons. Cis-trans tests suggest that the action of the genes of the bithorax complex are polarized in the manner of the genes of bacterial operons (Lewis 1963).

Cytological evidence suggests that the series is associated with a complex of two doublet structures of the salivary gland chromosomes. Several instances have been found in which chromosomal rearrangements appear to have separated these two doublets; such cases were detected because of an associated inactivation of the fourth and fifth genes. In such rearrangements the functioning of the first three genes of the series was found to be unimpaired, even when, in one of the rearrangements, the trio had been shifted by transposition to the left arm of the third chromosome. These polarity effects associated with rearrangements are consistent with the polarity effects shown by the mutants in cis-trans comparisons.

Mutants at the different loci of the bithorax complex recombine with low frequencies in the range of 0.005 to 0.01 per cent. It has been relatively easy to identify all possible double mutant combinations. In addition it has been possible to synthesize not only certain triplet mutant combinations but also a quintuple mutant combination. In females heterozygous for the quintuple mutant combination and a normal third chromosome, there has been no evidence of negative interference.

Until recently recombinational analysis of the bithorax complex has

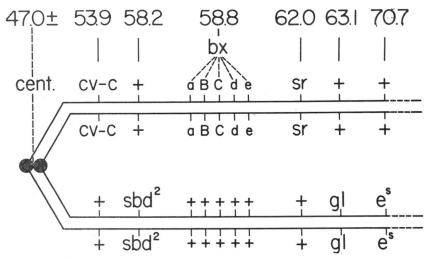

Fig. 3.3.—Diagram of the genetic constitution of attached-3R chromosomes heterozygous for a quintuple bithorax mutant combination and for closely linked marker genes. (Symbols: +, wild-type allele; *cent.*, centromere; *cv-c*, crossveinless-c; *sbd²*, stubbloid-2; *sr*, stripe; *gl*, glass; *e⁸*, ebony-sooty; *bx*, bithorax; *a*, bithorax-3; *B*, Contrabithorax; *C*, Ultrabithorax; *d*, bithoraxoid; and *e*, postbithorax.) The standard map locations are shown above the mutant symbols and are derived from Bridges and Brehme (1944), except that the location of *cv-c* is based on unpublished data kindly provided by Dr. Claude Hinton.

been handicapped because, in the autosomes of *Drosophila,* it has not been practical to recover more than one product of the meiotic tetrad. This difficulty has now been circumvented by the use of pseudoisochromosomes for the right arm of chromosome 3. Such "attached-3R" chromosomes are comparable to the well-known attached-X chromosomes of this organism and were synthesized some years ago in our laboratory by I. E. Rasmussen and E. Orias. These chromosomes permit a half-tetrad analysis of meiotic events; that is, two of the four products of a tetrad can be recovered by virtue of their sharing a common centromere.

It has been possible to construct, and to measure recombination in, females with an attached-3R chromosome in which one arm carries the quintuple bithorax mutant type (*a B C d e*) and the other arm carries the corresponding set of five wild-type alleles. Females carrying attached left arms (3L's) homozygous for a marker mutant, *radius incompletus* (*ri*), and attached-3R's of the genotype shown in Figure 3.3 were mated individually to males with attached-3L's marked with *ri* and attached-3R's marked with stripe (*sr*). (In such matings the attached-3L's usually segregate from the attached-3R's in much the same way that the Y chromosome of attached-X females segregates from the attached-X chromosome; the only viable progeny are those which receive one attached-3L chromosome and one attached-3R chromosome.)

Owing to the existence of marked cis-trans effects in the bithorax series, it is possible to recognize the simultaneous recovery of reciprocal recombinants derived from any one of the four recombination regions of the bithorax complex. Thus, in region I, the recombinant $a/B\,C\,d\,e$ (i.e., $a+++++/+\,B\,C\,d\,e$) has an extreme a phenotype; in region II, $a\,B/C\,d\,e$ has a combination of a and B effects; in region III, $a\,B\,C/d\,e$ is known to combine extreme d and e effects; and in region IV, $a\,B\,C\,d/e$ has an extreme e phenotype. By contrast the parental, or cis, arrangement ($a\,B\,C\,d\,e/+$) is virtually wild type except for slightly enlarged halteres. Several other recombinant and non-recombinant combinations can also be phenotypically identified, such as $a\,B\,C\,d\,e/e$, which has an extreme e phenotype, and $a\,B/+$, which has a moderate B phenotype. Moreover, certain types of events that would be indicative of gene conversion would be readily identifiable if they were to occur; for example, any of the above types of recombinants within the bithorax region which were not accompanied by recombination for the nearest outside-marker genes would represent possible gene conversions. Finally, certain types of double recombinants within the bithorax complex which would extract one of the single mutants, either B or d, would be readily detectable in certain combinations; for example, $B/+$ or $B/a\,B\,C\,d\,e$ is known to be viable and phenotypically easily identified, as is also $d/a\,B\,C\,d\,e$.

The results of the attached-3R experiment are shown in Table 3.1. In all, 16 recombinant strands have been verified by progeny testing. Such testing involved introducing the attached-3R's bearing the suspected recombinant types into triploids and isolating among the progeny of such triploids each strand of the attached-3R chromosome. In each case the occurrence of a recombinant strand within one of the bithorax regions was accompanied by a recombination of the outside-marker mutants. The marker-mutant recombination event was always consistent with the map order that had previously been deduced for the bithorax mutants from studies with nonattached-3R's. In this limited number of cases of recombination within the bithorax complex of attached-3R heterozygotes, interference was positive and complete. That is, there was no evidence of gene conversion. In this experiment, which involved approximately 221,000 progeny, the calculated frequency of recombination for regions I, II, and IV combined was roughly 1.5×10^{-4}. For technical reasons the frequency of recombination in region III could not be directly measured.

Table 3.1

Recombinant progeny for the bithorax regions and verified recombinant strands, derived from a mating of attached-3R females of genotype *a B C d e*/+ + + + + with attached-3R males homozygous for *sr* (see Fig. 3.3 for the full composition of the parental female and for a description of symbols). The number of recombinant progeny for the bithorax region that were successfully tested is shown in parentheses. These latter progeny were the source of the verified recombinant strands.

	Recombination regions within the bithorax complex							
	I	II		III		IV		Totals
Composition of attached-3R	*a*++++	*a B*+++	*a B*++++	*a B C*++	*a B C*++	*a B C d*+	*a B C d e*	
	+*B C d e*	++*C d e*	+++++*e*	+++*d e*	+++++	++++*e*	+++++*e*	
Observed number of flies	8 (5)	2 (0)	4 (2)	0	1* (1)	2 (1)	2 (2)	19 (11)
Number of verified recombinant strands	10	2	2		1*	2	2	16

* Phenotype overlaps wild type; hence some specimens may have been overlooked. Since the observed specimen was selected because of an associated recombination of outside markers, this case is omitted from the total number of verified recombinant strands.

Observed recombination frequencies between different genes of the bithorax complex are so low that the detection of intragenic recombination might require examining many more progeny than has been done thus far. It is also possible that one or more of the mutants are associated with minute rearrangements which have precluded the occurrence of intragenic recombination. Although all of the mutants used in the half-tetrad analysis appear to be normal in the salivary gland chromosomes, more sensitive criteria for rearrangement than this cytological test are obviously needed. One such criterion, discussed above under mutational tests, is suppressibility of the mutants by allele-specific (but not gene-specific) suppressor mutants. A test of this kind has been carried out for the bithorax series with a recessive, allele-specific suppressor—namely, the suppressor of Hairy-wing, located at 54.8 map units in the right arm of the third chromosome. The first known mutant allele, *su-Hw*, at this locus was found by Bridges, who showed that it had the ability when homozygous to suppress scute, Hairy-wing, cut, and, to some extent, forked and bar (Bridges and Brehme 1944). Although this mutant was lost before tests of allele specificity were carried out, a recurrence, designated *su²-Hw*, turned up during study of the bithorax complex.

The *su²-Hw* mutant has been found to suppress only certain alleles of a wide variety of mutant genes. The loci at which almost complete suppression has been detected are as follows: yellow, Hairy-wing, scute, cut, lozenge, forked, bithorax, bithoraxoid (loci *a* and *d* in the *bx* complex), *cubitus interruptus,* and, as recently found in our laboratory by G. Del Campo, diminutive and Beadex. Usually only one of a number of different alleles that have been tested is suppressed. This is especially striking for the yellow, scute, and lozenge loci. Among a large number of alleles tested at each of these loci, only one allele apiece was suppressed by *su²-Hw*—namely, *y²*, *sc¹*, and *lz¹*, respectively.

Among the five mutants of the bithorax complex which were used in the attached-3R experiment described above, two (*bx³* at the *a* locus and *bxd¹* at the *d* locus) are suppressed by *su²-Hw* while the remaining three are not. It is of interest that *bx³* and *bxd* in homozygous lines have each on one occasion undergone reversion to wild type, apparently by back mutation. The suppressor and reversion results only suggest that *bx³* and *bxd* may be true point mutations.

A unique property associated with the bithorax complex is the occurrence of a "transvection effect" (Lewis 1954). This effect was discovered when trans-heterozygotes for certain mutants of this complex were made structurally heterozygous for chromosomal rearrangements involving the right arm of the third chromosome. Under these circumstances, the mutant phenotype of a given trans-heterozygote (for example, $a +/+ C$) is frequently made more extreme than that of the corresponding heterozygote with structurally homozygous third chromosomes. Such phenotypes have been described elsewhere (Lewis 1963). Only those rearrangements which cause a cytologically observable disruption in pairing of the bithorax regions (*89E* of the salivary gland chromosomes) give the transvection effect. The existence of this phenomenon implies that the wild-type alleles of the trans-heterozygote are able to cooperate with one another even though they are in opposite chromosomes; moreover, they cooperate more efficiently when the chromosomes are paired (i.e., in the absence of an associated rearrangement) than when the chromosomes are unpaired. It is not known whether this cooperation occurs at the level of transcription or translation of the DNA message or whether it occurs at some level that involves diffusion of products of chromosomally localized enzymatic reactions.

The bithorax complex promises to be a suitable system for studying the genetic control of developmental pathways. A model has been presented elsewhere (Lewis 1963, 1964) that formally accounts for the manner in which the individual genes of the bithorax complex control the level of development achieved by certain body segments of the fly. This model is based on an analogy with the behavior of inducible operons in bacteria (Jacob and Monod 1961). The bithorax genes appear to control developmental pathways which recapitulate some of the phylogenetic steps that must have occurred during the evolution of the Diptera from primitive arthropod ancestors.

Summary

At first glance, the genes of higher organisms appear to be distributed throughout the chromosomes in a more or less random fashion with respect to their functional role in development. An increasing number of exceptions to this rule have been uncovered as the gene concept has come to be scrutinized more and more closely. "Gene" is here used in the sense of the code-message unit that codes for the production of a specific polypeptide. Whenever an apparently allelic series of mutants exhibits functional diversity, it is often difficult to distinguish whether such diversity resides within different sites of a single gene or within different pseudoallelic loci of a gene complex. Attention is drawn to the various genetic methods that can be used to distinguish operationally between these two possibilities. The emphasis in this paper has been placed upon those examples of functionally complex mutant series which turn out to be of the gene-complex type. In bacteria, an entire sequence of reactions in a biochemical pathway is frequently found to be controlled by an operon—a gene complex in which the functioning of individual genes of the complex is regulated in a coordinate manner. Operons for the primitive biosynthetic pathways of living organisms seem to have become fragmented in higher organisms, as judged by the scarcity of operons of this type in *Neurospora* and yeast. Nevertheless genes involved in biosynthetic or developmental pathways of relatively recent origin may well turn out to be linked together as gene complexes in higher organisms. This will be especially likely if the genetic control of such pathways has evolved by a process of gradual functional differentiation of a set of tandemly duplicated genes. It seems likely that many, but not all, gene complexes have originated by such a process; however, supporting evidence is lacking, except in one case—namely, the two-gene complex which codes for the production of the nearly identical beta and delta polypeptide chains of human hemoglobin. The study of gene complexes that affect morphological or other kinds of developmental processes promises to advance our knowledge of the genetic control of developmental pathways in much the same way that the study of bacterial operons has advanced our knowledge of the genetic control of biosynthetic pathways.

Literature Cited

AHMED, A., M. CASE, AND N. H. GILES, 1964. The nature of complementation among mutants in the *histidine-3* region of *Neurospora crassa*. Brookhaven Symp. Biol. **17**: 53–65.

AKSOY, M., AND H. LEHMANN, 1957. The first observation of sickle-cell hemoglobin E disease. Nature **179**: 1248–1249.

AMES, B. N., AND P. E. HARTMAN, 1963. The histidine operon. Cold Spring Harbor Symp. Quant. Biol. **28**: 349–356.

AMES, B. N., P. E. HARTMAN, AND F. JACOB, 1963. Chromosomal alterations affecting the regulation of histidine biosynthetic enzymes in *Salmonella*. J. Mol. Biol. **7**: 23–42.

AMES, B. N., AND R. C. MARTIN, 1964. Biochemical aspects of genetics: The operon. Ann. Rev. Biochem. **33**: 235–258.

BAGLIONI, C., 1962. The fusion of two peptide chains in hemoglobin Lepore and its interpretation as a genetic deletion. Proc. Nat. Acad. Sci. U.S. **48**: 1880–1886.

————, 1963. Correlations between genetics and chemistry of human hemoglobins. *Molecular Genetics,* pp. 405–475. Edited by J. H. Taylor. Academic Press, New York.

BARRATT, R. W., 1961. Studies on gene-protein relations with glutamic dehydrogenase in *Neurospora crassa*. Genetics **46**: 849–850.

BENZER, S., 1955. Fine structure of a genetic region in bacteriophage. Proc. Nat. Acad. Sci. U.S. **41**: 344–354.

———, 1957. The elementary units of heredity. *The Chemical Basis of Heredity*, pp. 70–93. Edited by W. D. McElroy and B. Glass. The Johns Hopkins Press, Baltimore.

BENZER, S., AND S. P. CHAMPE, 1962. A change from nonsense to sense in the genetic code. Proc. Nat. Acad. Sci. U.S. **48**: 1114–1121.

BOYER, J., L. RUCKNAGEL, J. WEATHERALL, AND E. J. WATSON-WILLIAMS, 1963. Further evidence for linkage between the β and δ loci governing human hemoglobin and the population dynamics of linked genes. Amer. J. Human Genet. **15**: 438–447.

BRIDGES, C. B., 1935. Salivary chromosome maps. J. Hered. **26**: 60–64.

———, 1936. The Bar "gene," a duplication. Science **83**: 210–211.

BRIDGES, C. B., AND K. S. BREHME, 1944. The mutants of *Drosophila melanogaster*. Carnegie Inst. Wash. Publ. No. 552.

BRINK, R. A., 1932. Are the chromosomes aggregates of groups of physiologically interdependent genes? Amer. Natur. **66**: 444–451.

BRODY, S., AND C. YANOFSKY, 1963. Suppressor gene alteration of protein primary structure. Proc. Nat. Acad. Sci. U.S. **50**: 9–16.

CARLSON, E. A., 1959a. Allelism, complementation, and pseudoallelism at the dumpy locus in *Drosophila melanogaster*. Genetics **44**: 348–373.

———, 1959b. Comparative genetics of complex loci. Quart. Rev. Biol. **34**: 33–67.

CATCHESIDE, D. G., AND A. OVERTON, 1958. Complementation between alleles in heterocaryons. Cold Spring Harbor Symp. Quant. Biol. **23**: 137–140.

CEPPELLINI, R., 1959. Discussion. *Ciba Foundation Symposium, Biochemistry of Human Genetics*, p. 135. Edited by G. E. W. Wolstenholme and C. M. O'Connor. Little, Brown and Co., Boston.

CHOVNICK, A., 1961. The garnet locus in *Drosophila melanogaster*. I. Pseudoallelism. Genetics **46**: 493–507.

CHOVNICK, A., A. SCHALET, R. P. KERNAGHAN, AND M. KRAUSS, 1964. The rosy cistron in *Drosophila melanogaster*: Genetic fine structure analysis. Genetics **50**: 1245–1259.

CRICK, F. H. C., L. BARNETT, S. BRENNER, AND R. J. WATTS-TOBIN, 1961. General nature of the genetic code for proteins. Nature **192**: 1227–1232.

DOUGLAS, H. D., AND D. C. HAWTHORNE, 1964. Enzymatic expression and genetic linkage of genes controlling galactose utilization in *Saccharomyces*. Genetics **49**: 837–844.

DUNN, L. C., 1956. Analysis of a complex gene in the house mouse. Cold Spring Harbor Symp. Quant. Biol. **21**: 187–195.

DUNN, L. C., AND E. CASPARI, 1945. A case of neighboring loci with similar effects. Genetics **30**: 543–568.

EDGAR, R. S., AND R. H. EPSTEIN, 1965. Conditional lethal mutations in bacteriophage T4. *Genetics Today*, vol. 2, pp. 2–16. Edited by S. J. Geerts. Proc. XI Int. Congr. Genet., The Hague, The Netherlands. Pergamon Press, Oxford.

EPSTEIN, R. H., A. BOLLE, C. M. STEINBERG, E. KELLENBERGER, E. BOY DE LA TOUR, R. CHEVALLEY, R. S. EDGAR, M. SUSMAN, G. H. DENHARDT, AND A. LIELAUSIS, 1963. Physiological studies of conditional lethal mutants of bacteriophage T4D. Cold Spring Harbor Symp. Quant. Biol. 28: 375–394.

FINCHAM, J. R. S., AND A. CODDINGTON, 1963. The mechanism of complementation between *am* mutants of *Neurospora crassa*. Cold Spring Harbor Symp. Quant. Biol. 28: 517–527.

FINCHAM, J. R. S., AND J. A. PATEMAN, 1957. Formation of an enzyme through complementary action of mutant "alleles" in separate nuclei in a heterocaryon. Nature 179: 741–742.

FORREST, H. S., E. GLASSMAN, AND H. K. MITCHELL, 1956. Conversion of 2-amino-4-hydroxy-pteridine to isoxanthopterin in *Drosophila melanogaster*. Science 124: 725–726.

FREESE, E., 1963. Molecular mechanism of mutations. *Molecular Genetics,* pp. 207–269. Edited by J. H. Taylor. Academic Press, New York.

GANS, M., 1953. Etude genetique et physiologique du mutant z de *Drosophila melanogaster*. Bull. biol. France et Belg., Suppl. No. 38, 1–90.

GILES, N. H., M. E. CASE, AND C. W. H. PARTRIDGE, 1965. Evidence for an aromatic (arom) operon in *Neurospora crassa*. Genetics 52: 444-445.

GILES, N. H., C. W. H. PARTRIDGE, AND N. J. NELSON, 1957. The genetic control of adenylsuccinase in *Neurospora crassa*. Proc. Nat. Acad. Sci. U.S. 43: 305–317.

GREEN, M. M., 1959. Spatial and functional properties of pseudoalleles at the white locus in *Drosophila melanogaster*. Heredity 13: 302–315.

——, 1963. Pseudoalleles and recombination in Drosophila. *Methodology in Basic Genetics,* pp. 279–290. Edited by W. J. Burdette. Holden-Day, San Francisco.

——, 1965. Genetic fine structure in Drosophila. *Genetics Today,* vol. 2, pp. 37–49. Edited by S. J. Geerts. Proc. XI Int. Congr. Genet., The Hague, The Netherlands. Pergamon Press, Oxford.

GREEN, M. M., AND K. C. GREEN, 1949. Crossing-over between alleles at the lozenge locus in *Drosophila melanogaster*. Proc. Nat. Acad. Sci. U.S. 35: 586–591

GREEN, M. M., AND K. C. GREEN, 1956. A cytogenetic analysis of the lozenge pseudoalleles in *Drosophila*. Z. Induktive Abstammungs- u. Vererbungslehre 87: 708–721.

HARTMAN, P. E., Z. HARTMAN, AND D. ŠERMAN, 1960. Complementation mapping by abortive transduction of histidine-requiring *Salmonella* mutants. J. Gen. Microbiol. 22: 354–368.

HAWTHORNE, D. C., AND R. K. MORTIMER, 1960. Chromosome mapping in *Saccharomyces*: Centromere-linked genes. Genetics 45: 1085–1110.

HERZENBERG, L. A., 1964. A chromosome region for $gamma_{2a}$ and $beta_{2A}$ globulin H chain isoantigens in the mouse. Cold Spring Harbor Symp. Quant. Biol. 29: 455–462.

HEXTER, W. M., 1958. On the nature of the garnet locus in *Drosophila melanogaster*. Proc. Nat. Acad. Sci. U.S. 44: 768–771.

HOLLIDAY, R, 1964. A mechanism for gene conversion in fungi. Genet. Res. 5: 282–304.

HOROWITZ, N. H., 1965. The evolution of biochemical synthesis—retrospect and prospect. *Evolving Genes and Proteins*, pp. 15–23. Edited by V. Bryson and H. V. Vogel. Academic Press, New York.

HOROWITZ, N. H., AND R. L. METZENBERG, 1965. Biochemical aspects of genetics. Ann. Rev. Biochem. 34: 527–564.

HORTON, B. F., AND H. J. HUISMAN, 1963. Linkage of the β-chain and δ-chain structural genes of human hemoglobins. Amer. J. Human Genet. 15: 394–397.

HUNT, J. A. AND V. M. INGRAM, 1959. The genetic control of protein structure: The abnormal human haemoglobins. *Ciba Foundation Symposium, Biochemistry of Human Genetics*, pp. 114–143. Edited by G. E. W. Wolstenholme and C. M. O'Conner. J. & A. Churchill, Ltd., London.

INGRAM, V. M., 1961. Gene evolution and the haemoglobins. Nature 189: 704–708.

INGRAM, V. M., AND A. O. W. STRETTON, 1961. Human haemoglobin A$_2$: Chemistry, genetics and evolution. Nature 190: 1079–1084.

JACOB, F., AND J. MONOD, 1961. On the regulation of gene activity. Cold Spring Harbor Symp. Quant. Biol. 26: 193–211.

JUDD, B. H., 1959. Studies on some position pseudoalleles at the white region in *Drosophila melanogaster*. Genetics 44: 34–42.

———, 1964. The structure of intralocus duplication and deficiency chromosomes produced by recombination in *Drosophila melanogaster,* with evidence for polarized pairing. Genetics 49: 253–265.

LAUGHNAN, J. R., 1961. The nature of mutations in terms of gene and chromosomal changes. *Mutation and Plant Breeding*, pp. 3–29. Nat. Acad. Sci., Nat. Res. Council, Washington, D.C., Publ. No. 891.

LEWIS, E. B., 1951. Pseudoallelism and gene evolution. Cold Spring Harbor Symp. Quant. Biol. 16: 159–174.

———, 1952. Pseudoallelism of white and apricot in *Drosophila melanogaster*. Proc. Nat. Acad. Sci. U.S. 38: 953–961.

———, 1954. The theory and application of a new method of detecting chromosomal rearrangements in *Drosophila melanogaster*. Amer. Natur. 88: 225–239.

———, 1955. Some aspects of position pseudoallelism. Amer. Natur. 89: 73–89.

———, 1956. An unstable gene in *Drosophila melanogaster*. Genetics 41: 651.

———, 1963. Genes and developmental pathways. Amer. Zool. 3: 33–56.

———, 1964. Genetic control and regulation of developmental pathways. *Role of Chromosomes in Development*, pp. 231–252. Edited by M. Locke. Academic Press, New York.

MACKENDRICK, E. M., AND G. PONTECORVO, 1952. Crossing over between alleles at the *w* locus in *Drosophila melanogaster*. Experientia 8: 390.

MITCHELL, M. B., 1955. Aberrant recombination in *Neurospora*. Proc. Nat. Acad. Sci. U.S. 41: 935–937.

MULLER, H. J., 1922. Variation due to change in the individual genes. Amer. Natur. 56: 32–50.

———, 1935. A viable two-gene deficiency phaenotypically resembling the corresponding hypomorphic mutations. J. Hered. 26: 469–478.

MULLER, H. J., A. A. PROKOFJEVA-BELGOVSKAJA, AND K. V. KOSSIKOV, 1936. Unequal crossing over in the bar mutant as a result of duplication of a minute chromosomal section. Compt. Rend. Acad. Sci. U.S.S.R. 2: 87–88.

MURRAY, N. E., 1963. Polarized recombination and fine structure within the me-2 gene of Neurospora crassa. Genetics 48: 1163–1183.

NELSON, O. E., 1962. The waxy locus in maize. I. Intralocus recombination frequency estimates by pollen and by conventional analyses. Genetics 47: 737–742.

NELSON, O. E., AND C. Y. TSAI, 1964. Glucose transfer from adenosine diphosphate-glucose to starch in preparations of waxy seeds. Science 145: 1194–1195.

NIRENBERG, M., P. LEDER, M. BERNFIELD, R. BRIMACOMBE, J. TRUPIN, F. ROTTMAN, AND C. O.'NEAL, 1965. RNA codewords and protein synthesis. VII. On the general nature of the RNA code. Proc. Nat. Acad. Sci. U.S. 53: 1161–1168.

NOTANI, G. W., D. L. ENGELHARDT, W. KONIGSBERG, AND N. D. ZINDER, 1965. Suppression of a coat protein mutant of the bacteriophage f2. J. Mol. Biol. 12: 439–447.

OLIVER, C. P., 1940. A reversion to wild type associated with crossing over in Drosophila melanogaster. Proc. Nat. Acad. Sci. U.S. 26: 452–454.

PETERSON, H. L., AND J. R. LAUGHNAN, 1963. Intrachromosomal exchange at the bar locus in Drosophila. Proc. Nat. Acad. Sci. U.S. 50: 126–133.

RAFFEL, D., AND H. J. MULLER, 1940. Position effect and gene divisibility considered in connection with three strikingly similar scute mutations. Genetics 25: 541–583.

RIZET, G., P. LISSOUBA, AND J. MOUSSEAU, 1960. Les mutations d'ascopores chez l'ascomycète Ascobolus immersus et l'analysis de la structure fine des gènes. Bull. soc. franç. physiol. vegetale 6: 175–193.

RUDKIN, G. T., 1965. The relative mutabilities of DNA in regions of the X chromosome of Drosophila melanogaster. Genetics 52: 665–681.

SCHROEDER, W. A., J. R. SHELTON, J. B. SHELTON, J. CORMICK, AND R. T. JONES, 1963. The amino acid sequence of the γ chain of human fetal hemoglobin. Biochemistry 2: 992–1008.

SMITHIES, O., 1964. Chromosomal rearrangements and protein structure. Cold Spring Harbor Symp. Quant. Biol. 29: 309–319.

SMITHIES, O., G. E. CONNELL, AND G. H. DIXON, 1962. Chromosomal rearrangement and the evolution of haptoglobin genes. Nature 196: 232–236.

SOUTHIN, J. L., AND E. A. CARLSON, 1962. Comparison of micromaps obtained by direct and indirect methods of recombination in the dumpy region of Drosophila melanogaster. Genetics 47: 1017–1026.

STADLER, D. R., AND A. M. TOWE, 1963. Recombination of allelic cysteine mutants in Neurospora. Genetics 48: 1323–1344.

STADLER, D. R., A. M. TOWE, AND N. MURRAY, 1965. Intragenic and intergenic recombination in Neurospora. Genetics 52: 477.

STADLER, L. J., 1954. The gene. Science 120: 811–819.

STADLER, L. J., AND M. H. EMMERLING, 1956. Relation of unequal crossing over to the interdependence of R^r elements (P) and (S). Genetics 41: 124–137.

STADLER, L. J., AND M. G. NUFFER, 1953. Problems of gene structure. II. Separation of R^r elements (S) and (P) by unequal crossing over. Science 117: 471–472.

STEPHENS, S. G., 1951. Possible significance of duplication in evolution. Advance. Genet. 4: 247–267.

STRETTON, A. O. W., AND S. BRENNER, 1965. Molecular consequences of the amber mutation and its suppression. J. Mol. Biol. 12: 456–465.

STURTEVANT, A. H., 1925. The effects of unequal crossing over at the Bar locus in *Drosophila*. Genetics 10: 117–147.

WEIGERT, M. G., AND A. GAREN, 1965. Amino acid substitution resulting from suppression of nonsense mutations. I. Serine insertion by the *Su-1* suppressor gene. J. Mol. Biol. 12: 448–455.

WELSHONS, W. J., 1958. The analysis of a pseudoallelic recessive lethal system at the notch locus of *Drosophila melanogaster*. Cold Spring Harbor Symp. Quant. Biol. 23: 171–176.

WELSHONS, W. J., AND E. S. VON HALLE, 1962. Pseudoallelism at the notch locus in *Drosophila*. Genetics 47: 743–759.

WHITEHOUSE, H. L. K., 1963. A theory of crossing over by means of hybrid deoxyribonucleic acid. Nature 199: 1034–1040.

WHITEHOUSE, H. L. K., AND D. J. HASTINGS, 1965. The analysis of genetic recombination on the polaron hybrid DNA model. Genet. Res. 6: 27–92.

WOODWARD, D. O., 1959. Enzyme complementation *in vitro* between adenylsuccinaseless mutants of *Neurospora crassa*. Proc. Nat. Acad. Sci. U.S. 45: 846–850.

YANOFSKY, C., 1963. Amino acid replacements associated with mutation and recombination in the *A* gene and their relationship to *in vitro* coding data. Cold Spring Harbor Symp. Quant. Biol. 28: 581–588.

4

Properties of Genes

*M. Demerec**

Research carried out at Brookhaven National Laboratory
under the auspices of the U.S. Atomic Energy Commission.

Because this volume commemorates the centennial of the publication of Mendel's work, it seems appropriate to emphasize historical aspects of the problems considered. Therefore in my discussion of gene structure, gene size, and gene number, I intend to give a good deal of attention to the progress made during early stages of genetic research.

Structure of Genes

Throughout the first half-century of the history of genetics, our concept of the physical structure of genes remained more or less static. The gene was generally regarded as the unit of a genetic system, an indivisible entity in the processes of recombination, self-reproduction, and mutation. Even early in that period, however, there was recognition of certain unusual patterns of genetic behavior that stimulated studies in a number of laboratories and initiated doubts about the gene as an indivisible unit. I have in mind specifically the attempts made to explain variegation in plants and step-allelism in the scute locus of *Drosophila melanogaster*.

"Mendelian" characters in plants expressed as color variegation in flowers, leaves, or seeds attracted the special attention of early geneticists because of their unusual type of hereditary behavior. Beginning in 1892, even before the rediscovery of Mendel's paper, Hugo de Vries, working with several varieties of *Antirrhinum majus,* observed that a variety having red-striped flowers might produce many variations in the "striping," including small dots, narrow or broad streaks, and colored sectors extending over a large part of the flower. One plant might produce wholly red flowers, or it might have one or more branches that bore only sectored or wholly red flowers. Occasionally, moreover, he

* Deceased, April 12, 1966.

found red-flowered plants that produced both red-flowered and variegated progeny. The change from striping to self-color that undoubtedly was occurring in the variegated plants he regarded as a case of atavism: a reversion to the original, normal red color (de Vries 1901).

Results of a study of similar flower-color variegation in *Mirabilis jalapa* were reported by Correns (1902), who concluded that red-sectored flowers, red flowers on variegated plants, and completely red-flowered plants were a consequence of changes in dominance of the factor responsible for color. After further studies of the same material he defined these changes as heritable shifts from the homozygous to the heterozygous state, producing a phenotype identical with that found for contrasting characters in sexual hybrids (Correns 1910). Some years later, in discussing results of experiments dealing with chlorophyll variegation in *Capsella bursa-pastoris,* Correns (1919) proposed a hypothesis to explain the unusual behavior of variegated characters. According to his theory a gene might be regarded as a large molecule made up of several identical constituent atom groups. The number of groups might vary genetically and, under the influence of environmental conditions, might either increase or decrease. The presence of any particular number of groups within the molecule was assumed to be responsible for a certain type of variegation, that is, a certain pattern of distribution of the recessive and dominant phenotypes in leaves or flowers. Only two states of a gene would be stable: one having the minimum number of constituent groups and determining the stable recessive, the other having the maximum number and determining the stable dominant.

In the United States, Emerson (1913, 1914, 1917) was the first investigator to study variegation problems carefully, and he introduced a concept which removed variegation from the list of characters that were difficult to fit into the Mendelian pattern of inheritance and placed it in a separate class of Mendelian characters determined by frequently mutating or unstable genes. Investigating variegated pericarp color in maize, he interpreted changes from variegation to self-color to be the result of mutations of unstable genes occurring in somatic cells. He assumed that color would develop in all pericarp cells directly descended from a cell in which the gene responsible for variegation had mutated to the dominant state, and that, among the gametes arising from such a modified cell, one half would carry the dominant and the other half the variegation gene. Thus the allele of the pericarp-color locus responsible for variegation would be an unstable white allele, and red stripes on kernels would represent clones of cells derived from one in which that allele had mutated to the dominant state. Mutations occurring early in the development of a tissue would produce large clones of cells appearing as large colored sectors, and mutations occurring late in ontogeny would produce small sectors. Therefore the size of a sector would be an indication of the time of occurrence of a mutation. If sectors were classified according to geometrically increasing area, such that each different "class center area" was twice the size of the preceding class center area, then each class would comprise those individuals in which mutations had occurred at approximately the same division, and the whole range of consecutive classes would represent mutational events occurring during successive cell divisions. Emerson (1922, 1929) then applied this principle in quantitative studies of mutability.

To explain the lability of unstable genes, E. G. Anderson (personal communication to Emerson, 1920; Anderson and Demerec 1922) proposed, as a working hypothesis, that genes were compound structures or aggregates of self-propagating gene particles, and that unstable genes were composed of two (or more) kinds of particles, which assorted at random during mitotic divisions, representing the recessive state below a certain threshold in the ratio of one kind of particles to another and the dominant state above that threshold. The complex-gene theory was expanded by Eyster (1924, 1928, 1929), who called the gene particles "genomeres," a term suggested by P. W. Whiting.

The genomere hypothesis advanced the analysis of the unstable-gene problem, for it permitted certain predictions and prompted experiments to test them. If changes in unstable genes were caused by assortment of small units (genomeres) within them, experimentally observed mutation frequencies should fall within a range of computed probabilities. Anderson presented this problem to Sewall Wright, who worked out (but did not publish) theoretical expectancy curves for various gene models differing in number of genomeres and in threshold level. The data available from studies by Emerson (1929), Anderson and Eyster (1928), and Eyster (1929) showed, in part, a reasonable agreement with expectancy. Two predictions, however, were discordant with empirical data. The simplest form of the hypothesis stated that a considerable proportion of dominant mutant types would have a frequency of reversion approximately equal to the mutation frequency of variegated types, but equal frequencies were not noted. Also, according to the hypothesis, homozygous variegated types would be expected to show a higher frequency of dominant mutations than would heterozygous variegated types (approximately double). Emerson's (1922) findings indicated the opposite to be true.

During the same general period (1922–26) I undertook a comparative study of several unstable genes in the larkspur *Delphinium ajacis,* and a few years later the discovery of unstable genes in *Drosophila viri-*

lis introduced a way to study a number of problems that could not be solved with plant material. The results obtained with *Delphinium* (Demerec 1931) indicated that the mechanism responsible for variegation is not as simple as had been assumed in the genomere hypothesis. Data about mutability of the unstable gene responsible for rose flower color showed a mutation rate that remained approximately the same throughout the twelve cell generations under observation. These results did not agree with theoretical expectancies based on Wright's calculations. According to Wright, a constant mutation rate of about 7.5×10^{-5} per cell generation, which was observed in the unstable rose variety, would require about 4000 genomeres; with such a large number of components, thousands of cell generations would have to pass before the constant rate of change would be approached. Therefore a random assortment of genomeres could not be responsible for the horizontal mutability curve and the observed patterns of variegation. Further evidence against the genomere hypothesis emerged from studies of the unstable gene for lavender flower color. The mutation rate of the lavender-flower gene varies during ontogeny: It is high during early embryonic development and again during the last few cell divisions in flowers but very low during the intermediate stages.

Thus the findings with *Delphinium* raised serious doubts about the validity of the genomere hypothesis, and these doubts were reinforced by the results obtained in studies of unstable genes in *D. virilis*. Instability was generally restricted to certain stages of ontogeny in *D. virilis*. For example, the reddish-body gene is unstable only at the maturation division in heterozygous females (Demerec 1928); and one allele of the miniature-wing gene is unstable in both somatic and germinal tissues, whereas another is unstable in somatic tissues only (Demerec 1929*a*). It was also found that the rate of mutation can be influenced by the sex and genomic constitution of an individual. Five genes were isolated that affect the mutability of the unstable miniature gene (Demerec 1929*b*, 1930, 1932).*

The facts accumulated throughout several years of research with un-

* In work with bacterial mutants I have observed many that resemble these unstable mutants of higher organisms with regard to frequency of spontaneous reversion. (Usually, unstable types are not suitable for experiments and are discarded.) They vary from extremely stable (1×10^{-11}) to highly unstable (Demerec 1953). Their instability falls well within the range of that of the genes responsible for plant variegation, like rose flower color in *Delphinium*, which mutates with a frequency of about 7.5×10^{-5}. A close parallel to the type of unstable genes represented by the reddish-body gene of *D. virilis* is seen in the "selfer" mutants of *Salmonella typhimurium*, whose reversion frequency is increased by the proximity of a transducing fragment (Demerec 1963).

stable genes of *Delphinium* and *Drosophila* could be explained by the genomere hypothesis only if it was modified by a large number of supplementary assumptions. All the facts, however, were compatible with an alternative hypothesis visualizing unstable genes as chemically unstable units and changes in unstable genes as chemical changes (Demerec 1931, 1935, 1938).

Another explanation of unusual genetic behavior in terms of complex gene structure was advanced in the late 1920's and early 1930's by Serebrovsky (1930), Dubinin (1932), and others, who investigated the phenotypes of a number of "achaete-scute" alleles of *D. melanogaster.* Each different phenotype lacks specific individual bristles on the head, the thorax, or the scutellum so that each allele may be characterized by its own bristle pattern. The investigators found that different phenotypes could be arranged in a definite series according to bristle patterns (step-allelism), and that heterozygotes lacked only those bristles which were affected in common by both participating alleles. They concluded that the serial classification of alleles according to bristle patterns echoed a similar arrangement of parts of the achaete-scute gene locus. On this supposition they divided the locus into twelve elementary subunits, called "centres," each affecting a particular bristle or group of bristles, and assumed that each allele reflected one particular combination of these centres. According to their concept, the achaete-scute locus was made up of separate, regularly spaced, and linearly arranged functional units (Dubinin 1932). The evidence gathered in support of this view, however, was not convincing.

Thus, early attempts to define the gene as a unit of complex structure were unsuccessful, primarily because the experimental techniques available were not sufficiently discriminating to resolve constituent parts. More than twenty years went by before generally acceptable evidence of the physical complexity of genes was obtained. It came from studies made with microorganisms, namely, fungi, bacteria, and finally bacterial viruses.

One of the first contributions of microbial research to the problem of complex loci was the discovery by Bonner (1951) and by Giles (1951) of recombination between alleles in *Neurospora crassa.* The purpose of Bonner's experiments was "to determine whether . . . genic complexity could be found in *Neurospora,* and if so whether it could be demonstrated for a gene affecting a known reaction." His results were positive: He observed recombinants in crosses among five alleles of the "*Q*" locus, which blocks the ability of the organism to convert 3-hydroxyanthranilic acid to niacin. Similar results were obtained by Giles in tests with several alleles of the inositol locus.

Soon afterward Pontecorvo (1952) and Roper (1953), analyzing the close linkage seen in genetic tests of three biotin mutants of *Aspergillus nidulans,* proposed—as an alternative to close physical linkage among three genes—that the three biotin mutants were alleles of a single gene locus, resulting from mutations at three different sites within it.

Within the next two years, reports of work with *Salmonella typhimurium* indicated that complex structure might be a general property of all gene loci (Demerec *et al.* 1954, 1955; Demerec 1955). To study patterns of spontaneous and induced reverse-mutability of various mutant characters, we analyzed about 200 auxotrophs and about 50 galactose-negative mutants. The first step was to determine which phenotypically similar mutants were allelic. The plan was to intercross similar mutants by the transduction technique, on the assumption that recombinants would appear when the markers crossed were nonallelic but not when they were allelic. Although the method was successful, the basic assumption proved to be inaccurate. Results showed clearly that mutant alleles *do recombine,* though with a frequency considerably lower than that observed with two nonallelic mutants. Our findings revealed (Demerec *et al.* 1954) "that a gene locus extends over a section of a chromosome and that changes occurring in different regions of this section give rise to different alleles. . . . regions within a section may separate, and recombine—by a process analogous to crossing over—with homologous regions within a locus of another chromosome." At the time of the first report, intragenic recombination between allelic mutants had been observed in 26 different gene loci belonging to seven phenotypic groups, that is, in every case where two or more alleles were available for tests. This finding justified the conclusion that complex structure is not a special feature of certain gene loci in *Salmonella* but a general property of all loci, a conclusion that has been confirmed by further studies in our laboratory as well as in several others. By now we have performed recombination experiments with more than a hundred *S. typhimurium* genes without detecting any exception to this apparently general rule.

The fine work of Benzer (1955, 1956) with *r*II mutants of coliphage T4 provided evidence that the organization of genic material in bacteriophages is similar to that observed in bacteria and fungi. Moreover, it furnished the basis for a model of a gene locus, in which the sites of different recombining allelic mutants correspond to a few or even one nucleotide pair, in accordance with the Watson-Crick model of the DNA molecule.

There is now ample direct evidence from work with various groups of microorganisms, as well as both indirect and some direct evidence from work with higher organisms (*Drosophila,* man), that genes in all organisms from viruses to mammals are complex in structure and basically similar in composition (see Lewis, Ch. 3). We can regard a gene locus as a heritable unit of function, a segment of a chromosome (in most instances a segment of a Watson-Crick DNA molecule), which specifies the structure of a single polypeptide chain and is made up of a large number of mutational sites—probably nucleotides—biologically separable by recombination. A site, then, is a subunit of a gene locus at which a mutation (chemical rearrangement) may occur but within which recombination has not been observed and presumably does not occur.

Size and Number of Genes

Soon after the first basic information about genes had been acquired, and particularly after it had been established that they are located in linear order in the chromosomes, attempts were made, with several organisms and by several methods, to estimate their number and size. One of the first estimates was presented by T. H. Morgan (1922) in a Croonian Lecture. By a method suggested by H. J. Muller, based on frequency of recurrence of mutations at known gene loci, Morgan calculated the total number of different genes in *D. melanogaster* to be about 2000. Dividing estimates of the volumes of chromosomes by this gene number, he estimated the average diameter of a gene as 6×10^{-2} μ.

A few years later similar calculations for *Drosophila* were published by Muller (1929). They were based on three kinds of data: (*a*) frequency of recurrence of mutations; (*b*) total frequency of crossing over divided by frequency of crossing over between genes as nearly adjacent as possible; and (*c*) symmetrical and asymmetrical crossing over between the genes for bar eye. The corresponding minimal values obtained for total number of genes were (*a*) 1150, (*b*) 1425–1800, and (*c*) 1400–1800. By dividing estimated chromosome volumes by the average estimated number of genes, Muller also calculated the average diameter of a gene as 6×10^{-2} μ.

Muller's discovery in 1927 that ionizing radiations are effective in inducing mutations revolutionized estimations of gene size and number. Estimations could now be based both on the justifiable assumption that a mutation may be caused by a single ionization within or very near a gene and on the relations of radiational properties to biological effects and to rates of induction of genetic changes. Gowen and Gay (1933) were among the first investigators to make such calculations of gene size and number in *Drosophila*. They concluded that the X chromosome carries a minimum of 1280 gene loci and the autosomes a minimum of 13,100, and thus "that there are not less than 14,380 loci occupied by genes which are vital to the normal morphology and well-being of the organism." They estimated the maximum volume of a gene to be about 1×10^{-18} cm^3.

Lea (1940) made another estimate of the number of genes in the X chromosome of *Drosophila*. He assumed that densely ionizing radiations (neutrons) produce sex-linked lethal mutations less efficiently, per ionization, than less densely ionizing radiations (X-rays), and he developed a theory correlating this effect with the target volume of individual genes. He estimated the average target radius of a gene as 1.89×10^{-7} cm and the number of genes in the X chromosome as 1860.

Still other approaches to estimation of gene number developed from cytological studies of chromosome structure. Using a superb staining technique and a fine optical apparatus, Belling (1931; see also Babcock 1933) was able to recognize a large number of chromomeres during meiotic divisions of chromosomes in several liliaceous plants. These he regarded as the structures in which individual genes are housed. In 1931 he wrote:

It was . . . ascertained that there were up to about 2500 pairs of chromomeres (and doubtless genes also) in the pollen-mother-cells (and hence in all other diploid cells) of Lilium. . . . At leptotene, minute, closely set beads (chromomeres) of different sizes have been demonstrated . . . in Lilium, Allium, Hyacinthus, and several other plants. At zygotene, the homologous chromomeres become paired (synapsed). At early pachytene, a successful case of destaining disclosed a minute, about submicroscopic, black dot at the center of each chromomere. This is either a bare gene, or close to one. Hence a chromomere is a gene with a covering of chromatin, usually different in volume for different genes.

A detailed cytological study of the X chromosome of the salivary gland of *D. melanogaster* (Bridges 1938) revealed the presence of at least 1024 bands. On the basis of contemporaneous speculations that each band represented the location of one gene, the minimal number of genes in the X chromosome would be about 1024.

New ways to estimate gene number and size have arisen from recent developments in molecular genetics, particularly the finding that DNA is the carrier of genetic information. The generally accepted Watson-Crick model postulates that genetic DNA consists of two polynucleotide chains running in opposite directions, coiled helically around a common axis and linked to each other by hydrogen bonds between the paired nucleotide bases, which face each other at regular intervals. Each chain consists of a sugar-phosphate backbone, with four bases—two purine (adenine and guanine) and two pyrimidine (thymine and cytosine)—attached to the sugars. The bonding between bases on the two chains is specific, so that adenine pairs only with thymine and guanine only with cytosine. Therefore the two chains of the molecule are complementary, the structure of one prescribing the sequence of bases along the other. Experimental evidence at present favors the assumption that genetic information is determined by the sequence of the nucleotides—that is, the monomers composed of one of the four bases, a deoxyribose sugar, and a phosphate.

Various calculations of gene sizes (reviewed by Clowes 1964) have been based on estimates of the number of nucleotide pairs the genes contain, estimates of the maximum number of mutational sites in the gene, ratios of map length to maximum intragenic recombination, and ratios of maximum to minimum recombination. For example, the size of the *lac* gene in *Escherichia coli* has been calculated as 3500 nucleotide pairs, that of the *tryA* gene as close to 800 pairs. Although such calculations suffer from a number of limitations, they do indicate considerable differences in size among different structural genes.

Recently Holley and his collaborators (1965) attained a significant goal in analysis of gene structure by determining the complete nucleotide sequence of an alanine transfer RNA isolated from yeast. As expected, the gene responsible for that RNA is very small, being composed of only 77 nucleotide pairs. In addition Hall and Sedat (1965) have recently reported that they have isolated a specific messenger RNA for synthesis of the decapeptide gramicidin S, and that molecular weight determinations show a chain of 36 nucleotides. Thus this is the smallest gene identified so far.

One of the best estimates for the total genic content of a bacterial cell is based on Cairns' (1963) measurement of the average length of the *E. coli* chromosome by radioautographs of chromosomes labeled with tritiated thymidine. He found that the length of the chromosome is 1100 μ or about 22 times the length of T2 DNA. According to this datum an *E. coli* chromosome has about 3.7×10^6 nucleotide pairs, which is fairly close to the value, 10^7, derived from chemical estimations of DNA per nucleus (see Clowes 1964).

Thus there is ample evidence from microorganisms that different genes may differ in size. The two extremes have been estimated as 36 and 3500 nucleotides. A reasonable guess based on available information is that the average length does not exceed 10^3 nucleotide pairs. Then taking 10^3 as an average number of nucleotide pairs per gene and 3.7×10^6 as the total number of nucleotide pairs per *E. coli* genome, we may conclude that *E. coli* has a minimum of 3700 different gene loci. The functions of some of these genes are not detectable by our present analytical methods.

Indications of the existence of such genetically cryptic, or perhaps inert, DNA material were derived from our analysis of the *cysC* region of the *S. typhimurium* chromosome (Demerec, Gillespie, and Mizobuchi 1963). The *cysC* region contains a cluster of five cysteine genes (*cysC, D, H, I,* and *J*). Transduction studies of recombination between mutant *cys* markers distributed along the region showed a total length of 137 arbitrary units, 75 units of which constitute a "silent section," located in the middle of the gene cluster between *cysD* and *cysH*. Tests with deletions covering about 95 per cent of the silent section revealed that it contains no genes affecting growth rate or any other property detectable in our experiments.

A good illustration of a cryptic gene is the suppressor of *leu500* in *S. typhimurium* described by Mukai and Margolin (1963). Earlier studies (Demerec and Z. Hartman 1956) had indicated that the region of the chromosome between a cluster of four *try* loci and the neighboring *cysB* cluster is considerably longer than the section covered by the four *try* loci. Mukai and Margolin found that deletion mutations anywhere throughout this intermediate region had no detectable effect except suppression of the *leu500* mutant gene, which is located a considerable distance from *try*; thus the region carries a *leu500*-suppressor gene locus, in which single-site mutations have been induced by treatment with 2-aminopurine. Judged by recombination frequencies, several additional genes can be accommodated in the region between *try* and *cysB*.

Inert DNA, if it exists, must play some role in the harmonious functioning of the genome, for otherwise it would have been eliminated in the course of evolution. It might, for example, act simply as a spacer that exists in short, medium, or long segments depending on the requirements of adjacent genes, or it might determine the starting or stopping point for the synthesis of messenger RNA.

Conclusions

The main contributions of Mendel's report, whose centennial we have honored here, are the initial evidence, well supported experimentally, that characters carried by two parents segregate in the offspring without undergoing any change, and Mendel's conclusion that factors present in the germ cells of the parents are responsible for the transmission of inherited characteristics. From that time forth these factors, the bearers of heredity that were later named genes, have been pictured as material particles possessing a high degree of stability. As time progressed, studies revealed that the genes are located in chromosomes and are, as a rule, present in every living cell of an organism.

Until a good model of physical gene structure became available, geneticists had calculated gene size in terms of diameter and radius, reflecting the prevalent visualization of genes as spherical bodies. The same point of view was suggested in Belling's chromomere hypothesis. In 1953, however, a new concept was introduced by the Watson-Crick model of DNA and its application to genetic material. But the idea that the gene is the functional unit of genetic systems has remained unchanged and has withstood several attempts at modification. I am confident that it will continue to do so.

Literature Cited

ANDERSON, E. G., AND M. DEMEREC, 1922. Studies of somatic mutations in variegated maize pericarp. III. An interpretation. Anat. Rec. 23: 90–91 (abstr.).

ANDERSON, E. G., AND W. H. EYSTER, 1928. Pericarp studies in maize. III. The frequency of mutation in variegated maize pericarp. Genetics 13: 111–120.

BABCOCK, E. B., 1933. John Belling. J. Hered. 24: 296–300.

BELLING, J., 1931. Chromomeres of liliaceous plants. Univ. California Publ. Bot. 16: 153–170.

BENZER, S., 1955. Fine structure of a genetic region in bacteriophage. Proc. Nat. Acad. Sci. U.S. 41: 344–354.

———, 1956. Genetic fine structure and its relation to the DNA molecule. Brookhaven Symp. Biol. 8: 3–5.

BONNER, J. M., 1951. Gene-enzyme relationships in *Neurospora*. Cold Spring Harbor Symp. Quant. Biol. 16: 143–157.

BRIDGES, C. B., 1938. A revised map of the salivary gland X-chromosome of *Drosophila melanogaster*. J. Hered. 29: 11–13.

CAIRNS, J., 1963. The chromosome of *Escherichia coli*. Cold Spring Harbor Symp. Quant. Biol. 28: 43–46.

CLOWES, R. C., 1964. Genetic fine structure in bacteria. *The Bacteria*, vol. 5, pp. 253–326. Edited by I. C. Gunsalus. Academic Press, New York.

CORRENS, C., 1902. Ueber Bastardierungsversuche mit Mirabilis-Sippen. Ber. deut. bot. Ges. 20: 594–608.

———, 1910. Der Übergang aus dem homozygotischen in einen heterozygotischen Zustand im selben Individuum bei buntblättrigen und gestreiftblühenden Mirabilis-Sippen. Ber. deut. bot. Ges. 28: 418–434.

———, 1919. Vererbungsversuche mit buntblättrigen Sippen. I. *Capsella bursa-pastoris albovariabilis* und *chlorina*. Sitzber. preuss. Akad. Wiss. 34: 585–610.

DEMEREC, M., 1928. Mutable characters of *Drosophila virilis*. I. Reddish-alpha body character. Genetics 13: 359–388.

——, 1929a. Changes in the rate of mutability of the mutable miniature gene of *Drosophila virilis*. Proc. Nat. Acad. Sci. U.S. **15**: 870–876.

——, 1929b. Genetic factors stimulating mutability of the miniature-gamma wing character of *Drosophila virilis*. Proc. Nat. Acad. Sci. U.S. **15**: 834–838.

——, 1930. A genetic factor affecting germinal mutability of miniature-alpha wing character of *Drosophila virilis*. *The Laws of Life,* pp. 45–56. Aventinum, Prague.

——, 1931. Behaviour of two mutable genes of *Delphinium ajacis*. J. Genet. **24**: 179–193.

——, 1932. Rate of instability of miniature-3 gamma gene of *Drosophila virilis* in the males in the homozygous and in the heterozygous females. Proc. Nat. Acad. Sci. U.S. **18**: 656–658.

——, 1935. Unstable genes. Bot. Rev. **1**: 233–248.

——, 1938. Eighteen years of research on the gene. Carnegie Inst. Wash. Publ. No. 501: 295–314.

——, 1953. Reaction of genes of *Escherichia coli* to certain mutagens. Symp. Soc. Exp. Biol. **7**: 43–54.

——, 1955. What is a gene?—Twenty years later. Amer. Natur. **89**: 5–20.

——, 1963. Selfer mutants of *Salmonella typhimurium*. Genetics **48**: 1519–1531.

DEMEREC, M., D. H. GILLESPIE, AND K. MIZOBUCHI, 1963. Genetic structure of the *cys-C* region of the *Salmonella* genome. Genetics **48**: 997–1009.

DEMEREC, M., P. E. HARTMAN, H. MOSER, D. KANAZIR, Z. E. DEMEREC, P. L. FITZGERALD, S. W. GLOVER, E. L. LAHR, W. E. WESTOVER, AND T. YURA, 1955. Bacterial genetics I. Carnegie Inst. Wash. Year Book **54**: 219–234.

DEMEREC, M., AND Z. HARTMAN, 1956. Tryptophan mutants in *Salmonella typhimurium*. Carnegie Inst. Wash. Publ. No. 612: 5–33.

DEMEREC, M., H. MOSER, J. HEMMERLY, L. BLOMSTRAND, Z. E. DEMEREC, P. L. FITZGERALD, S. W. GLOVER, J. F. HANSON, F. J. NIELSEN, AND T. YURA, 1954. Bacterial genetics I. Carnegie Inst. Wash. Year Book **53**: 225–241.

DUBININ, N. P., 1932. Step-allelomorphism and the theory of centres of the gene, achaete-scute. J. Genet. **26**: 37–58.

EMERSON, R. A., 1913. The possible origin of mutations in somatic cells. Amer. Natur. **47**: 375–377.

——, 1914. The inheritance of a recurring somatic variation in variegated ears of maize. Amer. Natur. **48**: 87–115.

——, 1917. Genetical studies of variegated pericarp in maize. Genetics **2**: 1–35.

——, 1922. Studies of somatic mutations in variegated maize pericarp. I. Relative frequency of dominant somatic mutations in homozygous and in heterozygous variegated pericarp. Anat. Rec. **23**: 90–91.

——, 1929. The frequency of somatic mutation in variegated pericarp of maize. Genetics **14**: 488–511.

EYSTER, W. H., 1924. A genetic analysis of variegation. Genetics **9**: 372–404.

——, 1928. The mechanism of variegation. Verhandl. V int. Kongr. Vererbungwiss. (1927) **1**: 666–686.

———, 1929. The bearing of variegations on the nature of the gene. Proc. Int. Congr. Plant Sci. (1926) **1**: 923–941.

GILES, N. H., 1951. Studies on the mechanism of reversion in biochemical mutants of *Neurospora crassa*. Cold Spring Harbor Symp. Quant. Biol. **16**: 283–313.

GOWEN, J. W., AND E. H. GAY, 1933. Gene number, kind, and size in *Drosophila*. Genetics **18**: 1–31.

HALL, J. B., AND J. W. SEDAT, 1965. Isolation and characterization of the messenger RNA for gramicidin S biosynthesis. Federation Proc. **24**: 282.

HOLLEY, R. W., J. APGAR, G. A. EVERETT, J. T. MADISON, M. MARQUISEE, S. H. MERRILL, J. R. PENSWICK, AND A. ZAMIR, 1965. Structure of a ribonucleic acid. Science **147**: 1462–1465.

LEA, D. E., 1940. A radiation method for determining the number of genes in the X-chromosome of *Drosophila*. J. Genet. **39**: 181–188.

MORGAN, T. H., 1922. On the mechanism of heredity. Proc. Roy. Soc. Lond. B **94**: 162–197.

MUKAI, F. H., AND P. MARGOLIN, 1963. Analysis of unlinked suppressors of an O^o mutation in *Salmonella*. Proc. Nat. Acad. Sci. U.S. **50**: 140–148.

MULLER, H. J., 1927. Artificial transmutation of the gene. Science **6**: 84–87.

———, 1929. The gene as the basis of life. Proc. Int. Congr. Plant Sci. (1926) **1**: 897–921.

PONTECORVO, G., 1952. Genetical analysis of cell organization. Symp. Soc. Exp. Biol. **6**: 218–229.

ROPER, J. A., 1953. Pseudo-allelism. Advance. Genet. **5**: 208–215.

SEREBROVSKY, A. S., 1930. Untersuchungen über Treppenallelomorphismus. IV. Transgenation scute-6 und ein Fall des "Nicht-Allelomorphismus" von Gliedern einer Allelomorphenreihe bei *Drosophila melanogaster*. Wilhelm Roux' Arch. Entwicklungsmech. Organ. **122**: 88–104.

VRIES, H. DE, 1901. *Die Mutationstheorie. Versuche über die Entstehung von Arten im Pflanzenreich,* vol. 1: Die Entstehung der Arten durch Mutation. Veit R. Co., Leipzig.

II

Mutation, Recombination, and Genetic Coding

5

Molecular Aspects of Genetics

M. Delbrück

Part II of this volume, "Mutation, Recombination, and Genetic Coding," concerns some of the *molecular* aspects of genetics—the denouement, as it were, of the detective story of genetics. One might expect that a review of molecular genetics would logically begin with a consideration of the *structure* of the genetic material, DNA, to be followed with a consideration of the two *normal* functions of DNA—replication and read-out. These are the two functions which DNA must perform all the time, its everyday business. Mutation and recombination are second-order effects, or errors in a sense. To be sure, without mutation and recombination we would not get very far in evolution, but ideally we might envisage an evolutionary stage in which life could carry on without mutation and recombination. The reader will note, however, that structure and replication are not included here, while read-out is represented only by its static element, the genetic code.

The chosen emphasis, for this part of the book, on mutation and recombination and on the genetic code reflects both the immediacy of these topics in current research and the breadth of genetics, whose subject matter can be covered sketchily at best in a multifaceted volume such as this.

I should like to point out that the mode of replication of DNA is by no means a settled matter. It is true, of course, that DNA replication is known to lead to a semiconservative distribution of the parental strands, as originally postulated by Watson and Crick and as first demonstrated so elegantly by Meselson, Stahl, and Vinograd, using density labels to distinguish the parental from the daughter DNA strands and an equilibrium density gradient to separate the parental duplexes from the daughter duplexes. Although this simple end result is known, some details remain puzzling and uncertain.

One of these details concerns the enzyme performing the function of normal replication. The enzyme DNA-polymerase, which was isolated by Kornberg from bacteria, was thought for a number of years to be the "replicase," but now seems much more likely to be involved in repair functions. The true replicase probably has not yet been isolated at all in functional form, nor has its mechanism of action been established.

Another aspect of replication which is still as puzzling as it was on the day Watson and Crick discovered the structure of DNA concerns the twisting of the DNA duplex during replication. The scheme of Watson and Crick requires that the two strands of the parental molecule be separated from each other during replication, implying that, in a bacterium, the entire length of the molecule (1000 times the dimension of the cell) rotates around its axis, like a speedometer cable, and at a rate of several hundred revolutions per second; furthermore, the molecule must be coiled like a skein of wool inside the bacterium. Whether this rotation is a physical reality no one has yet determined. Surely it should be possible to devise an ingenious physical technique that will permit an answer.

Read-out, we have learned, consists of two parts: *transcription* from DNA to messenger RNA and *translation* of messenger RNA into protein. The complex mechanisms of transcription and translation unfortunately could not be discussed here, for they delve deeply into biochemistry. However, the formal side of the read-out, the genetic code, is presented as the conclusion to this part. The breaking of the code is the most recent of the dramatic successes of molecular genetics; only during the last year have the bulk of the codons been identified. Hence it seems appropritate to culminate the survey of molecular aspects of genetics with a chapter by one of the foremost analysts of the code.

The two genetic error processes, mutation and recombination, have a longer, richer, and more complex research history than do the normal functions. For decades mutation and recombination of the genes were the only genetic properties that might lead to an unraveling of the mystery of the genetic material, and an enormous amount of effort has been spent at refining the tools of research in these areas. However, the historical development of molecular genetics has bypassed these lines of research. Our understanding of the basic chemistry of the genes did not come from research on mutation and recombination but from the new approaches opened up by the study of the genetics of microorganisms. We are now reaching the point where we may be able to interpret mutation and recombination in molecular terms and to apply these insights toward analysis of the higher organization of the chromosomes.

6

Changes in the Concept of Mutation and the Aims of Mutation Research

Charlotte Auerbach

Chronologically, mutation research up to the present day may be divided roughly into four periods, each characterized not only by its discoveries but even more by the questions that were asked, the types of experiment that were carried out, and the hypotheses that were formulated. During the first period, from the beginning of the century to 1927, the concepts of mutation and mutation rate were developed. In 1927 discovery of the mutagenic action of X-rays initiated the second period, which lasted to about 1945, and culminated in a unified theory of mutation. In its essentials, this theory was complete in the late 1930's, when it was presented in several reviews by Timoféeff-Ressovsky and his co-workers. Soon after the second world war, the biophysical view of radiation-induced mutations received comprehensive treatment in books by Lea and by Zimmer and Timoféeff, while Schrödinger discussed it in terms of quantum mechanics. By that time, however, experiments with ultraviolet light and chemical mutagens had revealed complexities that could not be fitted into the suggested biophysical framework. There followed a transitional period, in which the interpretation of many new and intriguing findings was hampered by ignorance of the chemical nature of the gene. This period ended in 1953. As more and more geneticists accepted DNA as the essential genetic material, there emerged the characteristic feature of the present period of mutation research: the primacy of chemistry and biochemistry in the planning and interpretation of experiments. Some think that the end of this period is already in view. I am inclined to agree with them, but I do not think that the end of mutation research is in view. On the contrary, I believe that we are just beginning to enter the most exciting period, when the necessarily oversimplified physical and chemical interpretations will be used as stepping stones for a biological analysis of the mutation process.

The whole field of mutation research has been dominated by the ideas and experiments of Muller. He provided the conceptual framework, formulated the decisive questions, worked out ingenious experimental techniques, and at all stages guided the interpretation of the increasing mass of data into a coherent theory. Many of the ideas and suggestions put forward by him at a time when the means for testing them were not yet available have later been proved correct.

The First Period (1900–27)

The concept of mutation

When Mendel carried out his experiments, he was interested in heredity pure and simple. When his results were rediscovered, Darwinism occupied the center of interest. The early geneticists devoted much of their attention to explanations of natural selection, based on the newly found theories of Mendel. Thus, the first questions asked about mutations concerned their suitability as raw material for selection; i.e., what were their frequencies and effects. The way in which these questions finally were answered belongs in the history of the evolution theory.

Already at this early stage and immediately after the discovery of the first presumed "mutations" by de Vries, geneticists asked questions about the causes of mutation. Of necessity, the answers were wholly speculative, but they are of interest as forerunners of later theories. One question, which has been debated ever since, cropped up at almost the same time as the concept of mutation, although it was not then specifically formulated: At what time in the life cycle of the genes—or "pangenes" as they then were called—do mutations preferentially arise? While de Vries believed that mutations occur at the time when the pangenes divide, Correns apparently envisaged that changes take place within existing genes. De Vries' distinction between progressive mutations, resulting from gain of hereditary properties, and retrogressive mutations, resulting from loss of those properties, is a forerunner of Bateson's presence-absence theory. It seems, however, that de Vries did not really visualize the physical gain or loss of pangenes but their activation or inactivation.

The presence-absence theory

Although this theory was based largely on the confusion between gene and character that is found in many of Bateson's writings, and although it is obvious that evolution could not have proceeded as a mere succession of loss mutations, experimental refutation of the presence-absence theory was extraordinarily difficult. It is true that observations soon turned up which contradicted the theory, but all these could be explained away by additional assumptions, which might have seemed plausible but were not testable. This has remained a popular way for protecting cherished theories against adverse experimental evidence.

Mutation rate

A decisive step forward was taken in the early 1920's, when Muller introduced the concept of mutation frequencies, or mutation rates, in *Drosophila*. It is this conceptual step, rather than the shortly ensuing discovery of the mutagenic action of X-rays, that marks the beginning of modern mutation research.

The Second Period (1927–45)
The production of mutations by X-rays

When Muller in 1927 and Stadler in 1928 reported the production of mutations by X-rays, the availability of a conceptual and experimental framework for mutation studies led to the tremendous burst of discoveries that followed close on the original one. For two decades, X-ray mutagenesis dominated almost all branches of genetics, and its role is far from being played out even now. It has provided a powerful tool that has been put to a multitude of different uses, including the fashioning of further tools of a remarkably delicate and intricate nature. Mutations and structural chromosome changes have been produced to order and have furnished the means for studying, among other problems, gene dosage effects, the mechanism of sex determination, position effects, and the mechanics of chomosome movement. The most important contribution of radiation mutagenesis was, however, the new evidence it provided on the nature of mutation itself.

Intragenic and intergenic changes

At an early stage in the X-ray work, it was found that radiation produces chromosome rearrangements as well as point mutations, and that rearrangements may resemble point mutations in phenotypes and segregation ratios. This observation led to a revival of the presence-absence theory in a modified and enlarged form.

It was claimed by some geneticists that all apparent gene mutations result from deletions, position effects, or restituted chromosome breaks. From an evolutionary point of view, this theory was as untenable as the original presence-absence theory; for if mutations are attributed to rearrangements of existing chromosome sections, then the rearranged sections must have been qualitatively different from each other to start with, and these primary differences must have arisen through qualitative mutations. In one version of the theory, the paradox was indeed recognized and the necessity for qualitative mutations in the course of evolution was admitted. This concession, however, was accompanied by the hypothesis that the mutations observed in experiments, even the spontaneous ones, are due to rearrangements or deficiencies. In this form, the theory was as difficult to disprove as had been the old presence-absence theory. Especially difficult to test critically was the concept that all X-ray induced mutations are connected with chromosome breakage.

Viewed from the present-day standpoint, the controversy has in part been resolved, in part it is seen to involve a question of terminology, and in part it persists in a slightly modified form. There can be no doubt that mutations may be the result of chemical changes of individual genes; this is obvious for base substitutions. Whether deletions or insertions of one or a few bases should likewise be classed among qualitative gene changes is a semantic question; I personally think they should. Although on close analysis they may be distinguished from base substitutions, the crucial fact remains that they, like base substitutions, cause mutational changes that are restricted to the limits of the individual cistron in which they occurred. There still remains the question whether there is a difference between deletions and rearrangements of whole genes on the one hand and corresponding changes within genes on the other or, expressed differently, between "intergenic" and "intragenic" changes.

The target theory

Regarding the nature and origin of mutations, the biophysical analysis provided a picture that remains impressive for its clarity but laid itself open to attack for its oversimplification. The focal point of this picture is the concept of genes as targets for hits by ionization. The narrow concept of the target as identical with the gene met with theoretical and experimental objections and soon was replaced by the concept of the target as a sensitive volume within which an ionization has a high probability of producing a mutation. Neither the size of the sensitive volume nor the probability that a hit on the target will produce a mutation—the "mutagenic efficiency of a hit"—was conceived as accurately fixed; both were admitted to be under environmental control to some extent.

Direct and indirect action of X-rays

Variations in the mutagenic efficiency of hits on the target could not then be interpreted. Most probably these occur during the processes that follow the initial lesion in the gene, but we are only on the verge of understanding some of those processes.

Radiochemical observations seemed to provide an explanation for variations in the size of the sensitive volume. It had been shown that ionizing radiations inactivate enzymes in aqueous solution by means of highly reactive free radicals. If this is true also for the action of radiation on genes, then the sensitive volume will change with any conditions that affect the diffusion rate of free radicals. There is little doubt that free radicals can act as intermediaries between ionizations and the gene, but the degree to which this happens has been much debated. Not long ago, a large proportion of all X-ray induced mutations was attributed to indirect effects via free radicals. Now, the pendulum has swung the other way, and direct effects of ionizations on DNA are considered the most important mechanism of X-ray mutagenesis. Whatever the contribution of indirect effects, it cannot change the essential features of the target theory; for the diffusion radius of free radicals is so small that the sensitive volume for indirect radiation effects is not much larger than the gene itself. It is not even large enough to explain the sometimes striking differences in sensitive volume between genes in different cell types.

The role of stable chemical intermediates in radiation mutagenesis

Sweeping attacks on the target theory were made soon after the discovery of chemical mutagens. The fact that chemicals can produce many of the same effects as X-rays was taken to indicate that X-rays, too, must act by chemical intermediates. This argument has always seemed inconclusive to me. The target theory is based on a vast and impressive body of radiation data; it cannot be disproved by observations of an entirely different nature. Similarity of ends does not imply similarity of means, and what we detect as mutations may well have been produced in a variety of vastly different ways. There is much more validity in the contrary argument. *Because* the target theory has been so clearly established, stable chemical intermediates with wide diffusion range can at best play a very minor role in mutagenesis by ionizing radiations. This conclusion would remain valid even if recent reports on mutagenic effects of X-irradiated organic media should be substantiated. The doses used in these experiments were extremely high and the results were slight. There is no reason why heavy irradiation of organic substances should not sometimes produce a mutagenic compound, but this has no bearing on the way in which lower doses produce mutations in directly irradiated cells. Ultraviolet light, too, may act in different ways under different circumstances of application.

In directly irradiated cells it produces mutations through its action on DNA, while higher doses of shorter wave length generate mutagenic peroxides in organic media.

The biophysical approach to spontaneous mutation

The biophysical approach was less successful in its interpretation of spontaneous mutation than in its explanation of radiation effects. Since natural background radiation was found insufficient to cause spontaneous mutations at the frequencies observed, and since no effective chemical mutagens had yet been detected, all spontaneous mutations were ascribed to the occasional occurrence of strong thermal oscillations in the neighborhood of a gene. Activation energies for mutations in *Drosophila* were calculated from spontaneous mutation frequencies in flies reared at different temperatures. However, both in its experimental design and in its underlying assumptions, this investigation neglected complexities of the spontaneous mutation process which at that time were unknown. Moreover, the possibility that spontaneous mutations may arise through errors during replication was left out of consideration.

The origin of spontaneous mutations has remained a subject for conjecture. Present-day speculations have to consider not only cosmic rays and thermal oscillations but also naturally occurring chemicals. Compared with the older speculations, they have the great advantage of starting with a precise idea of the chemical nature of the gene.

The Third Period (1945–53)

Chemical mutagens. Microorganisms

New means for mutation research became available during the second world war; with the re-establishment of international communication, this led to a great expansion of mutation work. The first chemical mutagens were discovered in the war years; their number increased rapidly and is still increasing now. The variety of mutagens available permitted comparisons among mutations that had been produced by a great diversity of means. Mutation work on fungi started shortly before the war and, soon after the war, was followed by the introduction of bacteria and viruses as test objects. The development of screening tests for mutations in microorganisms opened the way for experimentation on an unprecedented scale.

For nearly a decade, however, these rapid advances in breadth of approach were not matched by similarly rapid advances in depth, toward a better understanding of the molecular and cellular events involved in mutagenesis. As a result of this disproportionate growth, there was something curiously incomplete about the achievements of this period. New avenues of research were opened up, new phenomena were discovered, and new problems were piled on top of the old ones. Let me briefly mention a few of them:

New findings. New problems

(1) Originally it was thought possible that the chemical nature of mutagens might throw some light on the chemical nature of the gene and of mutation. However, the diversity of chemical mutagens was so great that it defied any attempt at a unified *chemical explanation of mutation.*

(2) Different mutagens were found to produce vastly differing ratios of rearrangements to point mutations. This suggested an essential difference between genes and *intergenic linkers,* but alternative explanations could not be ruled out and the question remained undecided. It is still undecided in spite of clear evidence that in *Drosophila* potential chromosome breaks and potential point mutations react differently to conditions of storage. While this shows a difference in the mechanisms by which intergenic and intragenic changes arise, it does not prove a chemical difference between the affected chromosomal regions.

(3) In chemically treated *Drosophila* chromosomes, mutations often arose after a delay of many cell cycles. This indicated a long-persisting state of *premutation,* the nature of which was much debated but could not be decisively established by experiment.

(4) Ultraviolet radiation was found to produce a different type of premutated state which persists for only one cell cycle and can be reversed by visible light, or, in certain bacterial systems, by inhibition of protein synthesis. This was the first indication of *repair mechanisms* in mutagenesis.

(5) The discovery of *mutagen specificity* in microorganisms aroused lively interest but little speculation, for which no chemical model was available. In the present period, this lack of speculation has been made good with a vengeance.

(6) Experiments with the chemostat indicated that, in certain bacterial systems, mutations may arise as *changes in the existing genes* rather than as errors of replication. This finding was so contrary to the then prevailing ideas that both the generality of the result and its meaning were queried. A renewed study of these observations has been taken up quite recently.

(7) In the chemostat experiments, *antimutagens* that suppressed purine-induced mutations also suppressed a proportion of spontaneous

mutations but no radiation-induced ones. This observation seemed to furnish a lead to the nature of at least one class of spontaneous mutations, but it has not been followed up.

Summary.—Looking back on this period as a whole, I remember that for those of us who were doing mutation research it was a time of excitement as well as of frustration. The excitement came from the fact that the simple outline of the biophysical picture of mutation broke open at many points to reveal new complexities. The frustration resulted from the lack of a suitable model which would allow speculation and lead to new types of experiments. It is true that the essential role of DNA in bacterial transformation had been shown already at the beginning of the period; but the existing tetranucleotide model made DNA such an unsuitable carrier of highly specific and diversified information that many geneticists hesitated to accept generalization of these findings. This was changed in 1953 with the Watson-Crick model of DNA which, with a time lag of a few years, started the present period of mutation research.

The Fourth Period (1953——)

The fourth period is dominated by the model of the gene as a sequence of nucleotide bases in DNA or RNA. This model has solved one fundamental problem in mutation research, has altered the aspect of most old problems, has raised many new ones, and has led to entirely new types of speculation and experiment. The advances have been so quick and in so many different directions that it is impossible for me to do justice to all the new concepts and aims that have emerged in the last ten years. Since my object in this review is to illustrate the changing aspect of mutation research rather than to discuss its achievements, I shall concentrate on those problems that have been handed on to us from previous periods.

The nature of mutation.—The central problem of mutation studies has always been the search for a chemical mechanism by which the most diversely mutated genes can still preserve their capacity for self-replication. This problem ceased to exist when the Watson-Crick model of DNA replication and mutation was accepted.

The causes of mutation.—We now take it for granted that mutations are chemical changes in DNA (or RNA), and we no longer ask *whether* a mutagen reacts with DNA but *how* it reacts with it. Some mutagens act in indirect ways or under special conditions of pH, ionic environment, etc. Analysis of these preliminary steps in mutagenesis may be very important for applied mutation work, but its theoretical interest is chemical rather than genetic. Great genetic interest centers, to the contrary, upon the final chemical changes in DNA, for these are the first steps in the biological process of mutation and to a large extent determine its outcome.

The simple nature of the nucleotide code imposes narrow limitations on the types of chemical change that are possible. Within the confines of the individual gene, these are restricted to base substitutions, deletions and insertions of bases, and, possibly, changes in base sequence by inversion or transposition. Great effort and ingenuity have been spent on determining for a variety of mutagens which particular type of change each is likely to produce. When applied to virus and bacteriophage and linked up with genetic analysis of the mutant strains as well as with chemical analysis of the mutant proteins, this approach has resulted in outstanding contributions to the analysis of the genetic code. At the same time, the internal consistency of the data and the agreement of the decoding key with that determined by entirely different means have confirmed the underlying hypotheses concerning the action of the selected mutagens in the studied systems. Their action in cellular organisms is not likely to be grossly different from that observed in viruses, and this has been confirmed for several fungi. On the other hand, attempts to use chemically induced forward and reverse mutations for determining base changes at mutant sites of bacterial and fungal chromosomes have not given any clear picture, no doubt for two reasons: differences between the *in vivo* and *in vitro* effects of some chemical mutagens, and complications arising from secondary processes which in cellular organisms intervene between the lesion in DNA and the detected mutation. Analysis of mutant proteins takes us closer to the mutant base sequence and, in *E. coli,* has indeed given results that agree with the expected effects of the mutagens used.

Mutagenic DNA-precursors.—One particular type of mutagenic action that by its very nature can be observed only in treated cells is that mediated by mutagenic precursors of DNA. Certainly base analogs appear to act only after incorporation in DNA but, even here, the early reliance on purely chemical data proved to be misleading. The massive and easily detectable incorporation of 5-bromouracil in place of thymine, which at first was considered the main source of mutagenic action, now appears to be much less mutagenic than its chemically hardly detectable incorporation in place of cytosine. Action via faulty DNA-precursors has been claimed also for a few other mutagens, but in no case was the evidence conclusive.

Mutation and gene replication.—The question of how mutagenic precursors act is closely bound up with one of the oldest problems in mutation research: Are all mutations caused by errors in gene replication? While those mutations acting via DNA-precursors must involve errors in replication, there is also clear evidence that spontaneous as well as induced mutations may arise as changes within existing genes. This fact is even more difficult to understand in the context of our present ideas about mutation than it would be in terms of the older, vaguer theories of mutagenesis. So far, we know of only one mutagenic treatment that might be expected to change one allele directly into another: the change of cytosine into uracil when RNA is treated with nitrous acid. All other mutagenic treatments are considered to produce first an intermediate chemical change that requires replication before it yields a mutation. Clearly, there is still a problem here. It is linked up with another old problem, that of mosaicism.

The problem of mosaicism.—Mutations that arise as replication errors should always give rise to mosaic clones or organisms; those that arise as changes in existing genes should generally also produce mosaics because most mutagens are presumed to act on only one strand of DNA, leaving the other strand unmutated. The actual findings do not agree with this expectation. They are complex and bewildering. Most mutagens produce both complete and mosaic mutations, but the ratio between the two varies between mutagens and organisms and may even vary between experiments carried out with the same mutagen applied to the same or closely related cell types. Attempts to explain complete mutations as the result of simultaneous lethal hits on the nonmutated, complementary strand of DNA have been contradicted by experimental evidence. A number of alternative hypotheses have been put forward but, so far, none has been proved. The most recent of these, and, to me, the most attractive, invokes the action of a cut-and-patch repair mechanism by which the base opposite the chemically changed one may be replaced in a complementary fashion. If the efficiency of this mechanism depended on cell type and experimental conditions, including the mutagen used, the great variability of the observations could be explained.

Delayed mutation.—The double-strandedness of DNA is not the only source of mosaic mutations. In *Drosophila,* several or many cell cycles may intervene between chemical treatment of a chromosome and the appearance of a rearrangement, deletion, or mutation. Originally, two main hypotheses were offered to account for this phenomenon. One of these postulated that the *Drosophila* chromosome is multistranded, that chemicals usually affect only one or a few strands, and that belated mutations appear when the sorting-out of mutated from nonmutated strands in successive mitoses has resulted in a cell with a preponderance of mutated strands. According to the other hypothesis, chemical treatment may create metastable molecular configurations which subsequently may lead to chromosome breakage or mutation.

The strandedness theory could be shown to be invalid for chromosome breakage because, in chemically treated *Drosophila* chromosomes, breaks may accumulate in the absence of replication. No similar evidence could be obtained for delayed point mutations but, if these are attributed to strand segregation, *Drosophila* chromosomes must contain very many strands to account for the often considerable mutagenic delay.

The molecular theory of mutagenesis attributes delayed mutation to repeatedly committed errors of replication by the same chemically changed template strand. While this hypothesis may explain certain observations in bacteriophage and bacteria, it clearly cannot account for the old findings on *Drosophila* nor for the very recent, similar findings on *Drosophila,* yeast, and *Neurospora:* The crucial point, and one that is often overlooked, is that in all these experiments one original mosaic gave rise to *several* mosaics for the same or a closely linked mutation, and this process repeated itself over several generations of flies and over many replatings of mosaic yeast colonies. Here, then, chemical treatment must have created instabilities which not only can produce mutations but can also replicate as instabilities.

The nature of these *replicating instabilities* is an intriguing puzzle. I suspect that the solution may be found not at the molecular level but in some supramolecular mechanism, involving perhaps a special type of rearrangement or the action of a controlling element. A number of analogies come to mind and suggest experimental approaches: Among the progeny of chemically treated mice, a pedigree of delayed visible mutation could be traced back to a translocation. In bacteria, a duplication has been shown to serve as the source of recurrent deletions. In maize, many loci become mutable through the action of controlling elements. Unstable mutations in bacteria have been tentatively attributed to the effects of episomes.

Repair mechanisms and secondary steps in the mutation process.— These long-persisting and replicating instabilities are quite different in nature from the short-lived premutational stages that by now are known to follow treatment not only with ultraviolet light but also with X-rays and at least with certain chemicals. Here the labile stage persists only until the next DNA replication and during this period can be reversed by a variety of repair mechanisms, at least some of which have been shown to be enzymatic in nature. Thus, whether a chemical change in DNA will yield a mutation depends to a large degree on the functioning of enzymatic processes in the living cell. Mutagenesis therefore must be thought of as a biological process in which a chemical change in DNA is only the first step, although an indispensable one. Indeed, the action of repair mechanisms is not the only secondary step in mutagenesis. Transcription of the new type of information, its translation into a new protein, the development of a new biochemical pattern in the cell, in many cases the rejoining of broken chromosome ends, and finally the establishment of a mutant clone often under stringent conditions of screening—all these are links in a chain of cellular processes that have to be carried out successfully before a primary change in DNA is expressed as a detectable mutation.

The study of the secondary steps in mutagenesis has hardly begun, although many observations stress their importance. The success of the molecular approach to mutation has been so dazzling that a tendency has developed to interpret all mutation data at the level of the DNA molecule. The many findings that cannot be fitted into this mold are either disregarded as irrelevant or, at best, laid aside until a time when the molecular approach will have expanded beyond its preoccupation with DNA to embrace events at more remote cellular levels. I feel that this is a dangerous restriction of scientific curiosity, which must lead to the loss of potentially important discoveries. Photorepair, dark repair, chemical mutagenesis, delayed mutation, suppressor mutations, and many other phenomena had first to be detected in the living cell before molecular hypotheses could be devised in explanation and could be tested *in vitro*.

Moreover, the biological approach is at present the only possible and fruitful way to analyze the increasing number of mutations and related changes that have been found to be the result of interactions between elements of the genome or between genes and cytoplasm—for example, the effects of mutator genes, mutable loci in maize and other organisms, paramutation, the segregation-distorter phenomenon in *Drosophila melanogaster*, and the maternal chromosome-breakage factor in *Drosophila robusta*. There is now also evidence for mutational changes in cytoplasmic elements, but these are outside the scope of this review.

Mutagen specificity.—This is one area of research where, in my opinion, progress has been held back by a narrow chemical approach. From the start, there has been a tendency to ascribe the preferential action of certain mutagens on certain genes or alleles to specific reactions between mutagens and genes. A more precise model was provided by the analysis of induced mutations in the *r*II region of phage T4. Here, some mutagens produce "hot spots," at which mutations are crowded together into specific sites; other mutagens show a more or less pronounced preference for one or two of the four nucleotide bases of DNA. Because of these findings the feeling has arisen that, in a general way, we can now account for mutagen specificity, although in cellular organisms complications may arise through prior reaction of the mutagen with cytoplasmic components or the chromosome-associated protein. This attitude discourages further analysis, for which chemical means are lacking.

I have never been able to share the belief that mutagen specificity must be caused by the selective action of a given mutagen on a certain base or base sequence in DNA. Certainly, there may be cases for which this is true, but I believe that these are the exception rather than the rule. Actually, a satisfactory molecular explanation even for the "hot spots" in bacteriophage has not yet been provided; moreover, their "temperature" depends not only on the mutagen and the site in DNA but also on the type of host cell used for screening. This indicates that secondary steps in mutagenesis play a role. I think that this may be true for most cases of mutagen specificity. Support for this assumption comes from many observations, of which I shall cite only four:

(1) When ultraviolet-treated bacteria are plated on a medium that inhibits protein synthesis, certain mutations fail to appear while others are not affected. Under these conditions, ultraviolet radiation specifically produces a certain type of mutation, and specificity probably resides at the level of the repair mechanism.

(2) In mutation experiments on a variety of fungi, ingredients of the plating medium suppressed certain mutations when these had been produced by one mutagen but not when they had been produced by a different mutagen. Here, specificity arose long after treatment.

(3) In bacteria, genes that were refractory to the action of a given mutagen became responsive when the metabolic pattern of the cell was changed by introduction of an unrelated mutant gene.

(4) Streptomycin, 5-fluorouracil, and other substances suppress specific classes of mutations by acting on the transcription or translation mechanism. If these substances were mutagenic, they would suppress certain types among the mutations that they themselves had induced. Perhaps this does happen with mutagenic alkylating agents, which have been shown to interfere with decoding *in vitro* and may well do so *in vivo*.

The assumption that mutagen specificity usually arises at a secondary level has the heuristic value that it encourages a type of analysis which may contribute to a better understanding of mutation as a complex biological process. It also plays a role in evaluating the possibilities of applied mutation research.

Applied mutation research.—This has two opposite aims. On the

negative side, the goal is to minimize mutational damage from mutagenic agents in the environment of modern man. On the positive side,
researchers would like to direct the mutation process in economically
important plants and microorganisms toward a preponderance or at
least a reasonable frequency of desirable mutants. The greater selectiv-
ity of chemical mutagens compared with ionizing radiation has opposite significance in these two projects. Estimates of genetic radiation
damage to man can be based with some degree of reliability on experiments with lower organisms; on the other hand, it is not likely that we
shall ever achieve more than a very modest control over the type of
mutation that is induced by ionizing radiation. For chemical mutagens
it is exceedingly difficult to derive estimates of genetic damage to hu-
mans from experimental data; perhaps it is impossible for all but the
most reactive and penetrating chemicals. There is, however, a distinct
hope that we may learn to increase the proportion of desirable mutants
after treatment with chemical mutagens by choosing the right ancillary
conditions, such as genotypical background, cell stage, and plating
medium. While these conditions are not likely to influence the primary
action of the chosen mutagen on DNA, they may act as selective sieves
which prevent the appearance of undesirable mutants or further that
of desirable ones. The search for such conditions requires a thorough
study of the biological aspects of mutagenesis.

7

The Molecular Basis of Genetic Recombination

Matthew Meselson

The previously unpublished experiments cited in this paper were performed with the support of a grant from the National Science Foundation.

The recombination of linked genetic factors must frequently, if not always, be ascribed to an interaction between homologous DNA molecules to yield DNA molecules having a nucleotide sequence partly that of one parent molecule and partly that of the other. What is the structure of a recombinant molecule produced by this remarkable interaction and what steps lead to its formation?

During the last few years, a combination of genetic and physico-chemical evidence, interpreted within the framework of the Watson-Crick model, has provided us with a rather detailed picture of the structures produced by recombination. According to this picture, the unreplicated or primary recombinant is an uninterrupted DNA duplex made up of pieces of the parent duplexes. That is, recombination occurs by breakage and joining of double-stranded DNA. At a site of joining, the complementary polynucleotide chains of a given parental segment terminate at different levels, separated by approximately 10^3 nucleotide pairs, so that complementary chains of different parentage overlap one another to form a hybrid region. Although the recombinant is made almost entirely of pieces of parental DNA, some of its material is newly synthesized; portions of the parental chains in the region of joining are removed and are replaced by copying of a complementary chain. The exact pattern of this removal and replacement cannot yet be specified. At least in many systems, and aside from the localized consequences of removal and replacement, recombinant molecules are produced in reciprocal pairs. A pair of structures with these various features is depicted in Figure 7.1.

Some features of the structures just described are securely established; others are less so. Almost nothing is known of the steps leading

4:4   5:3   6:2   5:3   4:4

Fig. 7.1.—Possible structures of two double-stranded DNA molecules following a single exchange between them. Solid and dashed lines represent polynucleotide chains from different parent molecules. Heavy solid regions indicate where parental chains have been excised and replaced by synthesis along a complementary strand of opposite parentage. The particular pattern of excision and synthesis is not to be considered unique. The meiotic output will consist of the two indicated structures plus a nonrecombinant chromosome of each parental type. Segregation ratios at the first post-meiotic mitosis are indicated at various levels.

to their formation. It is quite sure that bacteriophage recombination very frequently occurs by breakage and joining of double-stranded DNA molecules, but other mechanisms may exist as well. In the genetic transformation of bacteria following the uptake of extracellular DNA, single-stranded rather than double-stranded donor DNA is found integrated into the recipient chromosome. In higher organisms, evidence bearing on the structure of recombinant molecules is largely genetic and therefore is often indirect. But in spite of these and other reservations, there are strong reasons to believe that genetic recombination in a wide variety of forms, from viruses to higher plants and animals, will be found to possess fundamental aspects of mechanism in common. In this chapter I will attempt to summarize the development of current views of the molecular basis of genetic recombination and to indicate some of the problems which remain to be solved.

Breakage and Joining of Chromosomes

The recombination of linked hereditary characters in the sweet pea was reported by Bateson, Saunders, and Punnett in 1906, but they did not explain their results in terms of chromosome behavior. In the same year, Lock (1906) suggested that, if the linked characters studied by Bateson and his co-workers are determined by genes on the same chromosome, then their recombination might result from a limited exchange of materials between homologs during synapsis. The speculation that synapsed chromosomes exchange materials had already been advanced by a number of biologists and had subsequently received important experimental support from evidence that the number of separately assorting genes in an organism might exceed the number of its chromosomes. This was one of the phenomena which Janssens (1909) undertook to explain with the hypothesis, based upon his cytological observations of chiasmata in salamander spermatocytes, that synapsed chromosomes exchange parts by breakage and joining. More particularly, Janssens held that synapsed chromosomes break and join in pairs at a time in meiosis when the chromosomes have already split to form tetrads, and that a given exchange occurs at the same level in both members of a pair.

Although the recombination of linked characters was implicit in Janssens' hypothesis, he did not, at the time, comment specifically upon the matter. The idea that the recombination of linked characters results from the breakage and joining of homologous chromosomes was proposed by T. H. Morgan in 1911. Morgan interpreted his findings of recombination between sex-linked characters in *Drosophila* and the earlier results with the sweet pea in terms of Janssens' hypothesis, reaching the fundamental conclusion that the frequency of recombination between any two linked characters is a measure of the linear separation of the corresponding genes on the chromosome.

Confidence in Morgan's proposal and in its underlying assumption that the genes are arranged linearly along the chromosome was strengthened by Sturtevant's (1913) invention of the genetic map and his discovery that such maps are indeed linear. As more and more crosses were effected, it also became clear that recombination is, as would be expected on evolutionary grounds, a very exact process. Its occurrence generally leaves the map unaltered, causing neither deficiencies nor additions, nor any other alteration, even in the region of observed exchange.

Important information regarding the mechanism of recombination in meiosis was provided by analysis of the distribution of genetic exchanges among the four homologs comprising a tetrad. For this purpose, special systems had to be devised for the recovery and genetic analysis of more than one homolog from a given tetrad. By 1925 there was convincing evidence for the following conclusions (Anderson 1925; Bridges and Anderson 1925; L. V. Morgan 1925): (1) Exchange occurs pairwise among the four homologs. (2) Each pair of alleles segregates in a ratio of 2:2 among the four meiotic products, regardless of the number or distribution of exchanges. That is, recombination is reciprocal. (3) All four homologs of a tetrad may recombine.

Although the genetic data were in full accord with Janssens' picture of pairwise breaking and joining of homologs sometime after the chromosomes have duplicated, the cytological evidence had never been more than suggestive. As Wilson (Wilson and Morgan 1920) pointed out in a critique of Janssens' hypothesis, there was no compelling evidence that chromosomes actually break and join in normal meiosis. Although many investigators, including Wilson, considered that breakage and joining must nevertheless be the cause of recombination, cytology provided no direct support for this inference until very recently (Taylor 1965). It should be said in this connection that some authors seem to have misinterpreted the cytogenetic experiments of Creighton and McClintock (1931) and of Stern (1931) as proof of breakage and joining. These experiments showed that recombination of characters associated with a heteromorphic chromosome pair gives rise to chromosomes which are morphologically recombinant. Although this observation provided new evidence that specific genes are located at specific sites on the chromosomes and suggested that the genes themselves provide the structural continuity of the chromosomes, it did not demonstrate that chromosomes exchange materials. In particular, the correlation observed between genetic and cytologic events could have come about if "copy-choice" rather than material exchange were the basis of recombination.

Copy-Choice

An alternative to the idea that recombination involves an exchange of materials between chromosomes was proposed by Belling (1931), who, on the basis of certain cytological appearances in the lily, suggested the forerunner of what much later came to be known as the mechanism of copy-choice. According to this general hypothesis, recombination occurs in conjunction with the synthesis of new chromosomes. A pair of parental homologs acts as the template along which new chromosomes are formed, each new chromosome copying partly one and partly the other of the two parental structures. Therefore, if copy-choice were the sole mechanism of recombination, and if parental chromosomes are not systematically excluded from the meiotic output, no more than two of the four homologs in a tetrad can possibly be recombinant. But, as we have mentioned, genetic analysis had already led to the opposite conclusion. On this account, Belling (1933) abandoned the idea that recombination occurs without breakage and joining.

After long disuse, the copy-choice idea was revived in 1949 by Hershey and Rotman, following a suggestion of Sturtevant. They performed various bacteriophage crosses and examined the distribution of recombinants in phage yields from individual bacteria. A moderate correlation between reciprocal types was found for recombination in one interval but not in two others. Hershey and Rotman concluded that, if phage recombination is indeed nonreciprocal, recombinant phage chromosomes might be formed by a process different from the reciprocal breakage and joining thought to occur in higher organisms. In particular, they raised the possibility that phage chromosomes recombine by the mechanism of "partial replicas," a nonreciprocal form of copy-choice.

However, aside from the appealing analogy it permits with the situation thought to exist in higher organisms, a connection between reciprocity and breakage and joining is not logically necessary. In phage recombination, both copy-choice and breakage and joining may be imagined to operate either reciprocally or nonreciprocally.

Whether or not elementary acts of phage recombination generally yield complementary products is still uncertain, for there are serious experimental difficulties tending to obscure whatever reciprocity there may be. However, recombination between phage genes is strongly reciprocal in at least one situation specially devised to overcome such difficulties: namely, the recombination between prophage genes in partially diploid bacteria (Meselson, unpublished).

Copy-choice has also been considered as a mechanism for the integration of chromosome fragments and episomes into the chromosomes of bacteria. Among the phenomena in this category are transformation, lysogenization, transduction, and recombination following conjugation. Copy-choice has been invoked in the discussion of these phenomena not because they provide substantial evidence for a copying mechanism but only because they present certain problems which at times have seemed difficult to solve in terms of breakage and joining. One of these problems is to ensure that an odd number of exchanges does not take place between a fragment and the bacterial chromosome, an occurrence which could break the chromosome into two pieces.

At least in the case of lysogenization by λ and related temperate bacteriophages, we have an appealing solution to the above problem, suggested by Campbell (1962) and now supported by a good deal of physical and genetic evidence. The λ chromosome is able to exist either as a rod or a ring. When the chromosome of the free phage enters a host bacterium, a ring is formed. The ring form of the chromosome is presumed able to undergo a single reciprocal exchange with a homologous region of the bacterial chromosome. The result is a linear insertion of the λ chromosome into the chromosome of the bacterium. Reversal of these steps would occur when lysogenic bacteria are induced. Similar events could also account for the integration and liberation of episomes other than temperate phages. These events—duplication resulting from exchange with a ring and the production of rings by the reverse process—are already familiar in classical cytogenetics.

Campbell's suggestion specified neither copy-choice nor breakage and joining as the mechanism for the reciprocal exchanges postulated to account for lysogenization and induction. It is even possible that these exchanges occur by a type of breakage and joining not involved in ordinary genetic recombination. In this connection, it should be kept in mind that the joining of chromosome ends following induced or spontaneous breakage and such genetically determined breakage and joining events as the transposition in maize of the Dissociation element *Ds*, accompanied by chromosome breakage at the initial *Ds* site (McClintock 1951), may well reflect mechanisms of exchange fundamentally different from those found in ordinary genetic recombination. But the case in favor of some sort of breakage and joining and against copy-choice is strongly supported by recent observations that isotopically labeled phage chromosomes are added to and removed from the bacterial chromosome in the course of lysogenization and induction respectively (Menninger, Meselson, and Wright, unpublished; Prell 1965; Ptashne 1965).

Perhaps Campbell's explanation of the integration and liberation of episomes by reciprocal exchanges involving rings can be extended to cases in which regions of the bacterial chromosome are replaced by homologous regions of donor fragments, such as occurs in transformation, recombination following bacterial conjugation, and generalized transduction. Interstitial chromosome fragments in higher organisms often form rings. A DNA fragment in a bacterium might do the same. An even number of reciprocal exchanges between a ring and a homologous region of the bacterial chromosome would give a recombinant chromosome and a recombinant ring. The ring might soon be eliminated or, if unable to duplicate, it would be diluted out in the course of bacterial multiplication. An odd number of reciprocal exchanges would give a tandem duplication within which further reciprocal exchange might soon occur, leading to the same result. Again, whatever the detailed mechanism of exchange may be, there is direct evidence that it is based on a physical exchange of DNA segments. The integration of donor

DNA has been demonstrated in transformation (Fox and Allen 1964) and is indicated in the case of conjugation (Siddiqi 1963).

The last argument we shall cite against the general occurrence of copy-choice in genetic recombination concerns the conflict between the copy-choice hypothesis and the rather well-substantiated view that chromosomes duplicate semiconservatively even in meiosis (Taylor 1965; Chiang 1965). If its duplication is semiconservative, a chromosome must have one parental subunit at any level, regardless of the parentage of its newly synthesized companion. The template switching of copy-choice must therefore be restricted to the newly synthesized subunit. Aside from its structural implausibility, the unrestricted occurrence of this process would produce frequent long regions in which the two subunits of primary recombinant chromosomes would be of opposite parentage. Neither in classical nor in microbial genetics is there any evidence for such a state of affairs. Thus, if it occurs in the course of semiconservative duplication, copy-choice must be restricted to short intervals and could therefore not account for exchanges of relatively long blocks of linked genes.

Gene Conversion

By far the most suggestive genetic evidence for some form of copying in recombination, although not necessarily copy-choice itself, comes from tetrad analysis in fungi. In the great majority of tetrads, any given pair of alleles segregates in a ratio of 2:2 among the four products of meiosis. The usual reciprocity of recombination in a tetrad may be viewed as a corollary of this fact. Occasionally, however, a 1:3 segregation is observed for a marker, although other markers on the same chromosome have segregated normally. This rather rare phenomenon is called gene conversion or, more accurately, whole chromatid gene conversion. Plate 7.1 shows two cases of 1:3 segregation of a spore color character in the ascomycete *Bombardia lunata*. There is good evidence that conversion frequently or always extends over a short region rather than being confined to a single site. An intimate connection between conversion and reciprocal recombination is suggested by the fact that normally segregating markers on opposite sides of a converted region are very often recombined. Moreover, it may well be that the physical events manifested in the genetic phenomenon of conversion occur in most or even all recombinations; genetic studies indicate that, among tetrads selected for recombination between very close markers, the frequency of conversion in the immediate region of selected exchange is very high, in some cases even approaching 100 per cent. Unless the imposed selection for exchange in short intervals has also selected for a class of exchange events not at all typical of exchange in general, we may conclude that the conversion process occurs in the immediate vicinity of at least a large fraction of all exchanges.

The modern study of conversion began with Lindegren (1953, 1955) and Mitchell (1955), although 1:3 segregations had been investigated much earlier. Conversion has been observed to take place during meiosis and during mitosis in all species which have been tested for its occurrence. Although several different explanations of 3:1 segregation may be imagined, the one most commonly invoked is that a short segment at a given level on three of the four homologous chromosomes which comprise a tetrad is descended from only one of the parents because of localized excess copying of that parental type.

The Molecular Basis of Recombination

Breakage and joining of double-stranded DNA

It was pointed out earlier that Belling's 1931 hypothesis of recombination solely by copy-choice was contradicted by genetic evidence for the occurrence of breakage and joining. Thus, when the phenomenon of conversion is taken into account, the genetic analysis of recombination in higher organisms suggests that both copying and breakage and joining are operative. There has been much speculation concerning mechanisms of recombination that would explain the genetic data. But genetic analysis without knowledge of the molecular structures involved has not been able to penetrate beyond rather general insights into possible mechanisms.

The life forms which so far have allowed the closest coordination of genetic and structural investigations of recombination are bacteriophages. Phage crosses are usually brought about by infecting host bacteria with a mixture of two appropriately marked phages. After a short time, the infected cells lyse, releasing parental and recombinant type phage particles. Recombination frequencies may be utilized in the conventional manner to construct linkage maps. In each case examined so far, a single, unbranched linkage structure has resulted, corresponding to the single DNA molecule which constitutes the phage chromosome. Furthermore, map distances appear to be at least approximately proportional to distances along the chromosome.

In spite of the fact that the copy-choice hypothesis was first revived to account for the results of phage crosses, the first direct proof of recombination by breakage and joining was carried out with a phage

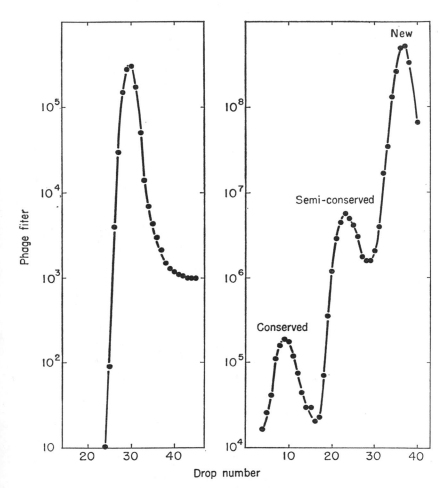

Fig. 7.2.—Left: Distribution of phage λ centrifuged to equilibrium in a CsCl density gradient. Successive drops correspond to successively lighter levels of the gradient. *Right:* Density-gradient distribution of the progeny of $^{13}C^{15}N$ labeled phage λ grown one cycle in multiply infected unlabeled bacteria. The buoyant densities of the three peaks show that they contain phages with fully labeled, half-labeled, and unlabeled chromosomes respectively.

—specifically with phage λ. Depending upon the conditions of infection and the strains employed, phage λ may either lysogenize its host or may multiply and lyse the cell, releasing several dozens of progeny. It is the latter response which occurs under the conditions used for genetic crosses and with which we are concerned here. The λ chromosome is a DNA duplex containing about 5×10^4 nucleotide pairs. When several λ chromosomes are injected into the same bacterium, as in a cross, some replicate semiconservatively and some do not replicate at all but simply reappear in new protein coats among the progeny. This is shown by the density distribution of the progeny of density-labeled parent phages allowed to multiply for one cycle in unlabeled bacteria, as may be seen on the right in Figure 7.2. It should be pointed out that the emergence of considerable numbers of chromosomes with intact parental DNA strands does not constitute evidence for recombination without chromosome breakage; the observed frequency of recombination between the ends of the λ map is rather low, leaving open the possibility that considerable numbers of chromosomes may not participate in recombination at all. However, if recombination does occur by simple breakage and joining, recombinant progeny from crosses performed with density-labeled parents should contain the label in discrete amounts, depending upon the site of selected exchange. This is exactly what is found. More specifically, two-factor crosses, when only one of the parental types is labeled, yield recombinants containing amounts of labeled DNA proportional to the fraction of the genetic map lying beyond the site of selected recombination in the direction of the marker from the labeled parental type (Kellenberger, Zichichi, and Weigle 1961; Meselson and Weigle 1961). This result has been repeated for recombination in various regions of the λ chromosome, including recombination between two markers in the same gene. An example is given in Figure 7.3 which shows the density distribution of parental and recombinant phages from a two-factor cross with one parent isotopically labeled. Both markers are in a gene situated about 20 per cent of the distance from one end of the linkage map. The markers are arranged so that wild-type phages produced by a single exchange receive 80 per cent of the linkage map from the labeled parent. As expected, three distinct modes of wild-type phages are observed, containing approximately 80, 40, and 0 per cent labeled DNA. These correspond to phages with chromosomes in which the DNA derived from the labeled parental type is respectively conserved, semiconserved, or new.

So long as the DNA of only one parental type is labeled, breakage and joining cannot be distinguished from a hypothetical mechanism which might be called breakage and copying. A fragment of a parental chromosome might be produced by breakage, but instead of forming part of a recombinant chromosome by joining with another fragment, it might become completed by copying along a template of opposite parentage. However, this mechanism cannot account for the results of

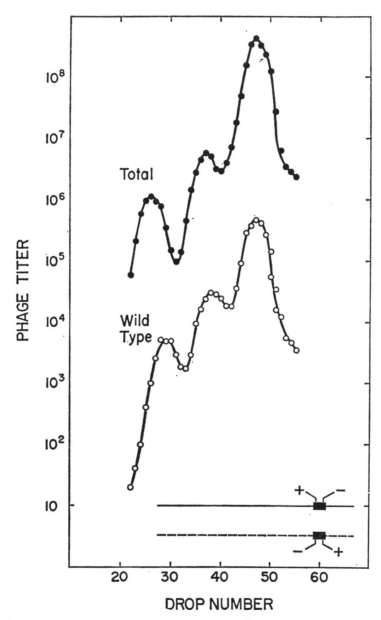

Fig. 7.3.—Density-gradient distributions of the total of all phage types and of wild-type recombinants from a cross of $^{13}C^{15}N$ labeled λsus *8* by unlabeled λsus *29*. The two mutations lie as indicated in the same gene, located about 20 per cent of the distance from one end of the linkage map.

crosses performed with parental types both containing labeled DNA
(Ihler and Meselson 1963; Meselson 1964). Among the progeny of such
crosses, recombinants are found with chromosomes formed entirely of
labeled DNA. This and other features of the density distribution of
the recombinants leave no doubt that recombination in phage λ frequently and possibly always occurs by breakage and joining of double-
stranded DNA molecules.

Joining via regions of hybrid DNA

If recombinant DNA molecules are formed by breakage and joining, what is the structure of the joint? The extreme precision of genetic recombination suggests that complementary base-pairing is somehow involved. Important evidence regarding the structure of the joint
has come from studies of the partial heterozygotes (hets) discovered
by Hershey and Chase (1951) among the progeny from phage crosses.
These phages are heterozygous over a short section of the genetic map
but segregate upon multiplication to yield homozygous offspring.
Plate 7.2 shows a plaque formed by a c/c^+ het (mottled) from a cross
of λc (clear) by wild-type λ (turbid). The behavior of hets suggested
to Hershey and Chase that they might be produced in the process of
recombination, possibly as intermediates in the normal formation of
homozygous recombinants. This view was developed by Levinthal
(1954), who, upon finding that phage T2 hets usually are recombinant
for a pair of markers bracketing the heterozygous region, suggested
that each newly formed recombinant might be a DNA duplex with a
short overlap of polynucleotide chains located between segments of
different parentage. According to this view, a het would simply be an
unduplicated recombinant molecule in which the overlap happens to
cover the locus of a marker under study. Segregation to give homozygous progeny would take place at the first semiconservative duplication. Although Levinthal considered that recombination most probably takes place by copy-choice, the discovery that phage recombination occurs by chromosome breakage led immediately to the view that
two chromosome fragments could be joined via a region in which
complementary polynucleotide chains form hybrid DNA, thus insur-
ing the great specificity and precision of recombination (Meselson and
Weigle 1961; Kellenberger, Zichichi, and Epstein 1962; Meselson 1962;
Doermann and Boehner 1963). Although the continued study of phage
heterozygosis has revealed quite unexpected and important complexities, there is now a considerable body of genetic and physical evidence

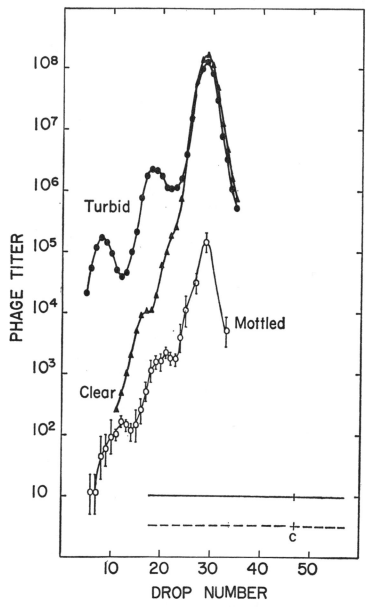

Fig. 7.4.—Density-gradient distribution of turbid, clear, and mottled plaque-forming progeny from a cross of $^{13}C^{15}N$ labeled λ by unlabeled λc. Error flags indicate 90 per cent confidence limits.

that the joint between chromosome fragments is indeed a region of hybrid overlap (Streisinger, Edgar, and Denhardt 1964; Tomizawa and Anraku 1964; Stahl 1965).

Direct evidence that λ hets are formed in association with the breakage and joining of chromosomes is shown in Figure 7.4, which depicts the density distribution of parental type phages and of hets from a cross of density-labeled λ by unlabeled λc. As expected from previous experiments, the progeny of the labeled parent (turbid) are found mainly in three distinct modes, corresponding to phages with conserved, semiconserved, and altogether new chromosomes. The distribution of the progeny of the unlabeled parent (clear) is in accord with the map location of the c locus, about one-quarter of the distance from one end of the λ map. If het chromosomes were produced by copy-choice rather than by breakage and joining, they would contain no heavy label. Instead, we see that they are found in distinct labeled modes with about three-quarters and three-eighths label, as though at least a sizable proportion of them were DNA duplexes composed of two different parental segments joined together at the region of heterozygosity. (The components expected with one-quarter and one-eighth label would not be resolved in the density gradient.)

Attempts have been made to determine whether the frequency of hets is consistent with the view that heterozygous overlaps are initially present at all sites of genetic exchange. Calculation indicates that the frequency of hets in T2 is close to the required value (Levinthal 1954). A similar calculation for λ indicates that hets are rarer than expected (Kellenberger, Zichichi, and Epstein 1962). But the question remains open, for there are serious uncertainties in both calculations. At least it may be said that heterozygosity is associated with a substantial fraction of all exchanges because, in both T4 and λ, regions sufficiently near to sites of selected genetic exchange are very often heterozygous, while more remote regions are not. This result is corroborated by the density distributions shown in Figure 7.4. The λc's in the region of the most dense peak of hets should be unreplicated recombinants with an exchange very near to c. Yet there are not many more λc's than there are hets. Indeed, some of the λc's in this region of the gradient almost certainly have drifted in from regions of less density, where their concentration is enormously greater. Furthermore, some hets may have been scored as parental types. Thus, at least a large fraction of chromosomes which have recombined near c are heterozygous for c.

The majority of T4 or λ chromosomes in a carefully made preparation are known to be DNA duplexes free of polynucleotide chain interruptions. In the case of T4, according to genetic evidence, there almost surely is one or more hybrid overlap per chromosome. Thus, it is likely that T4 heterozygotes are uninterrupted DNA duplexes (Tomizawa and Anraku 1964). In the case of phage λ, the relative rareness of hets indicates that only a minority of chromosomes possess overlaps. The usual chromosome structure might not be representative of the het chromosomes. But the properties of λ het chromosomes may be examined directly, for isolated λ chromosomes retain their infectivity and may be accurately assayed. Studies of infectious DNA from the progeny of λ crosses have shown that het chromosomes are single DNA duplexes which appear by a number of physical tests to be free of polynucleotide chain interruptions (Heinemann and Meselson, unpublished). Thus, we are led to conclude that the unreplicated product of genetic recombination in phages is an uninterrupted DNA duplex, as depicted in Figure 7.1.

The relatively rare phenomenon of post-meiotic segregation in ascomycetes (Olive 1959; Kitani, Olive, and El-Ani 1962; Lissouba *et al.* 1962) appears to be the counterpart of phage heterozygosis. One or two of the four products of meiosis are occasionally heterozygous for a given marker although outside markers are homozygous and segregate normally. The former situation, 5:3 segregation, is termed half-chromatid conversion, while the latter is sometimes described as aberrant 4:4 segregation. A high frequency of reciprocal recombination is found for a pair of markers bracketing a heterozygous site. If we accept the likely premise that each of the four homologs of a meiotic tetrad is simply a DNA duplex at any level (Gall 1963; Taylor 1965), then we may conclude that the features of chromosome structure responsible for post-meiotic segregation in fungi are likely to be essentially the same as the more fully characterized overlap regions of heterozygous phage chromosomes.

Removal and replacement of DNA in the region of joining

The idea that gene conversion might result from the removal and replacement of portions of DNA in regions of hybrid overlap has been put forward independently by Taylor, Haut, and Tung (1962), Holliday (1962, 1964), Whitehouse (1963), and Meselson (1964, 1965). The outcome of one possible form of removal and replacement is illustrated in Figure 7.1. Sometime during the course of breakage and joining, an excision process removes a terminal portion of one or more of the polynucleotide chains which subsequently are to be joined. (Because it removes a terminal portion of a chain, we shall refer to this sort of excision as *exonucleolytic*.) The excised DNA is replaced by copying along a complementary chain. If excision and copying should occur in a hybrid overlap region at a site heterozygous for a marker, homozygosity for the allele not excised will result. If, in a tetrad, this should occur on only one of the two homologs involved in an exchange, a half-chromatid conversion—that is, a 5:3 segregation—will be observed at the first post-meiotic mitosis. If the same allele is converted in both homologs, a 6:2 segregation or whole chromatid conversion is obtained. Both possibilities are depicted in Figure 7.1. (A further possibility not indicated in the figure is that opposite alleles will be converted in the two homologs, resulting in an apparently normal 4:4 segregation.)

Gene conversion has not yet been demonstrated in bacteria and phages. Its detection would require the recovery and genetic analysis of both chromosomes taking part in a given exchange. Although the required bacterial genetic techniques exist, they have not yet been applied to the study of conversion. In phage λ there is evidence that frequently a small percentage of the chromosome is removed and resynthesized during the course of recombination (Meselson 1964), but it remains to be seen whether this reflects the excision of DNA within regions of hybrid overlap.

The clustering of exchanges

When crosses are effected between parents multiply marked within a sufficiently short map interval, multiple exchange is generally found to be far more frequent than would be expected if each exchange occurred independently of the others. Such tight clustering of genetic exchanges, also called localized negative interference, has become well known since it was first intensively studied in *Aspergillus* by Pritchard (1955, 1960). The clustering of exchanges appears to be a general characteristic of recombination in all forms, having been found in *Drosophila*, several fungi, bacteria, and in bacteriophages. It differs from multiple exchange over long intervals in that only two parental homologs take part in the exchanges comprising any given cluster. In three-factor crosses, clustering may be detected as a heightened frequency of double exchange within sufficiently short intervals. This is shown for phage λ in Figure 7.5, which shows the excess of doubles—that is, the coincidence—measured in three-factor crosses over a wide range of interval lengths. Crosses with more than three close markers have shown that a cluster may often comprise more than two exchanges. Under the condition that the pattern of exchange is not influenced by the genetic markers themselves, it is possible to compute from genetic data the average number of exchanges per cluster and the average length of a cluster region. Calculations for phages T4 and λ indicate that, in a region where exchange has occurred, there are on the average approximately

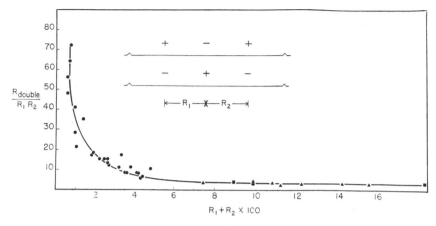

Fig. 7.5.—The relationship of the coincidence to the sum of the component recombination frequencies in each of 35 different three-factor crosses: ▲, crosses of Jacob and Wollman (1954); ■, crosses of Kaiser (1955); ●, crosses of Amati and Meselson (1965).

two or three exchanges and that the mean length of a cluster region is about the size of a gene (Stahl, Edgar, and Steinberg 1964; Amati and Meselson 1965). If further study should show that coincidence values rise rapidly within intervals even shorter than those examined so far, these estimates would require revision in the direction of shorter clusters with more numerous exchanges.

But if the mean number of exchanges per cluster were much greater than two or three, linkage of markers in a cluster region with those outside would be very weak or altogether lacking. If the markers should substantially influence the pattern of exchange, linkage relations could become grossly deranged. Evidence on this point is varied. In some investigations of intragenic recombination, linkage to outside markers is obscured or even completely deranged, and marker effects are extremely pronounced. In other cases, good linkage relations are preserved even in crosses involving intervals considerably smaller than the span of a single gene. It is not clear how much of the difference between various investigations can be ascribed to the types of markers chosen for study, the size of the intervals examined, or to differences in the characteristics of close exchange in different systems or regions of the chromosome. A striking case of bacterial transduction showing largely preserved linkage to an outside marker following selected exchange within intervals corresponding to only a few nucleotide pairs has been reported by Yanofsky and co-workers (1964). At least in this case, therefore, the number of exchanges per cluster seems not to be much greater than the value calculated for T4 and λ.

The primary recombinant structure shown in Figure 7.1 does not by itself account for the clustering of genetic exchanges. Operating within a region of heterozygous overlap, the exonucleolytic excision pictured in the figure can move the site of genetic exchange, but the number of exchanges is not influenced. Different results would be obtained if excision were endonucleolytic: Two new ends would be created by each excision. In an appropriately marked region, multiple genetic exchange within a short interval would be observed. As has been pointed out by Holliday (1962) and others, there may be a precedent for such a process in some of the events responsible for the repair of DNA damaged by ultraviolet light (Boyce and Howard-Flanders 1964; Setlow and Carrier 1964). Specifically, endonucleolytic excision might be provoked by poor complementarity within regions of heterozygous overlap. Excision would then operate to correct improper base-pairing, and extreme marker effects might occur, possibly depending on the particular nucleotides involved. However, it has not yet been proved that endonucleolytic excision occurs during normal genetic recombination. An alternative explanation for the clustering of exchanges is that excision is generally exonucleolytic and that clusters result from the iteration of the sort of breakage and joining event whose outcome is depicted in Figure 7.1. If the various enzymatic and mechanical requirements for breakage and joining should be satisfied at one place, the probability might be relatively great that they would be satisfied again nearby. Or, perhaps, one breakage and joining event actually induces another because of localized structural effects. In either case, exchanges would tend to cluster.

At least in principle, exonucleolytic and endonucleolytic excision might be distinguished by careful linkage studies in appropriately designed multi-factor crosses, because the elementary event in the former case is a single exchange whereas in the latter it is double. But, even if marker effects could be avoided, the distinction might be hopelessly obscured, depending on the distribution of breakage and joining sites and of overlap and excision lengths and frequencies.

A test of the general hypothesis that all or nearly all clusters result from events within an overlap between chromosome segments of opposite parentage has been devised and applied to phage T4 by Steinberg and Edgar (1962). The hypothesis predicts that a pair of markers just *beyond* the overlap on opposite sides will be recombined regardless of whether the number of exchanges selected *within* the overlap is odd or even. In apparent contradiction with the hypothesis, Steinberg and Edgar found that about half the time markers outside a selected tight double exchange are in the *non*recombinant configuration predicted by classical linkage relations. However, aside from possible difficulties of interpretation peculiar to the system, it is not certain that the outside markers were really outside the overlap region. Again, depending on the distribution of breaks and the lengths and distribution of overlaps and excisions, the distinction between linkage-preserving and non-linkage-preserving events in the overall mechanism of recombination might be badly obscured.

The localization of exchanges

Almost since the discovery of genetic recombination, attempts have been made to determine if exchange occurs with equal likelihood everywhere along a chromosome or if instead there is a tendency for it to occur in fixed places. The discovery of polarized conversion in exchange between close markers in *Ascobolus* by Lissouba and Rizet (1960) and the investigation of conversion and outside-marker recombination in a variety of other fungi show that certain exchange events are quite definitely not isotropic with respect to the linkage structure. There are three almost certainly interrelated phenomena which necessitate this conclusion:

(1) The rank order of conversion frequencies of certain closely linked spore-color markers in *Ascobolus* has been reported to resemble their map order (Lissouba 1961; Gajewski *et al.* 1963).

(2) Within certain short map intervals in *Ascobolus,* recombination between spore-color mutants is usually nonreciprocal. In any given two-factor cross, one of the two markers is generally found to have undergone whole-chromatid conversion, while the other segregates normally. Of interest here is the fact that the conversion exhibits a strong directional polarity: It appears that the marker lying in a particular map direction is the one that is usually converted. This direction is the same for marker pairs within certain regions but may be reversed in adjacent regions (Lissouba *et al.* 1962).

(3) Selection for exchange between close markers at some loci in *Neurospora* and *Aspergillus* stimulates recombination with outside markers on one side more than the other. The map direction of preferential stimulation is the same for selected exchange anywhere within certain limited intervals (Murray 1963; Siddiqi and Putrament 1963).

If it is accepted that conversion frequently occurs at a region of exchange, the first two observations may be explained by the postulate that exchange regions tend to occur in fixed places and that the probability of conversion falls off steadily on one or both sides. And, if exchanges occur in tight clusters, localization of the clusters in fixed places would also account for polarized stimulation of recombination with outside markers.

A fourth polar phenomenon, not yet established, might also be expected. The probability of hybrid overlap should decrease with increasing distance from a region of localized exchange. Therefore, unless marker effects obscure the phenomenon, the rank order of the frequencies of post-meiotic segregation for markers in certain short intervals should bear a definite relation to their map order.

Although the study of polarity has already progressed far enough to demonstrate that the localization of exchange events is common in fungi, many questions remain to be answered. Does localization occur in other organisms, especially in bacteria and viruses? Do polarized conversion rates fall off more or less smoothly on both sides of a maximum or is the fall-off abrupt on one side? An abrupt fall-off on one side might reflect a rather strict localization of initial break points. What are the detailed relations between the polarization of whole-chromatid conversion, the polarization of outside-marker recombination, and the possible polarization of post-meiotic segregation? Knowledge of these relations could be extremely informative with respect to the detailed pattern of events within an exchange region.*

The mechanism of genetic recombination

Even if we knew the exact structure of primary recombinant molecules, we would be far from understanding the steps leading to their formation. Polynucleotide chains are broken, but are breaks made before or after the initial synapsis by which homologous nucleotide sequences recognize each other? What structure is responsible for synapsis and how and where are breaks made? Many more questions could be asked about the mechanism of removal and replacement and of final joining.

One of the most fundamental problems of mechanism is whether recognition precedes breakage or follows it. The only molecular basis now known for sufficiently reliable recognition between homologs is the formation of complementary base pairs. Let us assume that the Watson-Crick structure is the basis of synaptic recognition and ask if it could form between two uninterrupted duplexes. Two duplexes could become unwound locally in homologous regions which, it might be argued, could then rewind to form regions of hybrid DNA. The

---

* A detailed analysis of the existing data, along with an interpretation in terms of possible patterns of hybrid overlap in various fungi, has been presented by Whitehouse and Hastings (1965).

difficulty with this scheme is that, without breaks, each right-hand turn of the hybrid helix generated in this way must be compensated by a left-hand turn. No one who has attempted to build a stable left-handed double helix with molecular models has succeeded. The formation of hybrid regions between duplexes should be energetically more favorable after the introduction of one or more single chain breaks. If breakage precedes recognition, breaks may be required in one or both of the parental duplexes. If both must break, there must be a great deal of breakage to ensure that breaks occur at or near corresponding sites on the two homologs, unless potential breakage sites are very rare. Such wholesale breakage could have escaped detection, considering the speed and efficiency of chromosome repair after radiation-induced breakage. However, a break on only one homolog might be sufficient to let hybrid DNA be formed. One or both free ends of a broken single chain might invade the homologous region of an intact duplex, once diffusion has brought them sufficiently close. This might be facilitated by the occurrence of transient unpaired regions in the unbroken duplex, for which studies of tritium exchange have provided some evidence (Printz and von Hippel 1965). Once started, hybrid regions must be allowed to grow to considerable lengths, for genetic analysis indicates that hybrid overlaps may often be as long as or longer than a gene. Somewhere in this complicated ritual, each chain must be broken, and DNA must be removed, replaced, and joined—all by specific enzymes. Clearly, much more must be learned about the biologically relevant conditions under which complementary DNA chains can be locally unpaired, about the stability of various configurations for synapsis, and about their rates of formation. And we would be in a far better position to guess at the structure of synapsed DNA if more were known of the specificity of the various endonucleases which may operate in recombination. Although formal genetic analysis will almost surely continue to help lead the way to a satisfactory understanding of the mechanism of recombination, detailed physical and chemical information must now be brought in.

Literature Cited

AMATI, P., AND M. MESELSON, 1965. Localized negative interference in bacteriophage λ. Genetics 51: 369–379.

ANDERSON, E. G., 1925. Crossing over in a case of attached-X chromosomes in *Drosophila melanogaster*. Genetics 10: 403–417.

BATESON, W., E. R. SAUNDERS, AND R. C. PUNNETT, 1906. *Report to the Evolution Committee of the Royal Society*, III. Harrison and Sons, London.

BELLING, J., 1931. Chrommomeres of lilaceous plants. Univ. California (Berkeley) Publ. Bot. 16: 153–170.

———, 1933. Crossing over and gene rearrangement in flowering plants. Genetics 18: 388–413.

BOYCE, R. P., AND P. HOWARD-FLANDERS, 1964. Release of ultra-violet light-induced thymine dimers from DNA in *E. coli* K-12. Proc. Nat. Acad. Sci. U.S. 51: 293–300.

BRIDGES, C. B., AND E. G. ANDERSON, 1925. Crossing over in the X-chromosomes of triploid females of *Drosophila melanogaster*. Genetics 10: 418–441.

CAMPBELL, A. M., 1962. Episomes. Advance. Genet. 11: 101–145.

CHIANG, KWEN-SHENG, 1965. Meiotic DNA replication mechanism in *Chlamydomonas Reinhardi*. Ph.D. thesis, Princeton Univ.

CREIGHTON, H. B., AND B. McCLINTOCK, 1931. A correlation of cytological and genetical crossing-over in *Zea mays*. Proc. Nat. Acad. Sci. U.S. 17: 492–497.

DOERMANN, A. H., AND L. BOEHNER, 1963. An experimental analysis of bacteriophage T4 heterozygotes 1. Mottled plaques from crosses involving six r_{II} loci. Virology 21: 551–567.

FOX, M. S., AND M. K. ALLEN, 1964. On the mechanism of deoxyribonucleate integration in pneumococcal transformation. Proc. Nat. Acad. Sci. U.S. 52: 412–419.

GAJEWSKI, W., A. KRUSZEWSKA, A. MARKAREWICZ, A. PASZEWSKI, S. SURZYCKI, AND H. BIELAWSKA, 1963. Conversion and crossing-over as recombination mechanisms in *Ascobolus immersus*. *Genetics Today*, vol. I, p. 11. Edited by S. J. Geerts. Proc. XI Int. Congr. Genet., The Hague, The Netherlands. The Macmillan Co., New York.

GALL, J. G., 1963. Kinetics of DNase action on chromosomes. Nature 198: 36–38.

HERSHEY, A. D., AND M. CHASE, 1951. Genetic recombination and heterozygosis in bacteriophage. Cold Spring Harbor Symp. Quant. Biol. 16: 471–479.

HERSHEY, A. D., AND R. ROTMAN, 1949. Genetic recombination between host-range and plaque-type mutants of bacteriophage in single bacterial cells. Genetics 34: 44–71.

HOLLIDAY, R., 1962. Mutation and replication in *Ustilago maydis*. Genet. Res. 3: 472–486.

———, 1964. A mechanism for gene conversion in fungi. Genet. Res. 5: 282–304.

IHLER, G., AND M. MESELSON, 1963. Genetic recombination in bacteriophage λ by breakage and joining of DNA molecules. Virology 21: 7–10.

JACOB, F., AND E. WOLLMAN, 1954. Étude génétique d'un bactériophage tempéré d'*Escherichia coli*. II. Mécanisme de la recombinaison génétique. Ann. Inst. Pasteur 87: 1–17.

JANSSENS, F. A., 1909. La theorie de la chiasmatypie. La Cellule 25: 389–411.

KAISER, A. D., 1955. A genetic study of the temperate coliphage lambda. Virology 1: 424–443.

KELLENBERGER, G., M. L. ZICHICHI, AND H. L. EPSTEIN, 1962. Heterozygosis and recombination of bacteriophage λ. Virology 17: 44–55.

KELLENBERGER, G., M. L. ZICHICHI, AND J. WEIGLE, 1961. Exchange of DNA in the recombination of bacteriophage λ. Proc. Nat. Acad. Sci. U.S. 47: 869–878.

KITANI, Y., L. S. OLIVE, AND A. S. EL-ANI, 1962. Genetics of *Sordaria fimicola*. V. Aberrant segregation at the *g* locus. Amer. J. Bot. 49: 697–706.

LEVINTHAL, C., 1954. Recombination in phage T2: Relationship to heterozygosis and growth. Genetics 39: 169–184.

LINDEGREN, C. C., 1953. Gene conversion in *Saccharomyces*. J. Genet. 51: 625–637.

———, 1955. Non-Mendelian segregation in a single tetrad of *Saccharomyces* ascribed to gene conversion. Science 121: 605–607.

LISSOUBA, P., 1961. Mise en évidence d'une unite génétique polarisée et essai d'analyse d'un cas d'interférence négative. Ann. sci. natur. bot. et biol. vegetale, 44: 641–720.

LISSOUBA, P., J. MOUSSEAU, G. RIZET, AND J. L. ROSSIGNOL, 1962. Fine structure of genes in the ascomycete *Ascobolus immersus*. Advance. Genet. 11: 343–380.

LISSOUBA, P., AND G. RIZET, 1960. Sur l'existence d'une unité génétique polarisée ne subissant que des échanges non réciproques. Compt. Rend. 250: 3408–3410.

LOCK, R. H., 1906. *Recent Progress in the Study of Variation, Heredity, and Evolution*. J. Murray, London.

McCLINTOCK, B., 1951. Chromosome organization and genic expression. Cold Spring Harbor Symp. Quant. Biol. 16: 13–47.

MESELSON, M., 1962. Genetic recombination at the molecular level. Pontificae Acad. Sci. Scripta Varia 22: 173–183.

———, 1964. On the mechanism of genetic recombination. J. Mol. Biol. 9: 734–745.

———, 1965. The duplication and recombination of genes. *Ideas in Modern Biology*, pp. 3–16. Edited by J. A. Moore. XVI Int. Congr. Zool. (1963). The Natural History Press, Garden City, New York.

MESELSON, M., AND J. WEIGLE, 1961. Chromosome breakage accompanying genetic recombination in bacteriophage. Proc. Nat. Acad. Sci. U.S. 47: 857–868.

MITCHELL, M. B., 1955. Aberrant recombination of pyridoxine mutants of *Neurospora*. Proc. Nat. Acad. Sci. U.S. 41: 215–220.

MORGAN, L. V., 1925. Polyploidy in *Drosophila melanogaster* with two attached-X chromosomes. Genetics 10: 148–178.

MORGAN, T. H., 1911. Random segregation versus coupling in Mendelian inheritance. Science 34: 384.

MURRAY, N. E., 1963. Polarized recombination and fine structure within the *me-2* gene of *Neurospora crassa*. Genetics 48: 1163–1183.

OLIVE, L. S., 1959. Aberrant tetrads in *Sordaria fimicola*. Proc. Nat. Acad. Sci. U.S. 45: 727–732.

PRELL, H. H., 1965. DNA transfer from prophage to phage progeny after zygotic induction. J. Mol. Biol. 13: 329–339.

PRINTZ, M. P., AND P. H. VON HIPPEL, 1965. Hydrogen exchange studies of DNA structure. Proc. Nat. Acad. Sci. U.S. 53: 363–370.

PRITCHARD, R. H., 1955. The linear arrangement of a series of alleles in *Aspergillus nidulans*. Heredity **9**: 343–371.

———, 1960. Localized negative interference and its bearing on models of gene recombination. Genet. Res. **1**: 1–24.

PTASHNE, M., 1965. The detachment and maturation of conserved lambda prophage DNA. J. Mol. Biol. **11**: 90–96.

SETLOW, R., AND W. CARRIER, 1964. The disappearance of thymine dimers from DNA: An error-correcting mechanism. Proc. Nat. Acad. Sci. U.S. **51**: 226–231.

SIDDIQI, O. H., 1963. Incorporation of parental DNA into genetic recombinants of *E. coli*. Proc. Nat. Acad. Sci. U.S. **49**: 589–592.

SIDDIQI, O. H., AND A. PUTRAMENT, 1963. Polarized negative interference in the *paba-1* region of *Asperigillus nidulans*. Genet. Res. **4**: 12–20.

STAHL, F. W., 1965. Recombination in bacteriophage T4. Heterozygosity and circularity. Symp. Biol. Hung. **6**: 131–141.

STAHL, R. W., R. S. EDGAR, AND J. STEINBERG, 1964. The linkage map of bacteriophage T4. Genetics **50**: 539–552.

STEINBERG, C. M., AND R. S. EDGAR, 1962. A critical test of a current theory of genetic recombination in bacteriophage. Genetics **47**: 187–208.

STERN, C., 1931. Zytologisch-genetische Untersuchungen als Beweise für die Morgansche Theorie des Kaktorenaustausches. Biol. Zentra'bl. **51**: 547–587.

STREISINGER, G., R. S. EDGAR, AND G. H. DENHARDT, 1964. Chromosome structure in phage T4. I. Circularity of the linkage map. Proc. Nat. Acad. Sci. U.S. **51**: 775–779.

STURTEVANT, A. H., 1913. The linear arrangement of six sex-linked factors in *Drosophila* as shown by their mode of association. J. Exp. Zool. **14**: 43–59.

TAYLOR, J. H., 1965. Distribution of tritium-labeled DNA among chromosomes during meiosis. I. Spermatogenesis in the grasshopper. J. Cell Biol. **25**: 57–67.

TAYLOR, J. H., W. F. HAUT, AND J. TUNG, 1962. Effects of fluorodeoxyuridine on DNA replication, chromosome breakage, and reunion. Proc. Nat. Acad. Sci. U.S. **48**: 190–198.

TOMIZAWA, J., AND N. ANRAKU, 1964. Molecular mechanisms of genetic recombination in bacteriophage II. Joining of parental DNA molecules of phage T4. J. Mol. Biol. **8**: 516–540.

WHITEHOUSE, H. L. K., 1963. A theory of crossing-over by means of hybrid deoxyribonucleic acid. Nature **199**: 1034–1040.

WHITEHOUSE, H. L. K., AND P. J. HASTINGS, 1965. The analysis of genetic recombination on the polaron hybrid DNA model. Genet. Res. **6**: 27–92.

WILSON, E. B., AND T. H. MORGAN, 1920. Chiasmatype and crossing-over. Amer. Natur. **54**: 193–219.

YANOFSKY, C., B. C. CARLTON, J. R. GUEST, D. R. HELINSKI, AND U. HENNING, 1964. On the colinearity of gene structure and protein structure. Proc. Nat. Acad. Sci. U.S. **51**: 266–272.

ZICKLER, H., 1934. Genetische Untersuchungen an einem heterothallischen Askomyzeten (*Bombardia lunata* nov. spec.). Planta **22**: 573–613.

8

An Experimental Analysis
of the Genetic Code

Heinrich Matthaei, Horst Kleinkauf,
Gesa Heller, Hans-Peter Voigt, and Helga Matthaei

This work was supported by a grant from the Deutsche
Forschungsgemeinschaft.

Some 80 years after Mendel's discovery of hereditary factors,
the chemical identity of the genetic material was established as nucleic
acids, compounds which were found a hundred years ago by Miescher
(1871). Since 1944, when Avery, MacLeod, and McCarty demonstrated
that DNA is the primary genetic substance, the science of gene structure and function at the molecular level has progressed mainly from
the effector molecules to their immediate products. This progress has
been a clear demonstration of how far simple mechanistic speculation
can go, with logical principles and a few basic facts, toward the formulation of useful working hypotheses. We allude in particular to the
hypotheses concerned with gene actions—the inherent direct or indirect
causes of all individual and universal properties of living systems: the
one gene-one enzyme hypothesis (Beadle and Tatum 1941), the one nucleotide triplet-one amino acid hypothesis (Gamow 1954, 1955), the
messenger ribonucleic acid (mRNA) hypothesis (Jacob and Monod
1961) postulating transcription of deoxyribonucleic acid (DNA) into a
ribonucleic acid (RNA) that directs protein synthesis, and the adaptor
hypothesis (Crick 1958) introducing another type of RNA (transfer
RNA: tRNA) for insertion of amino acids into the growing polypeptides according to the nucleotide sequence of mRNA. The necessary
counterpart and control of all speculation is, of course, careful and
critical observation, fostering evaluation of results and providing bases
for further productive speculative thinking that naturally flourishes in
a young science.

The synthesis of specific enzymes under genic control has been an
enigma to biologists and biochemists for a long time. This is partially
resolved now, in principle, by the demonstration of the sequential syn-

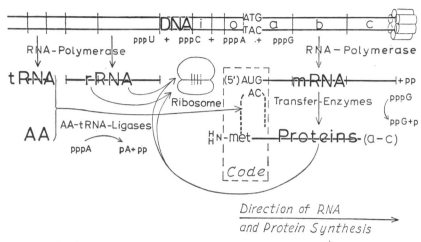

Genes(DNA), primary (RNA) and secondary Geneproducts(Proteins)

Fig. 8.1.—Synthesis of primary (RNA) and secondary (protein) gene products.

theses of two macromolecules from small molecules: the *transcription* of DNA nucleotide sequences into RNA nucleotide sequences and the *translation* of RNA nucleotide sequences into amino acid sequences (Crick 1963; Matthaei 1963; Nirenberg *et al.* 1963; Speyer *et al.* 1963). All known primary gene products are RNA's; the known secondary gene products are, strictly defined, primary structures of proteins (see Fig. 8.1). These polypeptide chains fold specifically into secondary (helical), tertiary (e.g., globular), quaternary (aggregated), and quintary (structure-incorporated) forms. Presumably all functional systems of the cell have component proteins; many of these constituents are enzymes which have specificities for catalytic interaction with certain small or large molecules.

An understanding of the initial steps in gene expression in terms of a decoding system is basic to the elucidation eventually of the general role of genes in living systems. Knowledge of the decoding system of the cell, central as it is, encourages us to hope for a complete scientific understanding of life in terms of related functional systems, integrated into cellular and higher organization and composed of molecules and atoms which interact specifically by certain chemical and physical properties that may be called "biochemical specificities." A major question to be answered by molecular biology is whether the atomistic understanding of macromolecular functions in terms of functions of their monomer building blocks (nucleotides in nucleic acids) will hold true, and if so, whether this model situation will be applicable, with or without modifications, to the function of the amino acid residues in proteins. Most trinucleotide groups in mRNA (that is, codons) have the chemical properties to interact somehow on the ribosome with aminoacyl adaptor RNA, so that at each triplet only one of twenty amino acids becomes incorporated into protein under the action of the transfer enzymes. The whole set of these homologous biochemical specificities, each usually corresponding to one particular amino acid, we have labeled the "genetic code."

There is apparently no direct interaction between the trinucleotide codons in mRNA and the corresponding amino acids, although until 1957 direct interaction was considered possible (Gamow 1954, 1955). According to Crick's (1958) successful adaptor hypothesis, the biochemical specificity for direct interaction with the codon resides in the tRNA as the carrier and adaptor for the amino acid. Furthermore, the hypothesis assumes the physicochemical principle of the interaction to be a hydrogen bonding between a base-complementary anticodon in the tRNA and the coding trinucleotide in mRNA. This principle, illustrated in Fig. 8.2, acts in the maintenance and possibly also the replicative synthesis of DNA structure by DNA polymerase. It could also lead to the base-complementary transcription of sections of one of the two DNA strands into tRNA, mRNA, and ribosomal RNA by the enzyme RNA polymerase. But at this time there is no decisive proof that either one of these polymerases or an enzyme-related site (for possible recognition of more or less perfectly paired codons and anticodons) on the ribosome would recognize paired bases as a countersite to their biochemical specificities involved in substrate recognition. Whereas it seems clear that the products of the replicating and transcribing enzymes are base complementary to their template cofactors (references in Matthaei 1963), we still have only one piece of direct information from analytical biochemistry concerning a codon-anticodon correspondence. Holley and co-workers (1965) have shown the existence of a triplet (3'-CGI*) in the nucleotide sequence of an alanyl

---

* The following notations and abbreviations are used in this chapter: *A*, adenosine; *C*, cytidine; *G*, guanosine; *I*, inosine; *T*, thymidine; *U*, uridine; *p* (e.g., ppA), phosphate (e.g., adenosine diphosphate). *AA*, amino acids: *ala*, alanine; *arg*, arginine; *asN*, asparagine; *asp*, aspartic acid; *cys*, cysteine; *glN*, glutamine; *glu*, glutamic acid; *gly*, glycine; *his*, histidine; *ilu*, isoleucine; *leu*, leucine; *lys*, lysine; *met*, methionine; *phe*, phenylalanine; *pro*, proline; *ser*, serine; *thr*, threonine; *try*, tryptophan; *tyr*, tyrosine; *val*, valine. DNA, deoxyribonucleic acid; *(m,r,s,t)RNA*, (messenger, ribosomal, soluble, transfer) ribonucleic acid. *TMV*, tobacco mosaic virus. DP, diphosphate; *TP*, triphosphate. *EDTA*, ethylenediaminetetraacetate; *Tris*, tris (hydroxymethyl) amino methane; *DEAE*, Cellex D anion exchange cellulose. A boldface star (*) indicates an isotopically labeled compound.

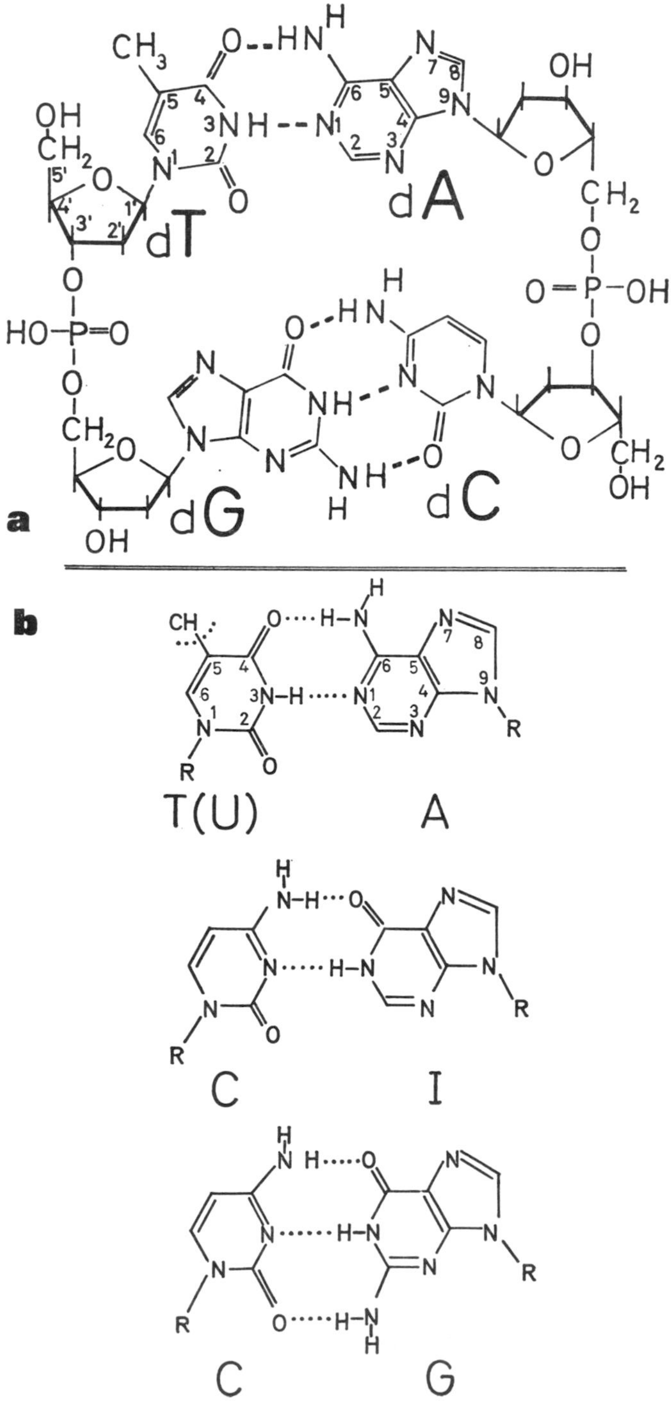
a
dT
dA
dG
dC
b
T(U)
A
C
I
C
G

tRNA (Fig. 8.3, top) which is base complementary and antiparallel (that is, running opposite to the direction of mRNA reading, from the 3' to the 5' hydroxyl end) at least to the alanine codon 5'-GCC (see Fig. 8.17). But the parallel complementary sequence 5'-CGG is available too, in the loop to the right in the tentative tertiary structure proposed in the upper right of Figure 8.3. Nucleotide sequence analyses of other tRNA species will be needed to characterize anticodons, but various functional tests as discussed below are also required. The code would appear to comprise, then, on the level of DNA a set of base-complementary codogens and anticodogens, on the level of mRNA the codons, and on the level of tRNA the anticodons if anticodons do exist in the original sense of Crick's hypothesis. This relation is illustrated in Figure 8.6. The real translation would occur by further biochemical specificities of the aminoacyl tRNA ligases, which recognize one or several analogous adaptors on one side and the corresponding amino acid on the other. The complete dictionary of biochemical specificities in the decoding system appears to contain a set of specific protein-amino acid interactions and a set of protein-RNA interactions in addition to the tRNA-mRNA interactions, the anticodons and codons. Translation specificity depends on the identities of the RNA and amino acid recognized by a given protein and the codon or codons recognized by a given tRNA.

The biochemical specificities in tRNA for recognition by the ligase appears indeed to be different from the still hypothetical anticodon (Yu and Zamecnik 1964; Weil *et al.* 1964): In Figure 8.4, the phenylalanine chargeability of soluble RNA (sRNA) is not reduced by formation of one mole of adenine-1-N-oxide per mole of sRNA, whereas lysine acceptance is inhibited by two-thirds (Seidel, Heller, and Matthaei 1966); however, phenylalanine anticodons should be mostly oxidizable and lysine anticodons should not. Similar evidence has been obtained by several laboratories working with different agents including ultraviolet irradiation, although the latter treatment did not reveal this difference between chargeability and transferability (Gottschling and Za-

---

Fig. 8.2.—a. Two adjacent DNA base pairs connected by the deoxyribose-phosphate backbone. The nucleosides (sugar-base compounds) are deoxythymidine (dT), deoxyadenosine (dA), deoxyguanosine (dG), and deoxycytidine (dC). *b.* Structure of hydrogen-bonded base pairs: thymine (uracil)–adenine (T:A; U:A), cytosine-hypoxanthine (C:I), and cytosine-guanine (C:G). In RNA, ribose with a 2' hydroxyl group replaces deoxyribose, and uracil replaces thymine (Watson and Crick 1953).

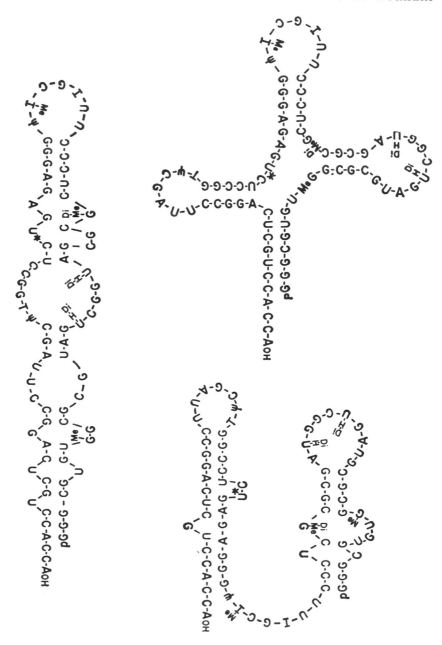

Fig. 8.3.—The nucleotide sequence of an alanine-accepting transfer RNA species, analyzed by Holley and co-workers (1965).

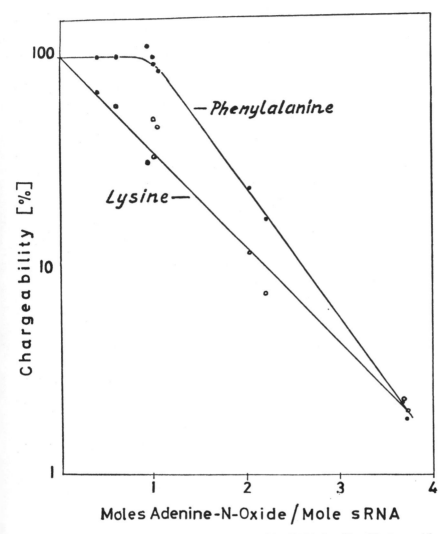

Fig. 8.4.—Inhibition of chargeability of soluble RNA by N-oxidation with monoperphthalic acid for the amino acids lysine and phenylalanine. This oxidation attacks only unpaired adenine and cytosine, according to Seidel and Cramer (1965).

chau 1965). But this type of evidence is indirect and needs to be extended by identification of the chemical changes and their position in the RNA sequence.

We shall report here on the analysis of the code in terms of a set of indirect correspondences: the identification of the individual amino acids coded by more than 60 trinucleotide permutations occurring in mRNA.

Discovery of the Code and
Base-Composition Analysis of Coding Units

In early 1961 Nirenberg and Matthaei set up what was hoped to be an assay system for mRNA. Volkin and Astrachan (1956) had shown earlier that an RNA with rapid turnover occurred in bacteria after a phage infection which, on the basis of its base composition, was phage DNA related. According to the older expectation of a template-functioning RNA (quoted in Matthaei 1963), this RNA could have been an mRNA. The possibility that ribosomal RNA might not be the messenger RNA was raised, also in 1961, by Gros *et al.* and by Brenner, Jacob, and Meselson. And there was a body of mostly speculative papers (quoted in Matthaei 1963) on properties of different codes which provided some guidance to experimental work: (1) The triplet nature of the codons; (2) the nonoverlapping reading feature; (3) the subsequently disproved ideas concerning commas; (4) the degenerate pattern which permits several codons per amino acid; (5) the so-called nonsense codons; and (6) the universality of one code possibly operating in all organisms.

Having all this in mind, Nirenberg and Matthaei treated cell-free extracts from the intestinal bacterium *Escherichia coli,* as obtained previously by several laboratories (Lamborg and Zamecnik 1960; Zillig, Schachtschabel, and Krone 1960), with deoxyribonuclease in order to destroy gene substance. These extracts were further incubated with the components required for protein synthesis, to destroy all endogenous mRNA, perhaps in a process similar to the rapid decay occurring in the cell or perhaps because of other ribonucleases present in the extracts. In any event, protein synthesis became dependent on added template RNA (Matthaei and Nirenberg 1961*a*). This system has been used for testing not only natural types of RNA but also synthetic polynucleotides, at first homopolynucleotides consisting only of large numbers of one of the four nucleotides occurring in natural mRNA. The experiment, almost ludicrous at that time, seems very reasonable today; it resulted in one of those excitingly large quantitative effects that leave little doubt about interpretation from the first observation. The synthetic polynucleotide polyuridylic acid stimulated the incorporation of only one of the 20 protein amino acids—namely, phenylalanine—into acid precipitable peptides (Matthaei and Nirenberg 1961*b*; Nirenberg and Matthaei 1961). It was soon found also that polycytidylic acid coded only proline. By ensuring conditions favorable to precipitation of the polypeptide product, Ochoa's co-workers first noted the synthesis of polylysine under the direction of polyadenylic acid (Gardner *et al.* 1962).

It was but a short step from study with homopolymers to those with polynucleotides containing two known bases in random order and prepared by the enzyme polynucleotide phosphorylase (reaction type depicted by equation 2, Fig. 8.5). The frequencies of the various amino acids coded by these polynucleotides were mostly in agreement with the triplet frequencies calculated from the polymers' base compositions. Thus, by late 1962, 49 base compositions of coding units direct-

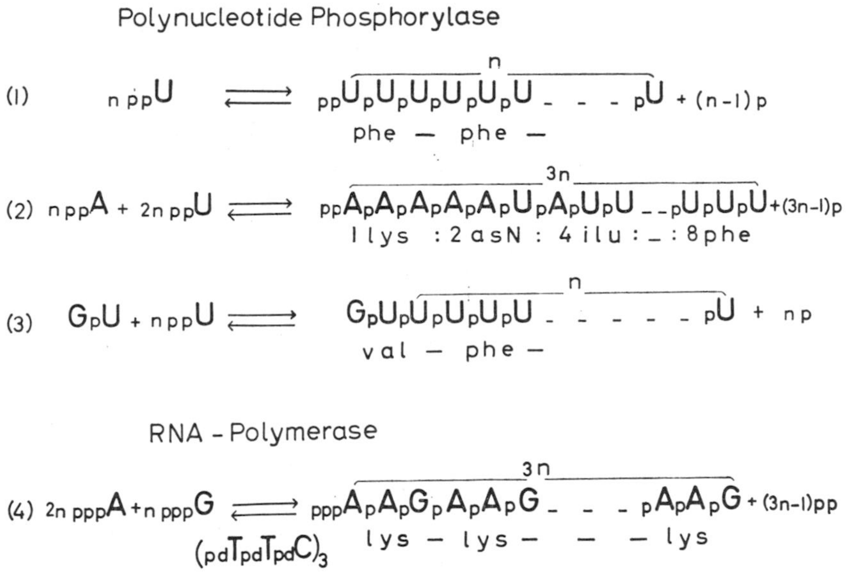

Polynucleotide Phosphorylase

$$(1) \qquad n\,\text{ppU} \; \rightleftharpoons \; \overbrace{\text{ppU}_p\text{U}_p\text{U}_p\text{U}_p\text{U}_p\text{U}}^{n} \; \text{-} \; \text{-} \; \text{-} \; _p\text{U} + (n-1)\,\text{p}$$
$$\text{phe} \; - \; \text{phe} \; -$$

$$(2) \; n\,\text{ppA} + 2n\,\text{ppU} \; \rightleftharpoons \; \overbrace{\text{ppA}_p\text{A}_p\text{A}_p\text{A}_p\text{A}_p\text{U}_p\text{A}_p\text{U}_p\text{U} \; \text{-} \text{-} _p\text{U}_p\text{U}_p\text{U}}^{3n} + (3n-1)\text{p}$$
$$1\,\text{lys} \; : 2\,\text{asN} : \; 4\,\text{ilu} : \_ : 8\,\text{phe}$$

$$(3) \qquad \text{G}_p\text{U} + n\,\text{ppU} \; \rightleftharpoons \; \overbrace{\text{G}_p\text{U}_p\text{U}_p\text{U}_p\text{U}_p\text{U} \; \text{-} \; \text{-} \; \text{-} \; \text{-} \; _p\text{U}}^{n} + n\,\text{p}$$
$$\text{val} \; - \; \text{phe} \; -$$

RNA - Polymerase

$$(4) \; 2n\,\text{pppA} + n\,\text{pppG} \; \rightleftharpoons \; \overbrace{\text{pppA}_p\text{A}_p\text{G}_p\text{A}_p\text{A}_p\text{G} \; \text{-} \; \text{-} \; \text{-} \; _p\text{A}_p\text{A}_p\text{G}}^{3n} + (3n-1)\text{pp}$$
$$(\text{pdT}_p\text{dT}_p\text{dC})_3 \qquad \text{lys} - \text{lys} - \quad - \quad - \text{lys}$$

Fig. 8.5.—Enzymatic syntheses of polynucleotides for decoding experiments.

ing one of the twenty different protein amino acids were known (Matthaei 1963; Nirenberg *et al.* 1963; Speyer *et al.* 1963). However, nothing was known about the sequences of the nucleotides within the codons. The concept of triplets of coding units was in agreement with but not proved by our data, and more direct evidence was required than that provided by the ingenious genetic experiments of Crick and co-workers (1962) on recombination of proflavin-induced mutants in the *r*II region of bacteriophage T4. The code already seemed to have the characteristic of degeneracy, and, from Wittmann's (1962) finding that a single base exchange in tobacco mosaic virus RNA effected the change of only a single amino acid in the coat protein, one felt quite convinced that the code would be read in a nonoverlapping fashion.

Ways for Determination of Coding Nucleotide Sequences

At the end of 1962, the code had been deciphered to the extent of 49 base compositions. Confidence in obtaining still more significant results with the same preparations and techniques was not sufficient to warrant continued attempts of this kind. The approach had been no more than preliminary from the outset, because it could never have permitted analysis of the coding nucleotide *sequences*. In this report we shall compare the results from systems in which random polymers are translated into polypeptide chains with data obtained in a simpler system which leads only to the binding of aminoacyl RNA to ribosomes specified by mRNA models of defined nucleotide sequence (that is, amino acid adaptation). These new data include 63 coding sequences observed in the *E. coli* strain A19 ribonuclease I^-.

In 1963 Matthaei summarized seven possible ways for deciphering the coding sequences (see Fig. 8.6). Five were functional biochemical analyses that would use specific interactions of an enzyme and ribosomes with mRNA and aminoacyl RNA. The sixth strategy was to analyze the nucleotide sequences of various tRNA species and then to correlate the sequences at a certain locus in the molecules with sequences that are compatible with their known codon-recognizing properties. The relation of the sequence at this locus and the codon sequence could then be established for each tRNA species; if the relation proved to have complementarity, the tRNA molecule could serve in cell-free synthesis of proteins of known sequence so that the nucleotide sequence of their mRNA could be deduced. But the seventh method, the direct biochemical analysis of the nucleotide sequence of an mRNA and its comparison with the amino acid sequence for which it codes, is still the ultimate correlation sought. It is difficult, however, to isolate an mRNA in well-defined form, and it is not yet possible to determine the sequence of even the smallest available mRNA.

The problem of further functional analysis was in part a synthetic one since mRNA models of defined nucleotide sequence had to be built for different approaches:

(1) Trinucleotides that are identical to an anticodon might give kinetic evidence of the sequence of the anticodon by specific competitive interaction with the aminoacyl RNA on the ribosome.

(2a) Di(oligo)nucleotide primed homopolynucleotides that have one different triplet at the 5′ end are useful in both adaptation and polymerization studies. Polynucleotide phosphorylase catalyzes the synthesis as described by equation 3 of Figure 8.5. n can be 1, and the trinucleoside diphosphates used by Nirenberg's group for adaptation

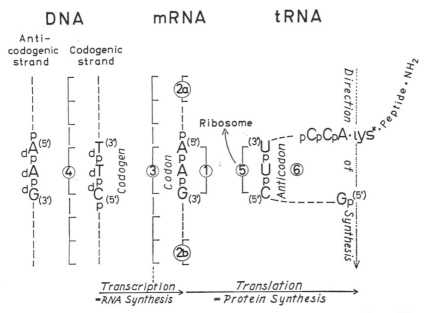

Fig. 8.6.—Ways for deciphering the coding nucleotide sequences (from Matthaei 1963). Numbers 1 to 6 refer to the suggested strategies for determining the identity of the specifically interacting groups.

studies are obtained (Nirenberg *et al.* 1965). Or n can be larger, as in the polymers of type $XpYpZ \ldots pZ \sim_{30}$ we have been using at Göttingen.

(2*b*) Trinucleotides can be obtained at the 3′ ends of homopolynucleotides by digestion of synthetic polynucleotides such as poly-UG with base-specific ribonucleases (Cramer, Küntzel, and Matthaei 1964). These polymers have not proved generally useful for deciphering coding sequences. Ochoa (1965) with his co-workers and Thach *et al.* (1965) have used this type of polymer to identify the direction of message reading.

(3) Polynucleotides can be synthesized by a chemical method or by enzymic transcription from: (4) oligodeoxytrinucleotides. Deoxypolynucleotides are more easily synthesized than polyribonucleotides because the 2′ hydroxyl group on the sugar renders polyribonucleotides labile both to hydrolytic attack and to undesired substitutions at the 2′ carbon, including formation of 2′–5′ instead of 3′–5′ phosphodiester linkages. Several polynucleotides of this sort have been synthesized by Khorana and collaborators (Nishimura *et al.* 1965; Nishimura, Jones, and Khorana 1965). The analytic application of synthetic polynucleo-

tides is elegant in principle: Decoding may be accomplished by identification of the peptides synthesized on ribosomes supplied by known polytrinucleotides. Results from the crude system that has been used so far, however, need ancillary support from the approach to be mentioned next. Furthermore, it seems unlikely that all of the possible kinds of polytrinucleotides could be used for coding the synthesis of the corresponding poly-amino acids, because many sequences are presumably not single stranded enough to be read by the ribosome (Nirenberg and Matthaei 1961).

(5) Trinucleotides, or even trinucleoside diphosphates, a border case of approach (2a), would, it was hoped, be accepted by the ribosome as a messenger sufficient for the specific binding of one corresponding molecule of aminoacyl RNA (Matthaei 1963).

Amino acid adaptation systems were developed independently by several laboratories in 1963–64 (Kaji and Kaji 1964; Matthaei *et al.* 1964; Nakamoto *et al.* 1963; Nirenberg and Leder 1964). The decoding results from cell-free systems are being verified by analysis of mutagen-related changes in the amino acid sequences of proteins synthesized

Table 8.1

Specificity in binding of phenylalanyl RNA and lysyl RNA to ribosomes. Reaction mixtures, composed of 54 $\mu\mu$moles 30S and 34 $\mu\mu$moles 50S ribosomal subunits, 400 $\mu\mu$moles sRNA containing 8 $\mu\mu$moles ^{3}H-labeled phenylalanyl RNA or 11.5 $\mu\mu$moles ^{3}H-labeled lysyl RNA in 350 μl of 0.01 M Tris-HCl (*p*H 7.8), and 0.01 M magnesium acetate, were incubated for 10 min at 37° C and filtered as indicated under Figure 8.7 (from Matthaei *et al.* 1964).

Polynucleotide added	30S+50S	30S	50S	Without ribosomes
nμmoles of ^{3}H-phenylalanyl RNA bound				
None	38	26	30	19
15 μg poly-U	**582**	**375**	37	11
15 μg poly-A	35	20	19	9
15 μg poly-C	35	52	40	53
15 μg poly-I	61	15	14	10
nμmoles of ^{3}H-lysyl RNA bound				
None	132	29	98	25
15 μg poly-U	68	21	71	15
15 μg poly-A	**1267**	**238**	**183**	23
15 μg poly-C	93	25	92	24
15 μg poly-I	74	14	72	17

Table 8.2

Characteristics of poly-U directed binding of phenylalanyl RNA to ribosomes. Reaction mixtures as indicated under Table 8.1, but with 15 $\mu\mu$moles 30S and 18 $\mu\mu$moles 50S ribosomal subunits and 15 μg polyuridylic acid (from Matthaei *et al.* 1964).

Modifications	nμmoles ³H-phenyl-alanyl RNA bound
Complete system	1350
−30S component	26
−50S component	1090
− polyuridylic acid	0
−Mg^{++}	−20
filtered with H_2O	554
−incubation (time=0)	63
+10 μg streptomycin	620
+20 μg RNase, 5 min postincubated	233
+15 μmoles KCl	1480
+2 μmoles β-mercapto-ethanol	1300
+100 mμmoles guanosine triphosphate	1280
+25 μg chloramphenicol	1225
+100 mμmoles puromycin	1375

within cells. The abundant agreement of the data presently available will be discussed below.

The System for Amino Acid Adaptation on the Ribosome

At the Symposium on Molecular Biology, held at Berlin in May 1964, we reported characteristics of a new simplified system in which aminoacyl sRNA becomes bound to ribosomes with a specificity that is dependent upon the type of mRNA added. Because the report of this symposium was published in a journal not generally available to biologists and biochemists (Matthaei *et al.* 1964), we would like to summarize the results here.

The mRNA directed binding of amino acid charged adaptors to ribosomes (called amino acid adaptation) was demonstrated with several polynucleotides. Table 8.1 shows the specificity of poly-U for phenylalanyl RNA and of poly-A for lysyl RNA. The isolated 30S subunit of *E. coli* ribosomes is active in the absence of the larger 50S component. The characteristics collected in Table 8.2 include another demonstration that 30S subunits are almost as active as 70S ribosomes. Phenylalanine adaptation requires polyuridylic acid template and magnesium ions. It is inhibited by streptomycin but not by chloramphenicol and puromycin. It does not respond to potassium chloride, mercapto-ethan-

ol, and GTP, which stimulate systems for peptide synthesis (Matthaei
and Nirenberg 1961b). Ribonuclease leads to loss of amino acid label
from the ribosomes. After hydrolysis of the amino acid tRNA ester
linkage at pH 9, at least 90 per cent of the lysine bound to the ribosomes in the presence of poly-A is regained as free amino acid.

A systematic study of all fractions obtained from *E. coli* ribosomes
dissociated into 30S and 50S subunits and separated by centrifugation
through sucrose density gradients has shown the receptivity of the 30S
particles for both labeled tobacco mosaic virus RNA used as an mRNA
model and for phenylalanyl RNA upon addition of excess poly-U (see
Fig. 8.7). Some preparations of 30S subunits were even as active as the
original 70S ribosomes. In Figure 8.8a, 30S subunits are equally active
in adapting phenylalanine both in the absence and in the presence of
50S subunits.

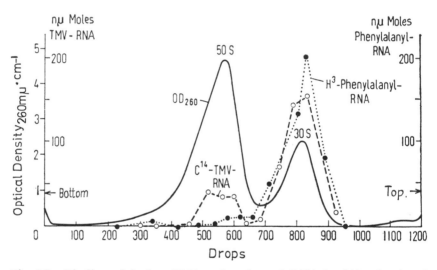

Fig. 8.7.—Binding of both mRNA and aminoacyl RNA by 30S subunits of
E. coli ribosomes fractionated in a sucrose density gradient. Particles dissociated in dialysis against 2.5×10^{-4} M magnesium acetate and 0.01 M Tris-HCl
(pH 7.6). Fractionation in 30-ml sucrose gradients from 5 per cent to 20 per
cent in same buffer during 6 hours at 25,000 rpm in Spinco rotor SW25-1;
50 µliters of each fraction incubated for 10 min at 37° C in 0.01 M Tris-HCl
(pH 7.8) and 0.01 M magnesium acetate with 2 µµmoles of ^{14}C-labeled tobacco
mosaic virus RNA or 400 µµmoles sRNA containing 8 µµmoles of ^{3}H-phenyl-
alanyl RNA and 15 µg of poly-pU respectively. Complexes were adsorbed by
filtration through cellulose nitrate filters with 0.01 M Tris-HCl (pH 7.2), 0.015
M magnesium acetate (from Matthaei *et al.* 1964).

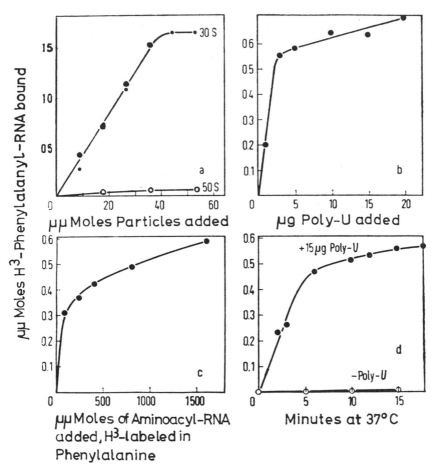

Fig. 8.8.—Adaptation of phenylalanine upon the addition of polyuridylic acid to 30S subunits of *E. coli* ribosomes. In (*a*) 30S (·), 50S (○), and (●) 30S + 50S were tested. Unless varied, reaction compounds were 15 μμmoles each of 30S and 50S ribosomal subunits, 15 μg of polyuridylic acid, 1200 μμmoles of aminoacyl RNA, carrying 19 nonlabeled amino acids, and 25 μμmoles ³H-phenylalanine. Systems were incubated in 0.01 м Tris-HCl (*p*H 7.8), 0.01м magnesium acetate at 37° C for 10 (*a, c*) or 15 (*b*) min, respectively (from Matthaei *et al.* 1964).

This system seemed to be potentially able to select the aminoacyl RNA corresponding to any trinucleotide added. However, in the following section on the determination of coding sequences by amino acid adaptation, we describe several purification procedures necessary for more satisfactory utilization of the system components, particularly of the mRNA models.

Analysis of the Code by Amino Acid Adaptation
on Polynucleotides of Type XpYpZ . . . pZ~$_{30}$

The first coding sequences known, in July 1964, were GUU coding valine (Leder and Nirenberg 1964) and UUG coding leucine (Cramer, Küntzel, and Matthaei 1964), both determined in an amino acid adaptation system. By May 1965, Nirenberg had tested 44 trinucleoside diphosphates, many of which significantly stimulated specific amino acid adaptations (Nirenberg *et al.* 1965). The major result of this work appeared to be the confirmation of the code's symmetry, as it had been postulated by Eck in 1963 on the basis of the amino acid exchanges known to occur in proteins and the net compositions of coding units determined from polynucleotide-directed polypeptide synthesis, described above. But there were also uncertainties which, we feel, resulted in part from impurities in the system used and in part from the relatively low efficiency of coding obtained with short pieces of mRNA. Furthermore, not all of the 44 trinucleotides were tested against all of the 20 protein amino acids.

In our work of the last two years, to be described here, we have attempted optimal purification of every component of the adaptation system. Nirenberg and Leder (1964) observed that longer polynucleotides have better efficiencies in coding, and in confirmation we have found that long polymers are at least 30 times more efficient than trinucleotides in our system. We hope to learn by the use of long polymers whether the ribosome may have a specificity for amino acid adaptation on the 5′ terminal triplet of XpYpZ . . . pZ~$_{30}$ polymers.

Purification of ribosomes

Purification of ribosomes seemed essential for the protection of both aminoacyl sRNA and mRNA, particularly since an exonuclease might be contaminating the ribosomes and degrading the mRNA starting from its 5′ end. For the same reason we chose the *E. coli* strain A19, which is a ribonuclease I^- mutant isolated by Watson and Gesteland at Harvard University.

To monitor the removal of ribonuclease, we developed a sensitive test primarily measuring exonuclease activity: ^{14}C-labeled polyuridylic acid serves as substrate, and the ribosomes (50 μμmoles) and polyuridylic acid (20 mμmoles uridylic acid; specific activity = 0.4 c/mole Up; chain length approximately 30 nucleotides) are incubated for 10 minutes at 33° C in the ionic environment described in Table 8.3 for the amino acid adaptation system, without the ammonium salt. Thereafter, 25-μl aliquots are spotted onto a 1 × 4 inch strip of Whatman

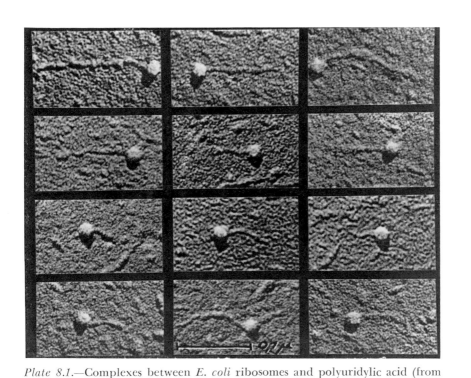

Plate 8.1.—Complexes between *E. coli* ribosomes and polyuridylic acid (from Matthaei *et al.* 1964). Electronmicrograph after fixation with 1 per cent uranium acetate (*p*H 4.2) and ultra-thin shadowing with platinum-carbon; 30 μμmoles of 30S and 50 μμmoles of 50S subunits were recombined for 15 min at 20° C with approximately 1000 μμmoles of polyuridylic acid (average chain length, 760 Å) in 5 ml 0.01 M Tris-HCl (*p*H 7.6) and 0.005 M magnesium acetate, and dried at 0° C on Formvar film.

3MM chromatographic paper on top of 10 µg of 3'-uridylic acid serving as a marker. The short chromatogram is developed in a descending direction with 3 parts of 1 M ammonium acetate (pH 5.5) and 7 parts of 95 per cent ethanol (Thach and Doty 1965; Voigt and Matthaei, unpublished) at room temperature. The Up spot is counted in a liquid scintillation spectrometer. When plotted at different stages of this purification, both time and enzyme concentration curves for the release of nucleotide from polyuridylic acid are linear at least up to one-quarter of the radioactivity added in the substrate. This range is used in the assays.

As shown in Figure 8.9, ribonucleolytic activity measured by this assay is logarithmically reducible to 10^{-3} times the level seen in the ribosomes after their initial sedimentation from the 30,000-g supernatant fluid of *E. coli* A19 extracts (Matthaei and Nirenberg 1961a). The ribosomes are purified to that extent by six washings at 3° C through the solution indicated in Figure 8.9 containing 0.5 M ammonium chloride and various diamines in standard buffer (Matthaei and Nirenberg 1961a).

After each sedimentation the ribosomes are suspended in standard buffer, centrifuged for 10 min at 5,000 g, aspirated, and brought to the concentration of the washing solution, and to approximately 240 OD_{260} units per ml. The suspension is kept in ice for 30 minutes and then sedimented for two hours at 4° C and 134,000 g. By this purification process, after six washings, 50 per cent of the ribosomes appear as active as before washing. The ribosomes may be stored in standard buffer at $-45°$ C for many months without appreciable loss in activity. They usually bind 1 mole of phenylalanyl RNA per 4 ribosomes at saturating concentrations of polyuridylic acid (Voigt and Matthaei, unpublished). The diamine compounds included in the washing solution help both to remove ribonuclease faster and perhaps to avoid loss by the ribosomes in specific adaptation activity (Voigt and Matthaei, unpublished). The latter capability of diamine compounds might be related to the fact that some of them are natural constituents of ribosomes (Zillig, Krone, and Albers 1959). We have observed marked stimulation of polyuridylic acid-dependent phenylalanine polymerization by *E. coli* extracts with 10^{-2} M cadaverine (1,5-pentanediamine) at saturating Mg^{++} concentration (see Figs. 8.10 and 8.11). There was no stimulation of the background incorporation seen in the absence of polyuridylic acid. Furthermore, in the presence of optimal concentrations of Mg^{++} plus cadaverine, another 30 per cent stimulation of phenylalanine incorporation was observed after addition of 10^{-2} M 1,7-heptanediamine (Voigt and Matthaei, unpublished). The concentrations used in this washing

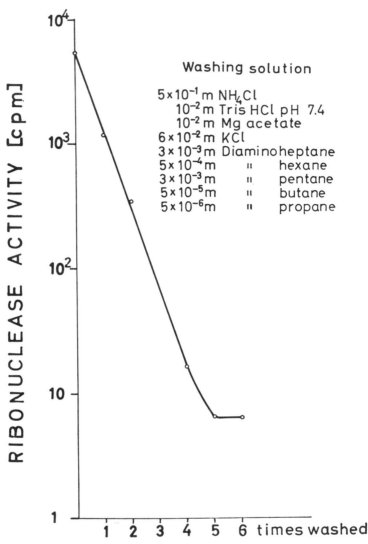

Fig. 8.9.—Purification of *E. coli* ribosomes from ribonucleolytic activity by washing in the ultracentrifuge (Voigt and Matthaei, unpublished). Ribonuclease assay and washing procedure described in the text. Formula of washing solution indicates final concentrations after mixing with ribosomal solution in standard buffer (Matthaei and Nirenberg 1961*a*). All diamine compounds were purest grades obtainable from Fluka, Switzerland.

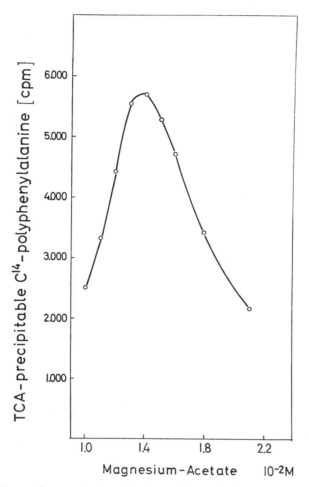

Fig. 8.10.—Dependence of phenylalanine polymerization on magnesium ion concentration. Each 200 μl reaction mixture contained (in μmoles per ml unless otherwise indicated) 86 Tris-HCl (*p*H 7.8), 55 KCl, magnesium acetate in amount indicated along the abscissa, 5.5 β-mercapto-ethanol, 0.7 ATP-K, 0.13 GTP-K, 0.07 CTP-K, 5.2 phosphoenolpyruvate, 24 μg pyruvate kinase, 0.15 ^{14}C-L-phenylalanine (specific activity = 5 c/mole), 0.02 of each of 19 non-labeled amino acids, 0.375 mg ribosomes, and 1.67 mg supernatant protein (after centrifugation at 165,000 *g* for 90 min, and dialysis overnight against standard buffer in the absence of Mg^{++}). After 60 min of incubation at 37° C, 100 μl aliquots were spotted on Whatman 3MM filter discs (25 mm diam), precipitated in 10 per cent trichloracetic acid at 0° C, hydrolyzed for 15 min in 5 per cent trichloracetic acid at 90° C, washed further for 3 min in 5 per cent trichloracetic acid, ether-ethanol (1:1), and ether, then dried and counted in 5 ml of 0.4 per cent PPO and 0.01 per cent POPOP in toluene in a liquid scintillation spectrometer. Counting efficiency was 53 per cent.

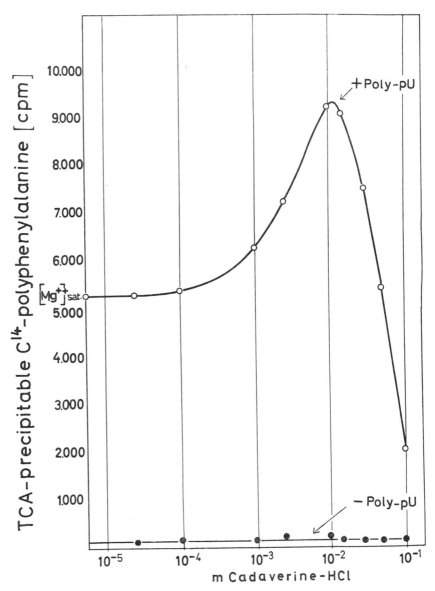

Fig. 8.11.—Further stimulation of phenylalanine polymerization by cadaverine (1,5-pentanediamine) at the saturating Mg++ concentration established in Fig. 8.10. For all other conditions, see legend to Fig. 8.10.

solution were determined by dialyses of ribosomes against varied concentrations of the diamines. Diamines help in maintaining ribosomal activity during dialysis, but apparently are not sufficient to preserve it completely.

Preparation of polynucleotides $XpYpZ \ldots pZ \sim_{30}$

Polynucleotide phosphorylase was purified over a hundred-fold from *Micrococcus lysodeikticus* by the procedure of Singer and O'Brien (1963) through the seventh step. Enzyme activity was monitored by a polymerization assay with ^{14}C-labeled UDP as substrate and saturating concentrations of ApA as primer at pH 8.8.

Polymer not migrating in the chromatographic system described above (with 4 parts of 1 M ammonium acetate at pH 5.5 and 6 parts of 95 per cent ethanol as solvent) was measured by radioactivity. Polymerization was completely dependent on dinucleoside phosphates added as primers in the following reaction mixtures (in μmoles per 1 ml): 150 Tris-HCl (pH 8.8), 10 MgCl$_2$ (3 for ADP), 0.4 K-EDTA, 40 nucleoside diphosphate, 1.3 dinucleoside* monophosphate (^{14}C-labeled for assay), 833 NaCl for UDP and CDP or 1000 (1190) NaCl and 800 (761) urea for ADP (IDP), and 200 μg of fraction VII polynucleotide phosphorylase. Samples were incubated at 33° C. For each enzyme preparation, preliminary experiments had to be performed to find the optimal concentrations of sodium chloride and of urea (Thach and Doty 1965) for obtaining good yields yet complete primer dependence.

The ratio of primer to substrate offered to the enzyme was 1:30. As can be seen from Figure 8.12, the fraction of tritium-labeled G*pU incorporated was smaller than the fraction of the substrate polymerized. Polynucleotide solutions were deproteinized by four extractions with phenol. Phenol was removed by two extractions with ether in a separatory funnel. Constituents in smaller quantities, like oligonucleotides and traces of phenol, were removed by fractionation in columns of Sephadex G50 (1.0 × 50 cm) in 0.1 M ammonium bicarbonate (pH 7.8). Examples of these chromatograms given in Figure 8.13 show by the exclusion shoulder indicated in the CpGpI . . . pI profile that the majority of the longer chains selected for coding experiments were slightly retarded. Chain length was estimated to be 30 nucleotides. The same value was also determined from analyses of the nucleoside to nucleotide ratio by high voltage electrophoresis after digestion with 0.3 M barium hydroxide (Matthaei *et al.* 1966*b*). All primers and substrates were analyzed and purified when necessary by recycling chromatography over DEAE-Sephadex A25 in 0.1 M ammonium carbonate (pH 9) to reduce impurities to less than 1 per cent.

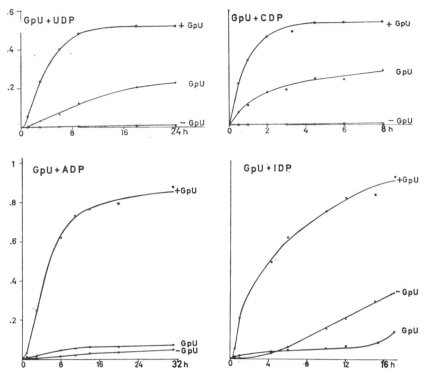

Fig. 8.12.—Synthesis of polynucleotides from nucleoside diphosphates primed by the dinucleoside monophosphate GpU. Fractions of substrate, polymerized in the absence and presence of GpU and of ³H-labeled G*pU, incorporated into polymer are plotted against time of incorporation at 33° C. Molar ratio of nucleoside diphosphate substrate to primer was 30 to 1. For reaction mixtures and assay procedure see text.

Synthesis and purification of aminoacyl sRNA

Soluble RNA was isolated from *E. coli* A19 ribonuclease I⁻ by the method of Berg and co-workers (Ofengand, Dieckmann, and Berg 1961). Of the sRNA isolated, 80 mg were purified further on Sephadex G75 (4.5 × 40 cm) in 0.01 M magnesium acetate, 0.01 M K-EDTA (*p*H 7.0), and 0.1 M Tris-acetate (*p*H 7.0) to remove mostly inactive material coming off in the exclusion peak. Further purification was done after the column was charged with a purified fraction from the 100,000-*g* supernatant fluid of A19 extracts.

The $OD_{260/280}$ value of these preparations was 0.49 and the charge-ability greater than 65 per cent. We have recently added a few phenol steps because at this stage of purity there were still traces of ribo-

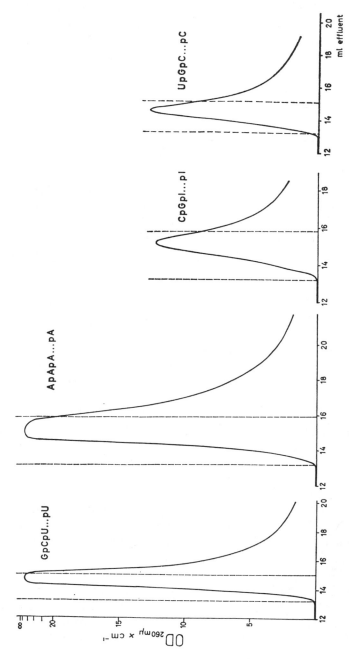

Fig. 8.13.—Selection of longest polymer chains of type XpYpZ . . . pZ∼₃₀ by passage over columns of Sephadex G50 (1.4 × 65 cm) in 0.1 M ammonium bicarbonate (*p*H 7.8) at room temperature. Long-chain material eluted between the dotted lines was used for decoding experiments.

nuclease activity detectable by the method of Neu and Heppel (1964). Charging was performed with saturating amounts of a fraction from the 100,000-g supernatant fluid of *E. coli* A19 purified over DEAE cellulose in a reaction mixture containing the following (in μmoles per ml): 2 ATP-K, 1 CTP-K, 10 MgCl$_2$, 50 KCl, 150 Tris-HCl (pH 7.4), 8.5 β-mercapto-ethanol, 8 potassium phosphoenolpyruvate, 20 μg pyruvate kinase, 0.08 (2 mg) sRNA, 0.05 of each of 19 nonlabeled L-amino acids, 0.05 of ^{3}H- or ^{14}C-labeled L-amino acid, 300 μg fraction with aminoacyl tRNA ligases (Heller and Matthaei, unpublished).

The aminoacyl RNA formed during 30 minutes of incubation at 36° C is purified by four extractions in a separatory funnel with phenol near 0° C after Mg-EDTA (pH 7) has been added to a concentration of 1.5×10^{-2} M to prevent nonenzymatic hydrolysis by traces of divalent cations possibly present in p.a. buffer salts used (Heller and Matthaei, unpublished). After removal of phenol by two precipitations of aminoacyl RNA from 70 per cent ethanol at 0° C, aminoacyl RNA is passed over Sephadex G25 (1×25 cm), which has previously been purified with phenol and EDTA, to obtain solutions of aminoacyl RNA free of ribonuclease, oligonucleotide material, and metal ion impurities destructive to the amino acid esters and their complexes with ribosomes. Data showing how this purification substantially affects the time curves of amino acid adaptation will be published elsewhere. The set of 20 aminoacyl RNA preparations used in these experiments was 62 per cent charged, as calculated from the one labeled amino acid of highest ^{3}H or ^{14}C specific activity available. This is clearly an underestimate, because it was based on OD$_{260}$ measurements before passage over Sephadex G25, at which stage the RNA still contains ATP and CTP.

Quantities and kinetics
of the refined amino acid adaptation system

The quantities incubated for template-specific amino acid adaptation are indicated in Table 8.3. From the curves of Figures 8.14 and 8.15 it was concluded that both 50 μμmoles of highly purified 70S ribosomes and 200 μμmoles of mRNA chains added per 100 μl were limiting. Maximum binding was reached at 33° C within 15 minutes, and the amount of aminoacyl RNA present in the system was shown to be saturating in all cases tested. Yield of arginyl RNA incorporation upon addition of CpGpC . . . pC$\sim_{30}$ as template can be derived from Figure 8.15. One-fifth to one-sixth of the arginyl RNA added is bound in the linear portion of the aminoacyl RNA concentration curve. This seems to be in reasonable agreement with the number of codons and adaptors available for the amino acid arginine (see Fig. 8.17) and also

Table 8.3

System for amino acid adaptation stimulated by $XpYpZ \ldots pZ_{\sim 30}$. All measurements after sorption to Millipore filters as mentioned under Figure 8.7.

Ribosomes[a]	50 $\mu\mu$moles
Polynucleotide chains,[b] approx.	200 $\mu\mu$moles
Soluble RNA[c]	800 $\mu\mu$moles
62% charged with 20 amino acids, average per labeled amino acid[d]	25 $\mu\mu$moles
Reaction mixture, incubated for 15 min. at 33° C	
Total volume[e]	100 μl
Mg acetate	1.6×10^{-2} M
Tris-acetate (pH 7.2)	3×10^{-2} M
KCl	6×10^{-3} M
NH$_4$ bicarbonate	1×10^{-2} M

[a] Calculated at 16 A$_{260}$ units: 1 mg/0.356 mμmoles of 70S.

[b] Average chain length = 30 nucleotides; 3 mμmoles of nucleotide.

[c] Calculated at 25 A$_{260}$ units: 1 mg/40 mμmoles of sRNA.

[d] Extreme values to this average were 3.0 $\mu\mu$moles of cysteine and 78 $\mu\mu$moles of leucine in 800 $\mu\mu$moles of sRNA.

[e] The $XpYpI \ldots pI$ polymers were tested in 1.0 ml of the same ionic environment.

with the very high degree of utilization of phenylalanine seen in the binding results described by Nirenberg and Leder (1964). The factor that limits the yields, in terms of mRNA added, to a few per cent therefore seems to be a nonfavorable equilibrium for mRNA binding (see Fig. 8.15). Still, a 3 per cent utilization of $XpYpZ \ldots pZ_{\sim 30}$ polymers is 30 times better than the 0.1 per cent usually obtained in coding with isolated trinucleoside diphosphates. Twenty-five per cent of our six-times washed ribosomes seem to be active in binding one molecule of phenylalanyl RNA when saturated with polyuridylic acid in normal standard buffer. The ionic environment chosen here and used throughout all experiments was designed to give high specificity in the coding by the polymers without too much loss in the efficiency obtainable at a higher ratio of divalent to monovalent cations.

The decoding results

For the first time all 64 triplets have been tested against all 20 protein amino acids. In Table 8.4 we present the coding results obtained with the 16 C-polymers of type $XpYpC \ldots pC_{\sim 30}$. The figures indicate $\mu\mu$moles of amino acid adapted in both absence and presence of these polymers under the conditions described in Table 8.3, except that the reaction mixtures were doubled for the cysteine, glutamine, and asparagine adaptations because of the lower specific activities of these amino acids. All assays were done in duplicate at least. Most of

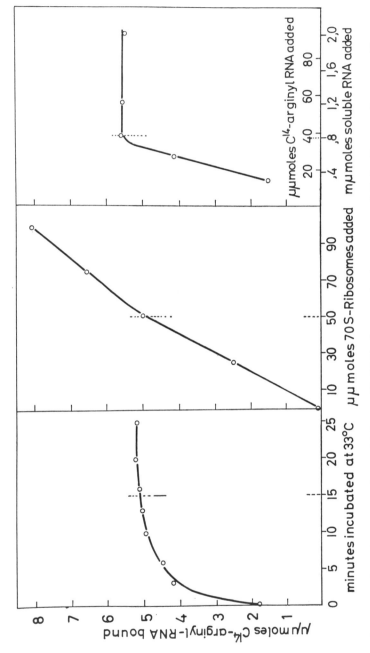

Fig. 8.14.—Adaptation of arginine on highly purified 70S ribosomes in the presence of CpGpGp . . . pC~$_{30}$ as coding template. Nonvaried conditions as specified in Table 8.3.

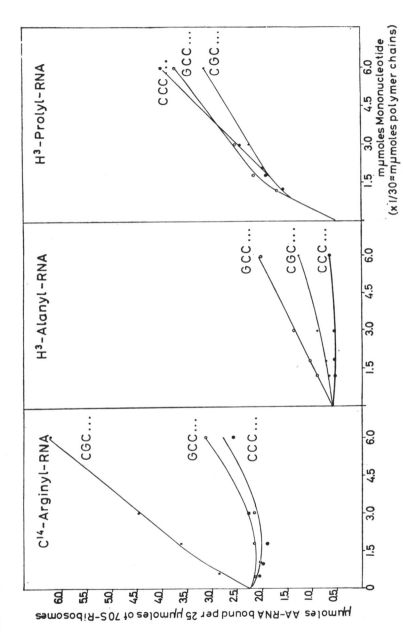

Fig. 8.15.—Adaptation of amino acids coded by polynucleotides CGC . . ., GGC . . ., and CCC . . ., respectively: polynucleotide concentration curves. Other conditions as specified in Table 8.3.

Table 8.4

Amino acid adaptations observed without and with the polymers $XpYpG \ldots pG_{\sim 30}$, as obtained in the system described in Table 8.3, in $\mu\mu$moles. Only the very small Millipore-filter blanks have been subtracted. Lightface figures indicate background adaptation; boldface figures indicate codon—amino acid assignments.

	Amino acid																			
	ala	arg	asN[a]	asp	cys[a]	glN[a]	glu	gly	his	ilu	leu	lys	met	phe	pro	ser	tre	try	tyr	val
Without polymer	0.80	1.66	0.29	0.63	0.49	2.45	0.30	1.11	0.13	0.34	2.38	3.28	0.60	1.35	0.29	1.03	0.87	0.88	0.87	0.71
UUC...	0.89	1.38	0.35	0.37	0.50	1.91	0.17	0.77	0.15	0.27	1.22	2.92	0.30	**1.51**	2.04	2.28	0.65	0.62	0.62	0.57
CUC...	0.90	1.60	0.24	0.43	0.38	1.99	0.20	0.85	0.18	0.28	**1.72**	2.45	0.33	0.44	2.48	2.65	0.86	0.60	0.68	0.56
AUC...	**1.87**	1.29	0.25	0.43	0.44	1.73	0.24	0.89	0.17	0.24	1.31	2.50	0.39	0.46	2.05	1.86	0.78	0.59	0.55	0.48
GUC...	0.83	1.22	0.24	0.44	0.53	1.78	0.21	0.87	0.16	0.31	1.13	1.59	0.22	0.44	2.39	2.75	0.97	0.61	0.59	**1.71**
UCC...	0.92	1.30	0.31	0.45	0.61	1.92	0.23	0.84	0.14	0.31	1.16	2.71	0.26	0.51	2.25	**2.54**	0.78	0.61	0.69	0.55
CCC...	0.95	1.42	0.34	0.42	0.55	1.98	0.21	0.91	0.16	0.24	1.26	2.58	0.28	0.45	2.38	2.11	0.83	0.61	0.61	0.53
ACC...	0.93	1.28	0.18	0.41	0.44	1.67	0.23	0.74	0.17	0.25	1.40	2.26	0.32	0.50	2.78	2.11	**1.85**	0.63	0.58	0.67
GCC...	**1.81**	1.47	0.32	0.42	0.44	1.81	0.24	0.81	0.17	0.24	1.15	2.43	0.21	0.44	2.35	2.22	0.88	0.67	0.54	0.58
UAC...	0.87	1.33	0.36	0.43	0.56	1.97	0.20	0.84	0.15	0.28	1.26	2.59	0.27	0.43	2.16	1.97	0.82	0.71	**1.80**	0.54
CAC...	0.92	1.41	0.27	0.43	0.31	1.88	0.18	0.90	**0.25**	0.30	1.23	2.45	0.26	0.45	2.56	2.26	0.89	0.58	0.64	0.62
AAC...	0.84	1.37	**0.49**	0.38	0.51	1.97	0.24	0.77	0.13	0.24	1.18	2.85	0.23	0.54	2.33	1.96	0.98	0.57	0.56	0.56
GAC...	0.68	1.10	0.32	**1.68**	0.32	1.73	0.24	0.69	0.18	0.23	1.23	2.08	0.27	0.44	1.80	1.79	0.93	0.67	0.50	0.45
UGC...	1.81	1.95	0.20	0.40	**1.06**	1.82	0.15	0.80	0.15	0.27	1.06	2.51	0.32	0.41	2.47	1.74	0.81	0.66	0.61	0.71
CGC...	1.60	**4.16**	0.31	0.45	0.43	1.84	0.19	0.82	0.14	0.26	1.46	2.36	0.33	0.48	2.37	2.02	0.64	0.61	0.58	0.56
AGC...	0.88	1.49	0.32	0.41	0.46	1.71	0.19	0.78	0.16	**0.54**	1.40	2.42	0.25	0.45	2.39	**2.43**	0.84	0.64	0.56	0.58
GGC...	0.87	1.47	0.29	0.39	0.49	1.43	0.24	**1.15**	0.19	0.26	1.32	2.55	0.25	0.41	2.23	2.21	0.92	0.70	0.64	0.57

[a] Values obtained for double reaction mixtures.

the boldface figures are far above the level of a fairly homogeneous series of background adaptations observed in both absence and presence of polymers not coding the particular amino acid. In Table 8.5 these results have been expressed as the percentage increase over the homopolymer blank. The table corroborates many of the data obtained, including those supporting the 65 amino acid assignments made to 63 of the triplet permutations in the system of *E. coli* strain A19. Table 8.5 also refers to the published work from Nirenberg's laboratory (Nirenberg *et al.* 1965) and to data from Khorana and co-workers (Khorana 1965).

There are some values in Table 8.4 which clearly exceed the homopolymer blank for reasons which we cannot yet define with certainty: UGC . . . and CGC . . . coding, like GCC . . . , for alanine could be interpreted as "pseudo-shifted" readings, the result of a reading of the first triplet after removal of the first letter, rather than a real one-nucleotide shift in the start of reading. Only from adaptations after removal of the traces of ribonucleolytic activity demonstrated in Figure 8.9 can we exclude the possibility of "pseudo-shifted" readings and interpret the observations as true reading of the triplet. This uncertainty is the major disadvantage at present in the use of XpYpZ . . . pZ polymers as compared to trinucleoside diphosphates, which have other disadvantages. But the polymers offer greater specificity in peptide synthesis and may be the only means for future studies of peptide synthesis. That pseudo-shifted reading is not general is seen from various examples given here: AGC . . . and GGC . . . do not code alanine as does GCC . . .; the four triplets XAC . . . do not stimulate threonine adaptation as ACC . . . does (see Table 8.4). Several other examples are given in Table 8.6. Analyses of polynucleotide preparations in which the triplet has apparently been read starting with the second nucleotide from the 5' end may reveal that some chains actually start with the second nucleotide because of some nucleolytic activity in the enzyme preparation by which the polynucleotide was made.

There are three amino acids, however, for which it has been difficult to obtain significant stimulations by some polymers in this system; they are leucine, proline, and serine. Whereas we know a proline codon to be given in poly-C since the first communication in 1961 (Nirenberg and Matthaei 1961), insignificant stimulations for the leucine codons UUA, CUU, CUC and for the serine codons AGU, AGC, and UCA have been found also by the laboratories of Nirenberg and of Khorana, respectively. Improvements to overcome this situation are being made and will be discussed.

Table 8.5

Significance of decoding results obtained with polynucleotides of type $Xp\Upsilon p\zeta \ldots$ $p\zeta_{\sim 30}$ in the adaptation system from *E. coli* A19. Figures indicate the percentage of stimulations over the homopolymer blanks. (See Addendum.)

1.	Nucleotide sequence 2.				3.
	U	C	A	G	
U	BNKphe 6000[a]	BNKser 17	BNKtyr 117	BNKcys 49	U
	BNKphe 180[b]	BNKser 23[b]	BNKtyr 200	Kcys 93	C
	B leu 20	Kser 9	leu 27		A
	BNKleu 64	BNKser 83[b]	leu 72	B Ktry 37[b]	G[c]
C	Bn leu 30	BNKpro 53[b]	BNKhis 220	B arg 685[b]	U
	Bnk leu 10	BNKpro 820[a]	BNKhis 81	BNKarg 216[b]	C
	leu 33	BNKpro 60	BNKglN 45	NKarg 41	A
	Kleu 29	Kpro 27[b]	N glN 25	Karg 14	G[c]
A	BNKilu 108[b]	BNKtre 323[b]	BNKasN 212	NKser 25; ilu 52	U
	(BNKilu)ala 98	BNKtre 123[b]	BNKasN 42	BNKser 10; ilu 107	C
	met 29	BNKtre 57	BNKlys 256[a]	BNKarg 42	A
	BNKmet 55[b]	Ktre 316	NKlys 17	arg 23	G[c]
G	BNKval 66[b]	BNKala 121	BNKasp 237[b]	BNKgly[d] 147[b]	U
	Kval 266[b]	B Kala 178	B Kasp 364	B Kgly[d] 67[b]	C
	Kval 41	B Kala 45	BNKglu 11[b]	B Kgly[d] 15	A
	Kval 35	Kala 84	Kglu 120	Kgly[d] 170[a]	G[c]

[a] Stimulation by homopolymers given in percentage increase over minus-polymer (i.e., ribosome) blank.

[b] From experiment No. 1; all other results from second experiment.

[c] G was replaced by I.

[d] Polymer synthesis started with IpI.

[B] Triplet in agreement with base composition determined in polynucleotide stimulated polymerization.

[N] Sequence determined by Nirenberg *et al.* (1965) by adaptation directed with trinucleotide diphosphates. Lower case letter (n) indicates authors' uncertainty because of small stimulations observed in aminoacyl RNA binding.

[K] Sequence determined by Khorana and co-workers (Nishimura *et al.* 1965) by adaptation directed with trinucleotide diphosphates. Lower case letter (k) indicates authors' uncertainty because of small stimulations observed. Italic letter (*K* or *k*) means triplet established by peptide synthesis directed with poly-dinucleotides or trinucleotides (Nishimura *et al.* 1965; Nishimura, Jones, and Khorana 1965).

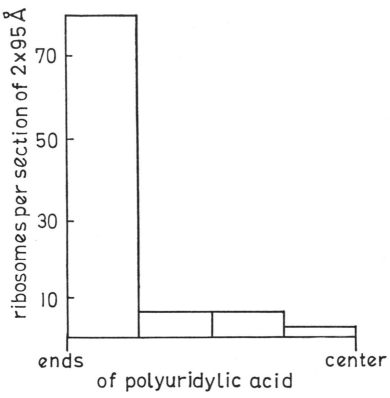

Fig. 8.16.—Terminal binding of ribosomes to polyuridylic acid: evaluation of 1358 ribosomes on an electron microscopic grid. Of 98 particles bound, 79 were attached to one end of polyuridylic acid. The 760 Å chain length of polyuridylic acid was not shortened by the ribosomes to a significant extent.

Specificity of ribosomes for 5′ ends of polynucleotides

At the Sixth International Congress of Biochemistry at New York, we communicated the electron microscopic observation by F. Amelunxen that ribosomes bind preferentially to one or both ends of polyuridylic acid *in vitro*. Electron micrographs are presented in Plate 8.1 and evaluated in Figure 8.16. The questions, to which ends of the polymers the ribosomes bind and if the binding leads to a precise reading of the very first triplet, may be answered by our studies with the polymers XpYpZ . . . pZ. We have seen in Figure 8.16 that about eight per cent of the ribosomes present in the adaptation system bind arginyl RNA because of the presence of CpGpC . . . pC$\sim_{30}$, whereas less prolyl RNA is bound simultaneously under these conditions. **As**

Table 8.6

Amino acid adaptation on the 5' terminal triplet of polynucleotides of type $Xp\Upsilon p\mathcal{Z}$ . . .
$p\mathcal{Z}$ ~₃₀, as obtained under the conditions of Table 8.3, in $\mu\mu$moles.

Amino acid	Triplet			Without polymer
	UCA---	CAA--	AAA-	
ser	**1.30**	1.11	1.22	1.43
glN	1.43	**1.72**	1.34	1.41
lys		6.15	**7.30**	3.35
	GUI---	UGI--	III-	
val	**1.34**	.93	.95	.36
try	.29	**.51**	.37	.23
gly	2.88	2.96	**3.70**	1.37
	GAC---	ACC--	CCC-	
asp	**3.45**	.61	.65	.67
tre	.93	**1.85**	.83	.17
pro	1.69	2.16	**2.40**	.30

stated above, only 25 per cent of the ribosomes seem active in binding
aminoacyl RNA upon the addition of synthetic mRNA. We have seen
examples in Table 8.4 indicating specificity of the ribosomes for 5' ends
of polynucleotides. Table 8.6 provides more evidence to support this
point: In UCA . . . , GUI . . . , and GAC . . . , reading of the triplet
almost never starts beyond the 5' terminal nucleotide. In turn, nucleotides standing ahead of the polymers with the sequences AAA . . . , III
. . . , and CCC . . . , for instance, seem to inhibit the reading of homo-
triplets so that their stimulation values approach those of the minus
polymer blanks; the extent of inhibition is related to the ratio of dinu-
cleotide primer ends to homopolymer ends present in the mRNA models. Further reduction in the traces of endonucleolytic activity remaining in the polynucleotide phosphorylase used to synthesize the mRNA
models (Matthaei *et al.* 1966*b*) should improve such experiments in the
future.

Discussion

It is highly desirable that decoding experiments testing all 64 triplets
against all 20 protein amino acids be performed with one set of parallel preparations, all assayed under the same conditions and in a relatively short period of time. Certainly all macromolecular components

should be taken from one strain of organism. In the most straightforward experiments with duplicate assays, some 3000 assay tubes, including blanks, are required. All this we have attempted to do. But optimal conditions for such extensive experiments will be reached only gradually.

Further experiments are required to improve the systems. Knowing the amino acid translations for 63 triplets in *E. coli* A19, we shall be able to determine the saturating concentration for each coding triplet instead of those for only some examples. Then when the amount of bound mRNA is also measured, it should be possible to learn whether the equilibria of mRNA binding or adaptation are different for various 5′ terminal triplets. This is of particular interest, for there is both genetic (Newton *et al.* 1965) and biochemical (Clark and Marker 1965; Waller 1963) evidence favoring the idea that only certain triplets serve as initiators for polypeptide synthesis. It is an open question whether chain-initiating aminoacyl RNA's might be acylated generally and might have special codons (Clark and Marker 1965). The range of initiating adaptors available might vary with varying patterns of de-repression in the cell and be a possible key to modulation, and may even lead to feedback regulation of de-repression if transcription should be coupled to translation by a ribosome. The fact that we found almost every triplet coding in terminal position, although apparently with quite different efficiencies, does not seem to support the idea that certain codons have a different meaning in an internal position (Nirenberg and Leder 1964; Nirenberg *et al.* 1965). The data obtained are in agreement with 41 of the 49 base compositions determined by cell-free polypeptide synthesis on random polynucleotides, where internal coding was presumably more frequent than terminal coding. The preference of ribosomes for the 5′ terminal end of mRNA, furthermore, is another indication that the direction of mRNA reading is from the 5′ to the 3′ hydroxyl end (Ochoa 1965; Thach *et al.* 1965), as is the direction of mRNA synthesis (Bremer *et al.* 1965).

The adaptation system should be improved further to give larger stimulations on the average by the use of (1) polymers with a higher ratio of primer to homopolymer 5′ ends, (2) isolated transfer RNA species to reduce blanks, (3) more completely purified ribosomes, and (4) a more favorable ionic environment. A major objection to the codon translations determined in cell-free systems for both adaptation and whole polypeptide synthesis is that there seems to be less specificity of coding in these systems than inside the cell. But here again, it is to be hoped that, with more experience, generally greater stimulations, and better knowledge of the natural environment and constituents of ribosomes, specificity may be improved by re-adjusting the artificial environment. On the other hand, certain ambiguous codons seen in cell-free systems (Matthaei 1963) may really be ambiguous in cellular protein synthesis as well. Codon–amino acid assignments made with acellular systems by different laboratories (see Table 8.5) are in excellent agreement with amino acid exchanges in mutant proteins, whether observed in single amino acid mutations of tobacco mosaic virus (Wittmann 1962, 1964) or in shifted-reading mutations in lysozyme (Streisinger, personal communication). Many more such correlations will be required to verify completely our present knowledge of the code.

There seem to be a few differences in the decoding systems operating in *E. coli* A19 as compared to those operating in *E. coli* B and W3100, two strains used with apparently similar results by Nirenberg and co-workers (1965). Sites and kinds of possible code mutations in strain A19, which was selected after mutagenic treatment with nitrosoguanidine, will be investigated soon. We found alanine, but not any isoleucine, coded by AUC. This would be a deviation from the rule that U and C have the same meaning at the third position in the triplet (see Fig. 8.17). There is ambiguity of the codons AGU and AGC which code the two amino acids serine and isoleucine with similar efficiency. And

1.	2. Nucleotide				3.
	U	C	A	G	
U	Phenylalanine Phenylalanine Leucine Leucine	Serine Serine Serine Serine	Tyrosine Tyrosine Leucine Leucine	Cysteine Cysteine Tryptophan	U C A G
C	Leucine Leucine Leucine Leucine	Proline Proline Proline Proline	Histidine Histidine Glutamine Glutamine	Arginine Arginine Arginine Arginine	U C A G
A	Isoleucine Alanine Methionine Methionine	Threonine Threonine Threonine Threonine	Asparagine Asparagine Lysine Lysine	Serine a. Isoleucine Serine a. Isoleucine Arginine Arginine	U C A G
G	Valine Valine Valine Valine	Alanine Alanine Alanine Alanine	Aspartic acid Aspartic acid Glutamic acid Glutamic acid	Glycine Glycine Glycine Glycine	U C A G

Fig. 8.17.—The mRNA code of *E. coli* strain A19 as tentatively derived by amino acid adaptation (Compare the Addendum.)

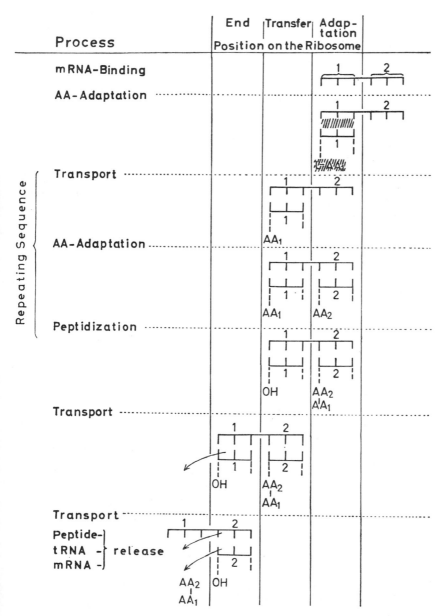

Fig. 8.18.—Schematic representation of sequential steps in polypeptide synthesis, according to the present working hypothesis. The simplest model case, the synthesis of a dipeptide directed by a hexanucleotide, is assumed.

we find leucine perhaps translated from both the codons UAA and UAG which, judged by mutagen-dependent reversibility, possibly are the nonsense codons occurring in ochre and amber mutations (Brenner, Stretton, and Kaplan 1965; Weigert and Garen 1965). It is also conceivable, although without support from other decoding data, that a chain-terminating transfer RNA species would normally supply these codons and carry a certain amino acid, which, after transfer, would have to be cut off from the polypeptide chain just received. For example, in Figure 8.18, let codon 2 be UAG and amino acid 2 be leucine; after transfer of amino acid 1 from its adaptor to amino acid 2, amino acid 2 would be cleaved off from amino acid 1 by an enzyme that could recognize, say, the adaptor number 2. The adaptation system would measure only the adaptation of amino acid 2, which might be leucine if our findings reflect a coding by the triplets UAA and UAG. It also remains to be clarified why the triplet UGA did not code any one of the 20 amino acids tested in A19. This triplet might be the signal for chain release used in both wild-type and suppressor strains. Nothing is known about its possible adaptor and the mode of its function.

Summary

(1) The decoding system of the cell is described in terms of its molecular members and their biochemical specificities.

(2) The amino acid translation for 49 coding triplets in mRNA was determined in 1961–62 by cell-free peptide synthesis directed with random polynucleotides as synthetic mRNA.

(3) Different types of synthetic RNA models of defined nucleotide sequence can be used to find the amino acid translation for the nucleotide sequences in mRNA by means of both peptide synthesizing and aminoacyl RNA binding cell-free systems.

(4) An amino acid adaptation system for mRNA directed binding of aminoacyl RNA to the ribosomes and their 30S subunits was described in 1964. A refinement of this adaptation system is discussed here for translation of the first triplet in XpYpZ . . . pZ~$_{30}$ polymers. The system involves (a) purification of E. coli ribosomes, even from ribonuclease I- strain A19, to one thousandth of their ribonucleolytic activities; (b) preparation and purification of both polynucleotide phosphorylase and polynucleotides synthesized with it; (c) purification of amino acid activating fractions and the aminoacyl RNA. The quantities of the components and the overall kinetics of the formation of adaptation complexes are reported.

(5) With the system components from E. coli strain A19, 65 amino

acid assignments were made to 63 trinucleotide sequences. Of the 49 base compositions found in polypeptide synthesis, 41 are in agreement with the determinations of coding nucleotide sequences. The code of *E. coli* A19 apparently displays a maximum of degeneracy.

(6) Ribosomes seem to have a marked specificity for the 5′ ends of many polynucleotides.

(7) The decoding results obtained and possibilities for further improvement of the system are discussed.

Addendum

A preliminary report of this work has been published in *Naturwissenschaften* **52**: 653–655 (1965).

Since this chapter was written, papers by Brimacombe *et al.* (1965) and by Söll *et al.* (1965) have reported many translations of trinucleoside diphosphates obtained in similar systems from *E. coli.* These are mostly in agreement with each other and with our results.

Further improvements of the aminoacyl RNA binding system, including the use of polynucleotides XpYpZ . . . pZ synthesized with 800- to 5000-fold purified preparations of polynucleotide phosphorylase, have led to the following corrections: AUC and probably also AUA code isoleucine; UAA and UAG do not stimulate leucine or any other protein amino acid above 10 per cent; UGA slightly codes cysteine; and AGU and AGC code only serine (Matthaei *et al.* 1966*a,b*).

Acknowledgment

It is a pleasure to thank Erika Gärtner, Karin Eckert, Renate Obermeier, Wiltrud Ludewig, Inge Röber, Jörg Schmidt, and Gernot Sander for their excellent cooperation. We also thank Dr. Hans Küntzel for some polynucleotides used in preliminary experiments.

Literature Cited

AVERY, O. T., C. M. MacLEOD, AND M. McCARTY, 1944. Studies on the chemical nature of the substance inducing transformation of pneumococcal types. J. Exp. Med. **79**: 137–158.

BEADLE, G. W., AND E. L. TATUM, 1941. Genetic control of biochemical reactions in *Neurospora*. Proc. Nat. Acad. Sci. U.S. **27**: 499–506.

BREMER, H., M. W. KONRAD, K. GAINES, AND G. S. STENT, 1965. Direction of chain growth in enzymic RNA synthesis. J. Mol. Biol. **13**: 540–553.

BRENNER, S., F. JACOB, AND M. MESELSON, 1961. An unstable intermediate carrying information from genes to ribosomes for protein synthesis. Nature **190**: 576–581.

BRENNER, S., A. O. W. STRETTON, AND S. KAPLAN, 1965. Genetic code: The "nonsense" triplets for chain termination and their suppression. Nature **206**: 994–998.

BRIMACOMBE, R., J. TRUPIN, M. NIRENBERG, P. LEDER, M. BERNFIELD, AND T. JAOUNI, 1965. RNA codewords and protein synthesis, VIII. Nucleotide sequences of synonym codons for arginine, valine, cysteine, and alanine. Proc. Nat. Acad. Sci. U.S. **54**: 954–960.

CLARK, B. F. C., AND K. A. MARKER, 1965. Coding response of N-formyl-methionyl-sRNA to UUG. Nature **207**: 1038–1039.

CRAMER, F., H. KÜNTZEL, AND J. H. MATTHAEI, 1964. Determination of the sequence of a code triplet. Angew. Chem. (Int. ed.) **3**: 589–590.

CRICK, F. H. C., 1958. On protein synthesis. Symp. Soc. Exp. Biol. **12**: 128–163.
———, 1963. The recent excitement in the coding problem. Progr. Nucleic Acid Res. **1**: 163–217.

CRICK, F. H. C., L. BARNETT, S. BRENNER, AND R. J. WATTS-TOBIN, 1962. General nature of the genetic code for proteins. Nature **192**: 1227–1232.

ECK, R. V., 1963. Genetic code: Emergence of a symmetrical pattern. Science **140**: 477–481.

GAMOW, G., 1954. Possible relation between deoxyribonucleic acid and protein structures. Nature **173**: 318.
———, 1955. On information transfer from nucleic acids to proteins. Bio. Medd., Danske Videnskab. Selskab **22**, No. 8.

GARDNER, R. S., A. J. WAHBA, C. BASILIO, R. S. MILLER, P. LENGYEL, AND J. F. SPEYER, 1962. Synthetic polynucleotides and the amino acid code, VII. Proc. Nat. Acad. Sci. U.S. **48**: 2087–2094.

GOTTSCHLING, H., AND H. G. ZACHAU, 1965. Ultraviolett-Inaktivierung der Phenylalanin- und Lysin-spezifischen Transfer-Ribonucleinsäuren. Biochim. Biophys. Acta **103**: 418–430.

GROS, F., H. HIATT, W. GILBERT, C. G. KURLAND, R. W. RISEBROUGH, AND J. D. WATSON, 1961. Unstable ribonucleic acid revealed by pulse labelling of *Escherichia coli*. Nature **190**: 581–585.

HOLLEY, R. W., J. APGAR, G. A. EVERETT, J. T. MADISON, M. MARQUISEE, S. H. MERILL, J. R. PENSWICK, AND A. ZAMIR, 1965. Structure of a ribonucleic acid. Science **147**: 1462–1465.

JACOB, F., AND J. MONOD, 1961. Genetic regulatory mechanisms in the synthesis of proteins. J. Mol. Biol. **3**: 318–356.

KAJI, H., AND A. KAJI, 1964. Specific binding of sRNA with the template-ribosome complex. Proc. Nat. Acad. Sci. U.S. **52**: 1541–1547.

KHORANA, H. G., 1965. Polynucleotide synthesis and the genetic code. Fed. Proc. **24**: 1473–1487.

LAMBORG, M. R., AND P. C. ZAMECNIK, 1960. Amino acid incorporation into proteins by extracts of *E. coli*. Biochim. Biophys. Acta **42**: 206–211.

LEDER, P., AND M. NIRENBERG, 1964. RNA codewords and protein synthesis, II. Nucleotide sequence of a valine RNA codeword. Proc. Nat. Acad. Sci. U.S. **52**: 420–427.

MATTHAEI, J. H., 1963. Wege zur experimentellen Analyse des Ribonuclein-säure-Code für die Protein-Synthese. Nova Acta Leopoldina **26**: 45–74.

MATTHAEI, J. H., F. AMELUNXEN, K. ECKERT, AND G. HELLER, 1964. Zum Mechanismus der Proteinsynthese. I. Die Bindung von Matrizen-RNS und Aminoacyl-RNS an Ribosomen. Ber. Bunsenges. Phys. Chem. 68: 735–742.

MATTHAEI, J. H., G. HELLER, H.-P. VOIGT, R. NETH, G. SCHÖCH, AND H. KÜBLER, 1966a. Analysis of the genetic code by amino acid adapting. Presented at 3rd Meeting Europe. Biochem. Soc., Warsaw.

MATTHAEI, H., AND M. W. NIRENBERG, 1961a. The dependence of cell-free protein synthesis in *E. coli* upon RNA prepared from ribosomes. Biochem. Biophys. Res. Commun. 4: 404–408.

MATTHAEI, J. H., AND M. W. NIRENBERG, 1961b. Characteristics and stabilization of DNAase-sensitive protein synthesis in *E. coli* extracts. Proc. Nat. Acad. Sci. U.S. 47: 1580–1588.

MATTHAEI, J. H., H.-P. VOIGT, G. HELLER, R. NETH, G. SCHÖCH, H. KÜBLER, F. AMELUNXEN, G. SANDER, AND A. PARMEGGIANI, 1966b. Specific interactions of ribosomes in decoding. Cold Spring Harbor Symp. Quant. Biol. 31 (in press).

MIESCHER, F. 1871. Ueber die chemische Zusammensetzung der Eiterzellen. Hoppe-Seyler's med.-chem. Untersuch. 4: 441–460.

NAKAMOTO, T., T. W. CONWAY, J. E. ALLENDE, G. A. SPYRIDES, AND F. LIPMANN, 1963. Formation of peptide bonds. I. Peptide formation from amino acyl-s-RNA. Cold Spring Harbor Symp. Quant. Biol. 28: 227–231.

NEU, H. C., AND L. A. HEPPEL, 1964. Some observations on the "latent" ribonuclease of *Escherichia coli*. Proc. Nat. Acad. Sci. U.S. 51: 1267–1274.

NEWTON, W. A., J. R. BECKWITH, D. ZIPSER, AND S. BRENNER, 1965. Nonsense mutants and polarity in the *lac* operon of *Escherichia coli*. J. Mol. Biol. 14: 290–296.

NIRENBERG, M. W., O. W. JONES, P. LEDER, B. F. C. CLARK, W. S. SLY, AND S. PESTKA, 1963. On the coding of genetic information. Cold Spring Harbor Symp. Quant. Biol. 28: 549–557.

NIRENBERG, M., AND P. LEDER, 1964. RNA codewords and protein synthesis. Science 145: 1399–1407.

NIRENBERG, M. W., P. LEDER, M. BERNFIELD, R. BRIMACOMBE, J. TRUPIN, F. ROTTMAN, AND C. O'NEAL, 1965. RNA codewords and protein synthesis, VII. On the general nature of the RNA code. Proc. Nat. Acad. Sci. U.S. 53: 1161–1168.

NIRENBERG, M. W., AND J. H. MATTHAEI, 1961. The dependence of cell-free protein synthesis in *E. coli* upon naturally occurring or synthetic polyribonucleotides. Proc. Nat. Acad. Sci. U.S. 47: 1588–1602.

NISHIMURA, S., D. S. JONES, AND H. G. KHORANA, 1965. Studies on polynucleotides. XLVIII. The in vitro synthesis of a copolypeptide containing two amino acids in alternating sequence dependent upon a DNA-like polymer containing two nucleotides in alternating sequence. J. Mol. Biol. 13: 302–324.

NISHIMURA, S., D. S. JONES, E. OHTSUKA, H. HAYATSU, T. M. JACOB, AND H. G. KHORANA, 1965. Studies on polynucleotides. XLVII. The in vitro synthesis of homopeptides as directed by a ribopolynucleotide containing a repeating trinucleotide sequence. New codon sequences for lysine, glutamic acid and arginine. J. Mol. Biol. 13: 283–301.

OCHOA, S., 1965. Ribonucleic acid interactions in translation of the amino acid code. Abstr. 2nd Meeting Fed. Europe. Biochem. Soc., Vienna, p. 273.

OFENGAND, E. J., M. DIECKMANN, AND P. BERG, 1961. The enzymic synthesis of amino acyl derivatives of ribonucleic acid, III. Isolation of amino acid-acceptor ribonucleic acids from *Escherichia coli*. J. Biol. Chem. 236: 1741–1747.

SEIDEL, H., AND F. CRAMER, 1965. Investigations concerning the secondary structure of soluble RNA from yeast. Biochim. Biophys. Acta 108: 367–375.

SEIDEL, H., G. HELLER, AND H. MATTHAEI, 1966. The influence of N-oxidation with monoperphthalic acid on the acceptor capacity of sRNA for lysine and phenylalanine. Biochim. Biophys. Acta (in press).

SINGER, M. F., AND B. O'BRIEN, 1963. Polynucleotide phosphorylase of *Micrococcus lysodeikticus*. II. Further purification of the enzyme and the arsenolysis of polyribonucleotides. J. Biol. Chem. 238: 328–335.

SÖLL, D., E. OHTSUKA, D. S. JONES, R. LOHRMANN, H. HAYATSU, S. NISHIMURA, AND H. G. KHORANA, 1965. Studies on polynucleotides, XLIX. Stimulation of the binding of aminoacyl-sRNA's to ribosomes by ribotrinucleotides and a survey of codon assignments for 20 amino acids. Proc. Nat. Acad. Sci. U.S. 54: 1378–1385.

SPEYER, J. F., P. LENGYEL, C. BASILIO, A. J. WAHBA, R. S. GARDNER, AND S. OCHOA, 1963. Synthetic polynucleotides and the amino acid code. Cold Spring Harbor Symp. Quant. Biol. 28: 559–567.

THACH, R. E., M. A. CECERE, T. A. SUNDARAJAN, AND P. DOTY, 1965. The polarity of messenger translation in protein synthesis. Proc. Nat. Acad. Sci. U.S. 54: 1167–1173.

THACH, R. E., AND P. DOTY, 1965. Enzymatic synthesis of tri- and tetranucleotides of defined sequence. Science 148: 632–634.

VOLKIN, E., AND L. ASTRACHAN, 1956. Phosphorus incorporation in *Escherichia coli* ribonucleic acid after infection with bacteriophage T2. Virology 2: 149–161.

WALLER, I. P., 1963. The NH_2-terminal residues of the proteins from cell-free extracts of *E. coli*. J. Mol. Biol. 7: 483–496.

WATSON, J. D., AND F. H. C. CRICK, 1953. A structure for deoxyribosenucleic acid. Nature 171: 737–738.

WEIGERT, M. G., AND A. GAREN, 1965. Base composition of nonsense codons in *E. coli*. Nature 206: 992–994.

WEIL, J. H., N. BEFORT, B. RETHER, AND J. P. EBEL, 1964. Effects of chemical modifications on the biological properties of s-RNA. Biochem. Biophys. Res. Commun. 15: 447–452.

WITTMANN, H. G., 1962. Proteinuntersuchungen an Mutanten des Tabakmosaikvirus als Beitrag zum Problem des genetischen Codes. Z. Vererbungslehre 93: 491–530.

——, 1964. Proteinanalyse von chemisch induzierten Mutanten des Tabakmosaikvirus. Z. Vererbungslehre 95: 333–344.

Yu, Chuan-Foa, and P. C. Zamecnik, 1964. Effect of bromination on the biological activities of transfer RNA of *E. coli*. Science 144: 856–859.

Zillig, W., W. Krone, and M. Albers, 1959. Untersuchungen zur Biosynthese der Proteine, III. Beitrag zur Kenntnis der Zusammensetzung und Struktur der Ribosomen. Z. physiol. Chem., Hoppe-Seyler's 317: 131–143.

Zillig, W., D. Schachtschabel, and W. Krone, 1960. Untersuchungen zur Biosynthese der Proteine, IV. Zusammensetzung. Funktion und Spezifität der löslichen Ribonucleinsäure aus *Escherichia coli*. Z. physiol. Chem., Hoppe-Seyler's 318: 100–114.

III

Gene Action

9

Some Old and New Problems Concerning Gene Action

Ernst Hadorn

It is impossible for me to sketch here all the steps which have led, since Mendel's time, to our present knowledge of gene action. I shall concentrate my introductory comments, therefore, on a few problems more or less related to the topics with which the following three chapters will deal.

Most present day speculations and theoretical considerations concerning gene action are based on three general theorems:

(1) Gene mutation or allelic substitution is based on qualitative changes within the molecular matrix of DNA (or RNA).

(2) All primary genic products are polypeptides.

(3) Genes can be turned on and off by control of the interaction among regulating factors.

I shall indicate how these theorems have superseded other and older conceptions, and at the same time I would like to mention some open questions which might be the subject of future research.

Some geneticists interpreted allelic differences as quantitative diversities within the genic substance. It was Goldschmidt (1927) who first based theories on that assumption. Different allelic quantities were presumed to act differently by producing one and the same agent in different amounts or at different speeds during development. To explain Mendelian traits which are often of alternative qualitative nature it was necessary to postulate rather sophisticated developmental systems where thresholds and limited phases for reaction were needed. Thus, the main concern was how to derive quality from quantity. Today we find ourselves most frequently confronted with just the reverse situation. The qualitative allelic differences between structural genes are at the base of a great many Mendelian traits which appear as quantitative differences. Thus we have to explain how quantity issues from quality. In this connection a new interpretation of Muller's (1932) hypomorphic and hypermorphic mutants might be needed.

149

The second theorem, which states that genic information can be translated only into a language encoded in the amino acid sequence of peptides, looks so well substantiated that any hereditary characteristic must be regarded as having developed by this specific molecular mechanism. But how are we to explain other apparently immediate gene products such as the blood-group antigens which also seem directly connected with allelic differences? How can differences in a peptide chain be the cause of differences in mucopolysaccharides? I do not think that we understand today the intricacies involved in such a "secondary translation."

The modern conception of genic action at the molecular level has given a definite answer once and for all, I think, to a question which has been disputed again and again since the time of Bateson's presence-absence theory. Mutant alleles, as well as normal genes, can no longer be considered solely as operational concepts indirectly derived from differences in phenotypes. Both are real genes; that is, both are molecular species of DNA, and increasingly many proofs are now at hand which show that both of the genes present in heterozygotes act independently side by side, each coding its specific peptide chain. Such a co-dominance was first found for human hemoglobins. Now more and more examples are becoming known in which different enzyme species are formed in the same heterozygous cell. From this we see that an amorphic mutant might appear when an aberrantly coded enzyme remains inactive. There are, of course, other and more direct ways leading to amorphic mutants: Apart from deficiencies, changes that interfere with transcription could occur in the structural gene, or mutation of operators and regulators might lead to a block in the activation of a structural gene.

This last remark already takes us into the realm of the third theorem. Not long ago the question whether all genes act throughout life and in all cells of an organism was still open for discussion and divergent interpretation. Though I am still somewhat skeptical about the ease with which genes are turned on and off, there is no doubt that gene action can be developmentally controlled—that is, interrupted or initiated. My own experience from studies on merogonic amphibian hybrids and on lethals (e.g., Hadorn 1961) has taught me that certainly not all factors of the genome are needed for the normal accomplishment of a given developmental process or for any specific differentiation. Thus, we could consider development to be based on a step-by-step activation of different genes along the time axis of ontogeny. But such ideas are founded mainly on indirect evidence.

The two chapters that follow will demonstrate how much we have progressed beyond the days of speculation based on indirect evidence.

In Chapter 10 Buttin, Jacob, and Monod will present recent findings of the Parisian school to which we owe the formulation and elaboration of the operon theory. Whereas in cell populations of *Escherichia coli* the shifts between periods of activity and inertness of genes can be observed on the enzyme level, Beermann's work provides visual proof that chromosomal loci pass through periods of fluctuating activity. Both of these fascinating topics are endowed with rather strongly suggestive overtones and seducing powers which could easily lead us astray from the field of facts to the far reaches of generalizations.

Nevertheless let me illustrate how an old enigma of genic action might be newly and fruitfully envisaged in the light of a mechanism which operates in gene controlling systems of bacteria. In multicellular organisms we are often confronted with patterns of pleiotropy where numerous phenes appear which cannot be related to or derived from a common biochemical or physiological cause. Such a case of mosaic pleiotropy is met, for instance, in the mutant lozenge-clawless (lz^{cl}) of *Drosophila* (Anders 1955; Hadorn 1961). In this genotype we observe changes in the inventory of ommochromes and pteridines. These biochemical phenes, however, are accompanied by a set of morphological aberrations which affect the facet structure of the eyes, the sensilla on the antennae, the formation of the tarsus, and the development of the internal genitalia of females where spermathecae and parovaria fail to be formed. It could be, of course, that even in such an embarrassing case all the phenes might stem from just one aberrantly coded peptide. But we may also conceive of other possibilities which could lead to manifold pleiotropic patterns. If in higher organisms regulator genes also exist which control the function of more than one structural gene (see Jacob and Monod 1961), then more than one peptide or enzyme would be affected as a consequence of only one allelic substitution. We could also speculate what might happen if a mutation affected the structure of ribosomes. If the ribosomes or other tools of translation were changed, a pleiotropy based on more than one aberrant peptide would again result (Hadorn 1965a). In any case, modern findings on gene regulating systems as they work in bacteria should suggest a reconsideration of the possible mechanisms that lead to pleiotropy in general.

Since, in Chapter 12, Gurdon will deal with problems of gene action during differentiation of higher organisms, I would like to conclude my introduction by presenting a few results that show how, in cultures of determined cells, new capacities for specific differentiations can arise (Hadorn 1963, 1964, 1965a,b,c, 1966). We have been working with cell populations derived from imaginal discs of *Drosophila* larvae. I shall refer here only to results which were obtained with cells of the male genital discs. Experiments using female genital discs or antennae and leg discs have led to analogous conclusions. The male genital disc not only contains the anlagen for the internal sex organs (vasa efferentia, paragonial glands, ductus ejaculatorius, and sperm pump) but also forms the external genitalia (penis apparatus, claspers, lateral plates) and the anal plates with the hindgut.

In the third larval instar the disc consists of an agglomeration of densely packed, small cells which all look alike, showing no sign of specific differentiation. But from fragmentation and irradiation experiments (Hadorn, Bertani, Gallera 1949; Ursprung 1959) as well as from the differentiating behavior of re-aggregated cell mixtures (Nöthiger 1964), we know that all cells of the disc are specifically determined. Thus the disc contains a mosaic of blastemas, and the cells of each blastema are determined for forming just one of the various elements which compose a genital apparatus.

We succeeded in culturing such determined cells of larval discs in the abdomens of adult flies. In this medium the cells have continued to divide prolifically for three years. Starting from a few original discs, we can separate as many subcultures as we like. We have only to transfer and to subdivide the cultures every fortnight. In the adult milieu the cells of the permanent cultures maintain their undifferentiated larval characteristics but do not lose the initial capacity for imaginal differentiation. This latent developmental ability can, at any desired moment, be tested by re-implantation of culture samples into larvae. In such a host the cells undergo metamorphosis to form normal adult organs. We have studied several thousands of such test implants from seventy-seven succeeding transfer generations (Hadorn 1966).

Samples from the first few transfer generations differentiated according to their original genital determination by forming anal plates, claspers, ductus, etc. (autotypic differentiations). This initial state of determination has been propagated for years now in many of the sublines.

However, besides those exhibiting autotypic behavior, we have observed cell lines stemming from cultivated primordia which no longer differentiate into genital organs. On the contrary, they switch into another and foreign state of determination which results in the differentiation of antennae, legs, wings, or thorax (allotypic differentiation). Such transdetermination happens regularly with a reproducible probability. Thereby certain sequences can be followed. From autotypic anal plate blastemas, allotypic primordia of antennae and legs arise first; thence, in a second transdetermining step, the quality for wing structures can be established; and, finally, the descendants of wing cells are often transdetermined into thorax blastemas. The latter will hardly change any more. Some of the transdetermining steps revert frequently; others rarely or never revert. In relation to Gurdon's results, we can state that cellular determination in *Drosophila* is certainly not based on irreversible nuclear or cytoplasmic changes.

The astonishing phenomenon of transdetermination confronts us with a multitude of unsolved problems (Hadorn 1965*c*). The switch leading from one cell type to another is certainly not due to genic mutation. It must be interpreted instead as an event which changes the gene control on which the specific determination for genitalia, legs, or head structures is based. Unfortunately we do not know what kind of cellular components act as "determinants." But it seems reasonable to assume that, in different organ-specific blastemas, different sets of genes act by producing specific determining entities which might be deposited in the cytoplasm. It is further feasible to assume that, in rapidly dividing cells, the gene-dependent constituents, on which a pre-existing determination had been based, become diluted. Consequently new synthesis is needed. Thus in our cell cultures, new messenger RNA, new ribosomes, and new cytoplasmic proteins must be synthesized. Our attention therefore might be concentrated on the following problem: Why do some of the cells form the same "determinants" as their ancestors, whereas in sister cells a new state of determination becomes established and maintained by cell heredity? The controlling mechanisms on which either stability or change of cell heredity is based remain to be elucidated (Hadorn 1966).

But whatever the solution, cellular determination appears in our cultures as a property which is subject to change. Thus we feel encouraged to seek more and better experimental devices with which to study this fundamental phenomenon of developmental genetics.

Literature Cited

ANDERS, G., 1955. Untersuchungen über das pleiotrope Manifestationsmuster der Mutante lozenge-clawless (*lz^{cl}*) von *Drosophila melanogaster*. Z. Vererbungslehre 87: 113–186.

GOLDSCHMIDT, R., 1927. *Physiologische Theorie der Vererbung*. J. Springer, Berlin.

HADORN, E., 1961. *Developmental Genetics and Lethal Factors*. Methuen & Co. Ltd., London; John Wiley & Sons, Inc., New York.

———, 1963. Differenzierungsleistungen wiederholt fragmentierter Teilstücke männlicher Genitalscheiben von *Drosophila melanogaster* nach Kultur in vivo. Develop. Biol. 7: 617–629.

————, 1964. Bedeutungseigene und bedeutungsfremde Entwicklungsleistungen proliferierender Primordien von *Drosophila* nach Dauerkultur in vivo. Rev. Suisse Zool. **71**: 99–115.

————, 1965*a*. Genetics on its way. *Genetics Today*, pp. lxiii-lxxii. Edited by S. J. Geerts. Proc. XI Int. Cong. Genet., The Hague, The Netherlands (1963). Pergamon Press, New York.

————, 1965*b*. Ausfall der Potenz zur Borstenbildung als "Erbmerkmal" einer Zellkultur von *Drosophila melanogaster*. Z. Naturforsch. **20***b*: 290–292.

————, 1965*c*. Problems of determination and transdetermination. Brookhaven Symp. Biol. **18**: 148–161.

————, 1966. Konstanz, Wechsel und Typus der Determination und Differenzierung in Zellen aus männlichen Genitalanlagen von *Drosophila melanogaster* nach Dauerkultur in vivo. Develop. Biol. **13**: 424–509.

HADORN, E., G. BERTANI, AND J. GALLERA, 1949. Regulationsfähigkeit und Feldorganisation der männlichen Genital-Imaginalscheibe von *Drosophila melanogaster*. Roux' Arch. **144**: 31–70.

JACOB, F., AND J. MONOD, 1961. On the regulation of gene activity. Cold Spring Harbor Symp. Quant. Biol. **26**: 193–211.

MULLER, H. J., 1932. Further studies on the nature and causes of gene mutations. Proc. 6th Int. Congr. Genet., Ithaca **1**: 213–255.

NÖTHIGER, R., 1964. Differenzierungsleistungen in Kombinaten, hergestellt aus Imaginalscheiben verschiedener Arten, Geschlechter und Körpersegmente von *Drosophila*. Roux' Arch. **155**: 269–301.

URSPRUNG, H., 1959. Fragmentierungs- und Bestrahlungsversuch zur Bestimmung von Determinationszustand und Anlageplan der Genitalscheiben von *Drosophila melanogaster*. Roux' Arch. **151**: 504–558.

10

The Operon:
A Unit of Coordinated Gene Action

Gérard Buttin, François Jacob, and Jacques Monod

This work has been supported by grants of the National Science Foundation, the National Institutes of Health, the Jane Coffin Childs Memorial Fund, the Commissariat à l'Energie Atomique, and the Delegation Generale à la Recherche Scientifique et Technique.

"There are various ways in which a gene can be defined; they are consistent with one another at certain levels of genetic analysis, but not at others. It is precisely at the levels at which inconsistencies arise that the interest of biochemistry in genetics and of genetics in biochemistry becomes greater." This statement by Pontecorvo (1952) is in fact an excellent summary of how genetics has evolved in the last decades.

The meeting of genetics with chemistry is rather recent. Only in the 1940's, with the discoveries by Beadle and Tatum (1941) and by Avery and his collaborators (1944), did the units of Mendel receive their first interpretation in chemical terms. When it was recognized that both the genes and the proteins are linear polymers, the aphorism "one gene-one enzyme" could be restated as "one nucleotide sequence-one peptide chain," a view which has been supported by all recent advances concerning the colinearity of the polymers (Sarabhai *et al.* 1964; Yanofsky *et al.* 1964), the mechanism of protein synthesis, and the nature of the genetic code. Ideally, as emphasized by Pontecorvo (1952), Benzer (1957), and Lewis (1963), the functional unit—that is, the nucleotide sequence—could be defined by the so-called functional cis-trans test in heterozygotes or heterocaryons. The genome or its elements could then be visualized as made up of long stretches of DNA, each of which is composed of adjacent functional units that are separated by a "punctuation" determining the beginning and the end of specific peptide chains.

155

In many instances, however, mutations have been obtained whose properties could not be incorporated into such a simple scheme, thus indicating that a more highly integrated unit exists than the unit of function and consequently that there is a second level of punctuation.

In bacteria, genes controlling the structure of enzymes belonging to the same pathway are often adjacent (Demerec and Hartman 1959). Some of the mutations that occur in such genes do obey the "one gene-one enzyme" rule, and, by the usual cis-trans test, it is possible to determine the functional unit responsible for a certain enzyme or peptide chain. Other mutations, however, violate this rule: they affect the production, not of a single enzyme, but of the whole series of enzymes determined by the adjacent functional units. Analysis of these pleiotropic mutations led to the inescapable conclusion that the series of adjacent genes constitute units of coordinate expression, which have been called *operons* (Jacob *et al.* 1960; Jacob and Monod 1961*a,b*).

Two classes of these mutations have so far been described: *Constitutive mutations (o^c mutations)* result in an increased constitutive synthesis of several functionally related, adaptive enzymes. *Polar point mutations,* besides destroying the activity of one enzyme as would be expected from a mutation in a typical structural gene, slow down the rate of synthesis of proteins specified by adjacent genes.

We would like to review here in some detail the presently known properties of both kinds of pleiotropic mutations and to show how the information supplied by their study can help both to transform the operon from a genetic concept into a biochemical structure and to elucidate the molecular basis of the adaptive regulatory mechanisms. This discussion will be centered mainly around observations concerning the inducible system of lactose utilization by *Escherichia coli.**

In *E. coli*, lactose metabolism is conditioned by the activity of the β-galactosidase. The intracellular accumulation of this sugar and related β-galactosides is dependent on the efficiency of a specific permeation system, called *β-galactoside-permease*. Both activities are governed by separate genes, referred to as the *z* and the *y* gene respectively, which are topologically associated in a complex lactose locus on the bacterial chromosome (Fig. 10.1). One more biochemical activity—that of the β-galactoside transacetylase—is governed by a structural determinant (*Ac*) located within the lactose segment and distinct from the adjacent permease determinant as shown by the existence of deletions in *y* which do not affect acetylase activity (Malamy, unpublished); the enzyme, which effects the acetylation of β-galactosides and β-thiogal-

---

* For bibliographic references concerning experimental work prior to 1961, the reader is invited to refer to the review by Jacob and Monod (1961*a*).

Fig. 10.1.—The lactose region on the chromosome of *E. coli. Ac, y, z* designate the structural genes of β-galactoside-transacetylase, β-galactoside permease, and β-galactosidase, respectively; *p*, promoter; *o, o* segment; *i*, regulator gene.

actosides using acetyl-CoA as an acyl group donor, has been purified and crystallized (Zabin 1963). Its role in cell metabolism is presently unknown.

The o^c Mutation and the Operator Function

A major clue to a mechanism that controls gene expression was the discovery that mutations can mimic the effects of permanent inducers. Two classes of regulatory mutations resulting in a constitutive synthesis of the lactose enzymes have been described: mutations of the *o* locus (o^c) and of a regulator gene (i^-).

The properties of the o^c mutations may be summarized as follows: Their map position is closely linked to the *z* structural gene, at one end of the lactose cluster; the constitutive synthesis of three proteins which they provoke is the result of a single mutation. The o^c alleles are dominant but affect only the expression of structural determinants located on the *same* chromosomal structure; the *o* site is not expressed independently from the adjacent cluster of lactose genes. The o^c mutations increase the rate of synthesis of galactosidase, transacetylase, and permease to the very same extent, although the level of synthesis is characteristic for each o^c mutation and can vary from 2 per cent to nearly 100 per cent of the activity of fully induced cells; regarding the regulatory process that is abolished by o^c mutations, the genetic information encoded in the *z-y-Ac* segment behaves as an integral message. The *z, y,* and *Ac* genes and the *o* site constitute a polycistronic unit of genetic expression, the *lactose operon.* The term "operator" has been used to designate the element, affected by o^c mutations, which directly regulates the expression of the operon as a whole. It may be useful to point out here that this definition does not imply any assumption concerning the biochemical nature of the operator, which, as we shall discuss in more detail later on, might be either the chromosomal *o* locus itself or an integral part of a cytoplasmic copy of the complete operon.

The definition of an operator, both genetic and functional, calls for investigations concerning its role in normal cell physiology as well as its biochemical nature. More specifically, we might ask two questions. (1) Besides the o^c mutations, two kinds of processes have been shown to affect specifically the regulation of all three lactose enzymes:

induction by galactosides and derivatives, and mutations at a different site, which we refer to as mutations of a regulatory gene. What are the functional relationships between operator, regulator gene product, and inducers? (2) Is the o segment, which governs the structure of an operator, a part of the first structural gene of the operon?

Operator function in regulatory circuits

An approach to the first question—the relationship of the operator with the other regulatory elements of the cell—must first admit the observation that o^c mutations do not drastically alter the response of the cell to the addition of specific inducers. Many, if not most, o^c mutants are only partially constitutive and can be further induced to maximal rate of enzyme synthesis by addition of a galactoside: This suggests that the o^c mutation decreases the sensitivity of the operator to a regulatory factor which, in the normal cell, prevents the expression of the lactose genes. This interpretation is fully supported and clarified by an analysis of the properties of the regulator gene mutations.

The regulator gene is located close to the lactose structural genes on the o side of the operon. Several experiments of mapping by three point tests (Jacob and Monod 1965), with different reference markers on the chromosomal segment containing the lactose operon, have established that the i gene is located beyond the o locus (Fig 10.1).

In wild-type cells, the i gene controls the expression of the lactose operon through a specific cytoplasmic product, as indicated by the recessive character of the i^- mutations. The recent observation by Bourgeois, Cohn, and Orgel (1965) that certain i^- mutations are suppressible by external suppressors (namely, suppressors of the "amber" mutation) known to act at the level of the translation of messenger RNA into peptide chain (Stretton and Brenner 1965) demonstrates that the i-gene product active in regulation is a protein, as already strongly suggested by earlier observations (Sadler and Novick 1965).

Actually, besides the i^- mutations, a second class of mutations of the regulator gene has been described. These mutations, called i^s (Willson et al. 1964), result in an entirely different physiological defect: as shown by the dominant lac^- phenotype which they exhibit even after addition of an inducer, the i^s mutants have lost the ability to respond to the presence of a β-galactoside. In spite of their entirely different phenotypical manifestation, the i^s and i^- mutations affect the same determinant; and not only do both occupy the same map location, but also, while diploid cells of genotype i^s/i^- exhibit the lac^- phenotype, cells of genotype $i^s i^-$ (obtained as lac^+ revertants of i^s mutants), carrying both defects on the same chromosomal structure, synthesize constitutively the lactose enzymes. The change observed in the apparent dominance of the i^s versus i^- mutations in such a cis-trans test cannot be explained if it is assumed that the mutations affect two determinants which are expressed through independent cytoplasmic products. Instead, on the basis of this genetic analysis, the protein specified by the regulator gene appears to possess two functionally different sites.

The simple model which accounts both for this observation and for the properties of the o^c mutants is that this protein recognizes the lactose operator, exerting thereby a permanent *repression* on the expression of the lactose genes; and that its ability to perform this regulatory function, be it enzymatic or not, is itself controlled in wild-type cells by the reversible binding of inducers.

The several assumptions in this model are supported by independent lines of experimental evidence. More precisely, the existence of regulatory circuits comprising a cytoplasmic factor which exerts a negative control is well documented by the isolation and study of constitutive mutants in other adaptive systems. On the basis of their properties of dominance, some of the constitutive mutations have already been identified with o^c mutations (Buttin 1963), while various recessive mutations could be classified as mutations of regulator genes (Echols, Garen, and Torriani 1961; Maas and Clark 1964). Further investigations are now desirable to establish which mutations among those classified as regulator mutations functionally correspond to the i gene of the lactose system, characterized as the site of both i^- and i^s mutations.

Consideration of the remarkable properties of the i^s mutants leads one to the conclusion that the repressor specified by the i gene is the site of action of the inducer. The alternative hypothesis which would account for the appearance of a *lac⁻* phenotype must assume that a structural mutation increases the affinity of the repressor for its cognate element; this is especially unlikely. Moreover, this latter hypothesis would predict that an i^s allele could repress the expression of partially constitutive o^c mutants more efficiently than could an i^+ allele; this is clearly not observed. The precise nature of the interaction between inducer and repressor remains unknown, but the properties of the induction process, quickly reversible and entirely "gratuitous," suggest that the inducer might exert its action by provoking an *allosteric* transition in the structure of the repressor protein (Monod, Changeux, and Jacob 1963). In any case, it seems legitimate to reject the specific hypothesis that assumes the repressor to be an enzyme which permanently inactivates an endogenous β-galactoside inducer and can be saturated by an exogenous supply of substrates or analogs of the substrates; the existence of two classes of structural mutants of the repressor cannot be explained in this model.

A definitive answer to the question of whether the repressor acts *directly* at the level of the operator rather than at the level of a cognate cytoplasmic intermediate, itself capable of recognizing the operator, is difficult to obtain from the analysis of genetic data; but a statistical survey of the defects shown by many lactose regulatory mutants does not suggest the existence of factors other than the repressor and the operator in the regulation circuit. The induction process being turned off in the i^s mutants, one may expect to find, among their revertants to the *lac*+ phenotype, mutants affected in any one of the genes governing the structure of an element required for the efficiency of the repression circuit. More than one thousand *lac*+ revertants from i^s mutants have been analyzed from this point of view (Jacob and Monod, unpublished; Bourgeois, Cohn, and Orgel, 1965). All synthesize constitutively the lactose enzymes and all mutations occupy map positions in the lactose region of the genome. When this chromosomal segment is transferred by sexduction to wild-type cells, some merodiploid cells synthesize the lactose enzymes constitutively, and the donors may be classified as o^c mutants (merodiploids: o^c i^s / o^+ i^+). In most merodiploid cells, the synthesis of the lactose enzymes requires the addition of an inducer, as expected from cells of genotype o^+ i^- / o^+ i^+; and the gene i can then be identified in all cases as the site of the recessive constitutive mutation by the observation that the normal inducible phenotype is never recovered when an i^- strain is used as a recipient instead of an i^+ strain. The existence of a different regulator gene, a defect of which should be complemented in i^- recipient cells, is never suggested.

The existence of lethal regulatory mutations cannot be formally ruled out, but it is not expected that alterations of a factor *specifically* required for the regulation of synthesis of the lactose enzymes will have a lethal effect in the selection of *lac*+ revertants of the i^s mutation.

A legitimate working hypothesis seems therefore to be that the regulatory circuit is closed through a direct binding of the specific repressor to the specific operator.

If the operator is the unique receptor site for regulatory signals which affect the expression of several lactose genes, it is an absolute requirement that the rate of synthesis of the different lactose enzymes must be affected to the very same extent by any factor, genetic or exogenous, which interferes with the functioning of the repression circuit—in other words, with the efficiency of the repressor-operator interaction. Evidence that this is indeed true has been accumulated, as a result of the development of accurate assays for the lactose enzymes and the availability of

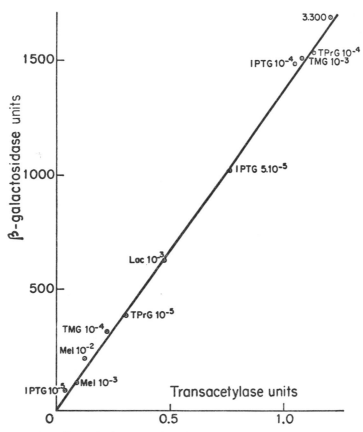

Fig. 10.2.—Coordinate induction of galactosidase and transacetylase. The rates of synthesis of both enzymes are expressed in arbitrary units. The point labeled 3.300 shows the activities of the enzymes in an extract of the i^- type mutant strain 3.300; all other points show activities in extracts of the wild-type strain 3.000, grown in the presence of the indicated concentration of various inducers. *Mel,* melibiose; *Lac,* lactose; *TMG,* thiomethyl-β-galactoside; *TPrG,* thiopropyl-β-galactoside; *IPTG,* thioisopropyl-β-galactoside (from Burstein 1964).

nonmetabolized inducers which have permitted systematic studies of the ratios of the enzymes' activities under conditions of complete or partial de-repression. The ratios of transacetylase and galactosidase activities remain constant in i^- mutants or in wild-type cells induced by various inducers, although the absolute activities of both enzymes can be varied by several orders of magnitude (Fig. 10.2). Moreover, the ratio is found to be identical to the ratio of the same activities measured for o^c mutants. Equally impressive is the fact that the same characteristic ratio of activities is observed when one modifies the absolute rates of synthesis by adding different concentrations of a nonmetabolizable inducer. In short, the genes clustered in the lactose locus respond as an integral unit to all alterations one can produce at the level of the cytoplasmic repressor as well as to mutations affecting the structure of the lactose operator.*

Such coordinate fluctuations in the rate of expression of clustered genes, first described in the pathway of histidine biosynthesis (Ames and Garry 1959), have now been reported for various polyenzymatic anabolic or catabolic systems. Evidence confirming that precise quantitative coordination is an intrinsic property of the unique operator, rather than that of the repressor, is supplied by an analysis of more complex adaptive systems. For example, the sequence of enzymes in arginine biosynthesis involves several structural genes distributed along the bacterial chromosome. Although they all appear to be controlled by a common regulator gene, their expression is affected in differing degrees by the addition of arginine, suggesting that the unique repressor acts with a different efficiency at the level of distinct operators (Gorini, Gundersen, and Burger 1961; Maas 1961; Vogel 1961; Mass and Clark 1964).

Relationship of the operator
with the structural genes in the operon

We would now like to discuss the evidence relevant to the second problem arising from the properties of the lactose operator: Do the o^c regulatory mutations affect the structure of a protein of the lactose operon? Several observations may be taken into consideration:

(1) The analysis of a large number of o^c mutants isolated under various conditions suggests that o^c mutations are obtained mostly, and perhaps exclusively, as deletions of a genetic segment. Mutants of this class normally arise spontaneously. The o^c mutations can be provoked by X-irradiation but not by a 2-aminopurine treatment. They do not

---

* It may be useful to emphasize here the necessity for clear distinction between factors which affect rates of protein synthesis through the specific repression circuit and factors which can affect individually the rates of synthesis of several proteins specified by the genes of an operon. This is perhaps best exemplified in the lactose system by the results obtained when the rates of β-galactosidase and transacetylase synthesis are measured in cells grown at various temperatures. The ratio of β-galactosidase activity to transacetylase activity is different in cells grown at 37° C from that ratio in cells grown at lower temperatures (Zabin 1963). However, the ratio characteristic for each temperature is constant in cells induced at various levels (Burstein 1964). The repression control remains fully coordinated, whereas the final expression of the genetic message appears modulated by some temperature-dependent unidentified factors.

seem to be suppressible by external suppressors, and no reversions to the wild type have been detected. No thermosensitive o^c mutants have been isolated when specifically sought. The o^c mutations, however, do not alter the properties of the β-galactosidase molecule as determined by its temperature and pH sensitivity. More precisely, the β-galactosidase produced by a mutant with the o and i loci deleted has been compared by Steers, Craven, and Anfinsen (1965) to the β-galactosidase produced by i- mutants: No differences between the enzymes were detected in immunochemical properties, constants of inactivation by urea or chymotrypsin, sedimentation constants, or electrophoretic mobilities. Identical amino acid composition and peptide maps have been reported for both enzymes. In both cases, the only NH_2 terminal amino acid found was threonine; this observation is of particular interest since, as we shall discuss below, the assembly of amino acids into any peptide chain appears to be initiated at the end of each cistron closer to the o site.

(2) Mutants have been isolated which carry deletions in the z gene including known z^- point mutations. One deletion (Beckwith 1964a) includes "extreme polar mutations" (see discussion of polar mutations), which could not be separated from the o^c mutations by usual mapping procedures; even in this deletion mutant, the inducibility of permease and acetylase is not altered.

The concordance of both series of observations indicates that the o locus is a segment independent of the z structural cistron.

We may then ask whether β-galactosidase is the first protein of the operon; we could suggest *a priori* that the o site is still part of a structural gene of the lactose operon coding for an as yet unknown protein. But this hypothetical protein would have to be unnecessary for lactose metabolism or, more generally, for any function essential to the growth of the cells, even in minimum mineral media; and experimental data (Jacob, Ullmann, and Monod 1964) appear to contradict directly this proposal.

These observations concern the properties of deletions extending over both the o segment and part of the z structural gene. More than 150 mutants of this type have been isolated from noninducible i^s mutants (as secondary mutants capable of synthesizing constitutively the galactoside-permease [Beckwith 1964a]). When they are mapped (Jacob, Ullmann, and Monod 1966), a remarkable situation is evident: the deletions extend over various lengths of the z structural cistron, but on the other side all the deletions include the i gene (Fig. 10.3). Moreover, in these strains the rates of permease and acetylase synthesis are limited to 10–30 per cent of their rates in fully induced cells and are not increased by the addition of a β-galactoside inducer.

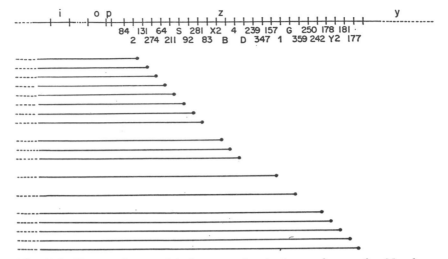

Fig. 10.3.—Extent of some deletions covering both *o* and part of *z*. Numbers refer to known *z⁻* point mutations.

This finding is in striking contrast to the properties of the o^c mutations which do not affect the *z* gene. As already pointed out, in partially constitutive o^c mutants the addition of an inducer stimulates the rate of synthesis of the lactose enzymes to the maximal value observed in wild-type cells, and no more than 20 per cent of these mutants simultaneously lose the activity of the *i* gene. There are clearly two classes of deletions which affect the *o* segment, operationally characterized by the fact that they do or do not also include the extremity of the *z* cistron. When—and only when—the beginning of the *z* cistron is deleted does one observe levels of operon expression far below the maximum and yet out of the control of the specific regulatory circuit; in these cases, the deletions cover the *i* gene.

For interpretation of these results, two assumptions appear necessary:

(1) There exists between *o* and *z* a genetic sequence which plays a particular role in the expression of the operon. (It might actually correspond to the very beginning of the *z* cistron or to the *z* end of the *o* segment, but certainly not to the other end of the latter.) Whatever the biochemical function of this site, which we shall refer to provisionally as a "promoter" (*p*) of operon action, its properties are different from the properties of an intercistronic punctuation. Deletions which simultaneously include part of the *z* and *y* genes are known, and they do not affect the expression or the regulation of the *Ac* gene (Malamy, unpublished). The properties of the *p* site are not explained if the *o* segment codes for an unknown protein of the operon; in this

hypothesis, the *o-z* punctuation would represent a regular intercistronic punctuation.

(2) The properties of the *z-o-i* deletion mutants suggest that the "promoter" is a genetic sequence *required* for the expression of the operon and that, following its deletion, the rescue of structural gene activity rests upon the successful association of the structural genes to another promoter and therefore to another unit of regulation. This hypothesis was formulated earlier to account for the changes in regulatory properties of the histidine operon which result from deletions starting in the first structural cistron (Ames, Hartman, and Jacob 1963).

If the hypothesis is correct, the joining of structural genes of one operon to the *p-o* end of a different operon should result in the subordination of those structural genes to the regulatory mechanism specific for the second operon. This prediction can be checked only if the nature of the new operon to which structural genes are assumed to become fused is itself known. But an attempt to fuse two well-identified operons usually requires the deletion of extensive segments of genetic material, an alteration which is likely to be lethal for the cells. This difficulty can be overcome if merodiploid cells are used in which the chromosome is intact, and the episome carries the segments with the desired rearrangements. Taking advantage of this situation, Jacob, Ullmann, and Monod (1965) studied the properties of deletions which fuse the lactose operon to an operon governing the synthesis of purines that comprises at least two cistrons (α and β) and is sensitive to a repressive control by adenine or guanine.

Various episomes carrying deletions all starting in the *z* gene but extending over different lengths of the episome were transferred to a recipient Lac_Δ strain (in which the whole lactose region was deleted). The extent of the deletion could be checked precisely by further transfer of the episome to recipient strains carrying appropriate markers.

Three classes of episomes, all of which carried the *Pur-α* segment, could be distinguished (Fig. 10.4) according to their deletions: both T_6 and *Pur-β* deleted (class *C*), T_6 alone deleted (class *B*), or neither deleted (class *A*).

The permease and transacetylase activities of the various Lac_Δ/F' strains were determined in the presence and absence of regulatory metabolites specific for the lactose and purine operons. In minimal medium, both proteins are synthesized constitutively but, depending on the strain, at a rate 5 to 20 times lower than that in induced $Lac_\Delta/F'lac^+$ control cells. In no strain was the synthesis affected by the addition of isopropyl-β-thiogalactoside, an inducer of the lactose operon. Addition of adenine had no detectable influence upon enzyme synthesis

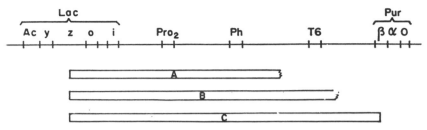

Fig. 10.4.—Schematic representation of the three classes of deletions affecting the episomes carried by *Lac*$_\Delta$ strains. *Lac,* lactose operon (see Fig. 10.1); *Pro*$_2$, gene governing the activity of an enzyme required for proline biosynthesis; *Ph,* structural gene of alkaline phosphatase; *T6,* gene governing the sensitivity to phage T6; *Pur,* purine operon (see text).

in strains carrying *A* or *B* class episomes. In striking contrast, addition of adenine to clones carrying an episome of the *C* class, and therefore an *Ac-y* segment fused to the *Pur-α* cistron, resulted in a repression of the permease and acetylase activities by more than 80 per cent. The subordination of the lactose genes to the purine control mechanism, demonstrated in this experiment, is further shown by the observation that all the conditions known to de-repress specifically the purine operon (purine starvation by growth of a strain carrying in its host chromosome a *Pur⁻* mutation topologically unrelated to the *Lac-Pur* segment, or by growth in the presence of azaserine) de-repressed the lactose genes carried by a *C* class episome. It is clear from these observations that the capacity to obey a regulatory signal is not an intrinsic property of the structural gene but of its integration into a more complex unit, and that the conditions of its expression can be entirely modified as a result of the substitution of a different regulatory segment for its normal one. Direct evidence is thus supplied that the operator is the unique receiving site for cytoplasmic regulatory signals; the conclusion that the same enzyme can be induced or repressed as a consequence of the substitution of one operator for another further illustrates the common basis of both kinds of adaptive controls.

The Polar Mutation

We would like now to consider the second class of mutations which establish the integral character of an operon: the *polar* mutations.

In contrast to the *o^c* constitutive mutations which occupy map positions at one end of the operon, the polar mutations are distributed all along the structural genes, and they affect the reading conditions of the genetic message. More precisely, the polar mutations (Franklin and

Luria 1961; Jacob and Monod 1961*b*) are identified by the following properties:

(1) Although most of them have been characterized as point mutations, they not only abolish the activity of one protein but also reduce the synthesis of proteins governed by adjacent cistrons.

(2) These mutations affect the expression only of the cistrons which are farther from the *o* end of the operon than is the site of the mutation, whence comes the term "polar." For example, polar mutations in the *z* cistron decrease the rate of synthesis of both permease and transacetylase; those in the *y* cistron, the rate of synthesis of acetylase only. The term "polar" is intended only to indicate the existence of an oriented process; it does not imply by itself that a quantitative gradient exists in the level of expression of adjacent cistrons affected by the pleiotropic mutation. The most impressive example of a polar system is supplied by the 15 histidine cistrons, along which polar mutations have been observed at various places (Ames and Hartman 1963).

(3) A polar mutation that reduces several enzymatic activities to barely detectable levels does not prevent the expression of the active alleles of the corresponding cistrons, carried by an extra chromosomal segment in merodiploid cells. But the polar mutation is not complemented by a set of alleles with mutations in any one of the structural cistrons.

These properties again clearly indicate that a cluster of genes, when affected by polar mutations, behaves as a supracistronic unit of genetic expression.

In the lactose system, some of the *z*⁻ polar mutants have map positions very close to the *o* segment, and because they almost completely shut off expression of the whole operon, they were initially thought to represent a particular class of operator mutants (*o*⁰). Further investigations of their properties did not support this interpretation, since deletions covering these mutations (which we propose to refer to as "z gene extreme polar mutations") do not alter the sensitivity of the operon to its repressor. Actually, the extreme polar mutations are located in the *z* gene, as indicated by the thermosensitivity of the galactosidase produced by their revertants.

Many lactose polar mutants, including the extreme polar mutants in the *z* gene, are suppressible by the extragenic suppressors of the "amber" and "ochre" nonsense mutations. As already mentioned, these suppressors act, not at the level of transcription of the gene into a messenger RNA copy, but at the level of the translation of the RNA message into protein chains, by unblocking chain termination at the site of the mutation. The recovery of expression of the *Ac* and *y* genes by suppression of a point mutation in the z gene during the translation of their RNA messages requires that the *Ac, y,* and z messages have remained encoded as a physically integral structure. This strongly suggests that the primary transcription product of an operon is an integral messenger RNA, the translation of which is oriented from the o end of the operon. Recent examinations (Newton *et al.* 1965) of a series of polar mutants of the lactose operon have already illustrated this conclusion. Supplementary evidence as well as considerable information relevant to the mechanism of translation is expected from further studies of the properties of nonsense polar mutations.

As a matter of fact, when measured in a sufficient number of *nonsense* mutants, the polar effect appears to depend strongly upon the map position of the mutation inside the mutated cistron. In the z gene, 16 groups of nonsense mutants have been distinguished by their map positions, as established by deletion mapping. The closer the mutation is to the o segment, the stronger is the polar effect on the synthesis of permease and acetylase (Fig. 10.5). Those nonsense mutations which occupy unambiguous map positions in the z gene, but close to the z-y punctuation, do not significantly affect the rate of synthesis of the two "distal" enzymes; the assembly of peptide chains can occur along distal genes even though the chain governed by a proximal gene is interrupted before completion. In other words, translation of the messenger for proximal cistrons does not need to go to completion in order for translation to be initiated at the next distal intercistronic punctuation. The existence of a gradient can be interpreted *a priori* in two ways: The significant factor in the map position of the nonsense mutation is the distance to the o-p end of the messenger; or the significant factor is the distance to the z-y punctuation itself.

Evidence supporting the second interpretation arises from the observation that a deletion which is located in the z gene between a nonsense mutation and the z-y punctuation, but respects both of them, strongly decreases the polar effect of the nonsense mutation.

The preceding findings on polarity have clarified to what extent the final expression of a cistron is affected by the modalities of the translation of the message that corresponds to an adjacent cistron, closer to the o locus. Interpretations of these observations, which are more relevant to the intimate mechanism of translation than to our present topic, will not be discussed here.

One may notice finally that only the properties of *suppressible* polar mutants of the lactose system have been investigated to any extent. Not all polar mutants are suppressible, however, and it is likely that the sur-

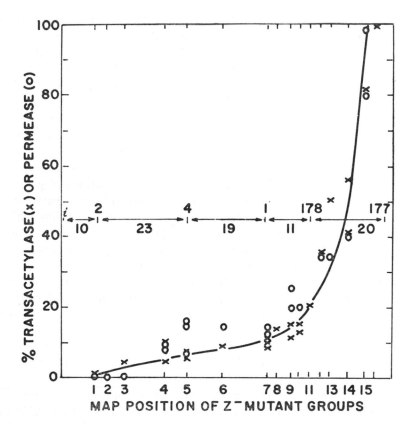

Fig. 10.5.—Relationship between map position of suppressible *z⁻* mutations and levels of β-galactosidase and transacetylase. The numbers on the abscissa represent groups of mutants located by deletion mapping. The genetic map position of some *z⁻* point mutants used as reference markers for deletion mapping and the frequencies of recombination between these mutants are reported on the graph (from Newton *et al.* 1965).

vey of other classes of polar mutants will be of a comparable interest in studies of the mechanism of gene action.

Genetic Punctuation and
Molecular Basis of Repression

The properties of the polar mutations strongly suggest that the molecular basis for coordinated expression of an operon is its transcription into an uninterrupted messenger RNA (mRNA) molecule. Moreover, some direct evidence has been obtained for the existence, in cell extracts, of high molecular weight RNA molecules which, on the basis of their property to form hybrids with specific DNA molecules, could be related to well-identified operons. Their sedimentation constants were in the range predicted for polycistronic mRNA molecules (Attardi *et al.* 1963; Guttman and Novick 1963; Martin 1963; Spiegelman and Hayashi 1963; Imamoto, Morikawa, and Sato 1965). It seems reasonable therefore to define the operon in biochemical terms as *the polydeoxyribonucleotide sequence which specifies an integral mRNA molecule.*

The products of polycistronic operons—mRNA and peptide chains —manufactured during the two steps of gene action which we can now distinguish operationally, appear as the expression of genomic segments of unequal lengths. This requires that a continuous genome carries at least two types of punctuation, capable of being interpreted by two different mechanisms: a punctuation in transcription which "cuts" operons and a punctuation in translation which "cuts" cistrons. The available data do not indicate whether the genome is composed of a sequence of adjacent operons separated by a single punctuation sign in transcription, which defines both the end of an operon and the beginning of the next one, or whether the size of an operon is limited by two punctuation signs, a "start" sign and a distinct "stop" sign (the "stop" sign being adjacent or not to the next "start" sign). However, the latter interpretation is supported by experiments (Beckwith and Signer, unpublished) which reveal that an episome-carried lactose operon can be integrated either clockwise or counterclockwise into the same region of a recipient chromosome. Because of the 3′-5′ polarity, an inversion involves a change in the DNA chain to be transcribed; therefore, the experimental result obtained would be expected only if one punctuation sign alone tells both where the transcription of this operon must start and which DNA chain will be transcribed. A distinct sign appears to be necessary to stop the transcription, and to prevent its reinitiation. In the absence of a specific "stop" sign, the integration of an operon with the wrong orientation should result in the simultaneous and antiparallel continuous copying of both DNA chains, an occurrence which, in all likelihood, would be lethal.

Besides its direct importance for our understanding of the structure of the genome, a precise knowledge of the location of the various signs of genomic punctuation could permit an approach to the still unsolved problem of the molecular basis of repression. We may illustrate this by examining the problem within the framework of three models which make specific predictions on the relative position of "start" signs for both transcription and translation with reference to the *o* regulatory segment (Fig. 10.6). Recently, the important conclusion was reached that

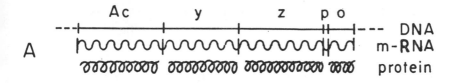

A

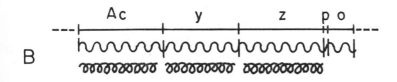

B

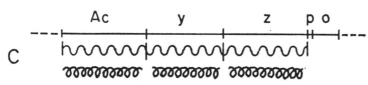

C

Fig. 10.6.—The three conceivable models on the cytoplasmic expression of the *o* segment. Model *A*, *o* segment transcribed and translated; model *B*, *o* segment transcribed but not translated; model *C*, *o* segment neither transcribed nor translated.

polarized transcription of DNA by the DNA-dependent RNA-polymerase and polarized translation of mRNA by polysomes both start from the *o* side of the operon. This follows from observations made independently in several laboratories: The translation of mRNA into protein has been shown to begin at the *o* end (Somerville and Yanofsky 1964); and both mRNA synthesis (Bremer *et al.* 1965; Maitra and Hurwitz 1965) and amino acid addition (Salas *et al.* 1965; Streisinger 1965; Thach *et al.* 1965) are initiated at the 5' free end of the mRNA, thus following the same direction. But the biochemical data do not tell whether transcription and translation start ahead of the *o* segment.

According to model A, the *o* sequence is both transcribed and translated. Two distinct hypotheses would lead to this specific prediction: Either the beginning of the first peptide, specified by *o*, has the regulatory properties characteristic of an operator (Szilard 1960), or, alternatively, the peptide coded by *o* is not an element of the repression circuit but must be synthesized (at the level of an RNA operator) before synthesis of the other peptides can take place (Stent 1964).

According to model B, the *o* segment is transcribed but not translated. In this model, the repressor may either stimulate the rate of degradation of the mRNA or block the reading of mRNA by the ribosomes (Beckwith 1964*b*).

According to model C, the *o* segment is neither transcribed nor translated; repression acts necessarily at the level of a DNA operator, the *o* segment itself (Jacob and Monod 1961*a,b*).

Genetic analysis of the structure of the operon favors model C: The promoter is interpreted as the necessary "start" sign for transcription and occupies a map position consistent with the hypothesis. In model B, the promoter must be interpreted as a unique punctuation in translation, governing, for example, the ribosome's initial binding at a precise location along an uninterrupted mRNA strand. This model still supposes the existence, ahead of the *o* segment, of a "start" sign for transcription, a supposition which is not supported by deletion mapping. In model A, not only does the latter objection hold true, but the properties of deletions which lead one to postulate the existence of the promoter site remain completely unexplained. Moreover, if one considers specifically the first hypothesis of model A, the observation that most o^c mutants are deletion mutants cannot be accounted for. In that first hypothesis, the regulatory function of a peptide specified by *o* is assumed to be governed by its affinity for the repressor, depending upon the integrity of a stereospecific site; this affinity should be affected equally by point mutations (including nonsense mutants in particular) or by deletions.

Definitive evidence concerning the biochemical function of the repressor, and hence the nature of the operator, cannot be expected from an analysis of genetic data alone. Various biochemical approaches have been attempted to discover the level of action of the repressor. Direct measurements of specific mRNA production in extracts of cells grown under various conditions of repression and de-repression again best agree with model C: The amount of RNA hybridizable with the lactose or galactose structural genes is considerably increased in constitutive mutants or in cells induced by inducers specific for these enzymatic systems (Attardi *et al.* 1963). The significance of these measurements has been challenged, however, by the observation that, even after inducer addition, no lactose-specific mRNA could be detected in extracts of a nonsense extreme polar mutant. The fact that this mutation is suppressible and known to block translation at its beginning has been taken as evidence that repression acts at the level of translation and ultimately controls transcription through a feedback mechanism (Beckwith 1964*b*).

Actually, under the conditions in which mRNA production can be measured in cell extracts, it is possible that mRNA molecules prevented, by repression, from entering a polysomal structure are degraded during the extraction step. Further investigations of the influence of polar mutations on the actual rate of mRNA synthesis remain desirable. On the other hand, the hypothesis that coupling occurs between transcription and translation is indeed attractive, and some experimental data have recently been reported (Grunberg-Manago and Gros 1964) which indicate that such a coupling might play a role in the overall regulation of mRNA synthesis. In this hypothesis, one may expect that a block in translation, as provoked by a nonsense mutation, will block transcription. However, it remains entirely conceivable that the coupling mechanism is nonspecific and could be superimposed upon a regulatory system involving specific repression, which defines the maximal amount of a specific mRNA molecule which can be synthesized under optimal conditions of translation in a wild-type cell. It is certain that the conditions under which the rate of translation can influence transcription remain to be analyzed, especially in view of reported examples of mRNA synthesis unaffected by amino acid starvation (Sekiguchi and Cohen 1964).

The preceding discussion of the operon concept has been concerned almost exclusively with the system of lactose utilization in *E. coli*. The question of whether such a clustering of genes into a unit of expression exists for other biochemical pathways has been answered by the increasing number of discoveries of operons controlling series of degradative as well as biosynthetic reactions in various microorganisms (reviews by Maas and McFall 1964; Ames and Martin 1964).

One must, of course, assume that the clustering of structural genes into polygenic operons, functioning as units of expression and regulation, possesses some selective value which maintained such an organization in the course of evolution, at least in the bacterial cell and for certain biochemical systems. Probably it is only when subtle types of regulation are required that the genes determining the enzymes of a given pathway become distributed all over the bacterial chromosome to form small operons, containing sometimes only one structural gene. We have evidence for such situations in the biosynthetic pathways of arginine and of pyrimidines, for instance. One cannot help wondering whether organisms more complicated than bacteria also contain polygenic operons. In fact, structural genes which in certain bacterial species are clustered within a single polygenic operon appear in yeast or *Neurospora* to be distributed in different chromosomes. Yet as the resolution of genetic analysis has increased, more and more operon-like clusterings have been observed, and even in higher forms many instances of such clusters have recently been described (see Demerec, Ch. 4; Lewis, Ch. 3). One should remain cautious, however, and refrain from assuming that operons occur in higher forms until the necessary genetic and biochemical tests have been performed.

It should also be pointed out that the regulation system of the lactose operon is especially simple from both the genetic and biochemical viewpoints: On the one hand, there is one single operon to which the regulator gene is closely linked, a peculiarity which allows the transfer of the system as a whole and makes genetic analysis relatively easy; on the other hand, the lactose system is perfectly independent and does not require integration into the general metabolism of the cell, for nothing more is required to switch on or off the whole system than a signal—the presence or absence of a β-galactoside. Similar autonomy obviously does not exist in most systems where an enzyme pathway is more or less directly related to the production or utilization of essential cellular components. One must then expect a much more complicated network of signals involving alternative induction and repression of enzyme synthesis, and this is indeed what is found in many regulatory systems. But more complicated circuits do not necessarily mean more complicated mechanisms. And in the systems which can be conveniently analyzed for both induction and repression of enzyme synthesis, the basic mechanisms appear formally similar to that involved in the lactose system.

Literature Cited

Ames, B. N., and B. J. Garry, 1959. Coordinate repression of the synthesis of four histidine enzymes by histidine. Proc. Nat. Acad. Sci. U.S. 45: 1453–1461.

Ames, B. N., and P. E. Hartman, 1963. The histidine operon. Cold Spring Harbor Symp. Quant. Biol. 28: 349–356.

Ames, B. N., P. E. Hartman, and F. Jacob, 1963. Chromosomal alterations affecting the regulation of histidine biosynthetic enzymes in Salmonella. J. Mol. Biol. 7: 23–42.

Ames, B. N., and R. C. Martin, 1964. Biochemical aspects of genetics: The operon. Ann. Rev. Biochem. 33: 235–258.

Attardi, G., S. Naono, J. Rouviere, F. Jacob, and F. Gros, 1963. Production of messenger-RNA and regulation of protein syntheses. Cold Spring Harbor Symp. Quant. Biol. 28: 363–372.

Avery, O. T., C. M. MacLeod, and M. McCarty, 1944. Studies on the chemical nature of the substance inducing transformation of pneumococcal types. J. Exp. Med. 79: 137–157.

Beadle, G. W., and E. L. Tatum, 1941. Genetic control of biochemical reactions in Neurospora. Proc. Nat. Acad. Sci. U.S. 27: 499–506.

BECKWITH, J. R., 1964a. A deletion analysis of the *Lac* operator region in *Escherichia coli*. J. Mol. Biol. **8**: 427-430.

———, 1964b. Restoration of operon activity by suppressors. *Structure and Function of the Genetic Material*, vol. 4, pp. 119–124. Abhandl. Deutsch. Akad. Wiss. Akademie-Verlag, Berlin.

BENZER, S. 1957. The elementary units of heredity. *The Chemical Basis of Heredity*, pp. 70–93. Edited by W. D. McElroy and B. Glass. Johns Hopkins Press, Baltimore.

BOURGEOIS, S., M. COHN, AND L. E. ORGEL, 1965. Suppression of and complementation among mutants in the regulatory gene of the lactose operon of *Escherichia coli*. J. Mol. Biol. **14**: 300–302.

BREMER, H., M. W. KONRAD, K. GAINES, AND G .S. STENT, 1965. Direction of chain growth in enzymic RNA synthesis. J. Mol. Biol. **13**: 540–553.

BURSTEIN, C., 1964. Contribution à l'étude de l'induction de l'operon lactose d' *Escherichia coli*. Thèse de doctorat, Université de Paris.

BUTTIN, G., 1963. Mecanismes regulateurs dans la biosynthèse des enzymes du métabolisme du galactose chez *Escherichia coli* K12. II. Le determinisme genetique de la regulation. J. Mol. Biol. **7**: 183–205.

DEMEREC, M., AND P. E. HARTMAN, 1959. Complex loci in microorganisms. Ann. Rev. Microbiol. **13**: 377–406.

ECHOLS, H., A. GAREN, AND A. TORRIANI, 1961. Genetic control of repression of alkaline phosphatase. J. Mol. Biol. **3**: 425–438.

FRANKLIN, N. C., AND S. E. LURIA, 1961. Transduction by bacteriophage P1 and the properties of the *lac* genetic region in *E. coli* and *S. dysenteriae*. Virology **15**: 299–311.

GORINI, L., W. GUNDERSEN, AND M. BURGER, 1961. Genetics of regulation of enzyme synthesis in the arginine biosynthetic pathway of *Escherichia coli*. Cold Spring Harbor Symp. Quant. Biol. **26**: 173–182.

GRUNBERG-MANAGO, M., AND F. GROS, 1964. Remarques sur les caractéristiques des ARN messagers et sur le code genetique. Bull. Soc. Chim. Biol. **46**: 1441–1497.

GUTTMAN, B. S., AND A. NOVICK, 1963. A messenger-RNA for β-galactosidase in *Escherichia coli*. Cold Spring Harbor Symp. Quant. Biol. **28**: 373–374.

IMAMOTO, F., N. MORIKAWA, AND K. SATO, 1965. On the transcription of the tryptophan operon in *Escherichia coli*. J. Mol. Biol. **13**: 169–182.

JACOB, F., AND J. MONOD, 1961a. Genetic regulatory mechanisms in the synthesis of proteins. J. Mol. Biol. **3**: 318–356.

JACOB, F., AND J. MONOD, 1961b. On the regulation of gene activity. Cold Spring Harbor Symp. Quant. Biol. **26**: 193–209.

JACOB, F., AND J. MONOD, 1965. Genetic mapping of the elements of the lactose system. Biochem. Biophys. Res. Commun. **18**: 693–701.

JACOB, F., D. PERRIN, C. SANCHEZ, AND J. MONOD, 1960. L'operon, groupe de gènes à expression coordonnée par un opérateur. Compt. Rend. **250**: 1727–1729.

JACOB, F., A. ULLMANN, AND J. MONOD, 1964. Le promoteur, élément genetique nécessaire à l'expression d'un operon. Compt. Rend. **258**: 3125–3128.

JACOB, F., A. ULLMANN, AND J. MONOD, 1965. Délétions fusionnant l'opéron lactose et un opéron purine chez *Escherichi coli*. J. Mol. Biol. **13**: 704–719.

LEWIS, E. B., 1963. Genes and developmental pathways. Amer. Zool. **3**: 33–56.

MAAS, W. K., 1961. Studies on repression of arginine biosynthesis in *Escherichia coli*. Cold Spring Harbor Symp. Quant. Biol. **26**: 183–191.

MAAS, W. K., AND A. J. CLARK, 1964. Studies on the mechanism of repression of arginine biosynthesis in *Escherichia coli*. J. Mol. Biol. **8**: 365–370.

MAAS, W. K., AND E. McFALL, 1964. Genetic aspects of metabolic control. Ann. Rev. Microbiol. **18**: 95–107.

MAITRA, U., AND J. HURWITZ, 1965. The role of DNA in RNA synthesis. IX. Nucleoside triphosphate termini in RNA-polymerase products. Proc. Nat. Acad. Sci. U.S. **54**: 815–822.

MARTIN, R. G., 1963. The one operon-one messenger theory of transcription. Cold Spring Harbor Symp. Quant. Biol. **28**: 357–361.

MONOD, J., J. P. CHANGEUX, AND F. JACOB, 1963. Allosteric proteins and cellular control systems. J. Mol. Biol. **6**: 306–329.

NEWTON, W. A., J. R. BECKWITH, D. ZIPSER, AND S. BRENNER, 1965. Nonsense mutants and polarity in the *Lac* operon of *Escherichia coli*. J. Mol. Biol. **14**: 290–296.

PONTECORVO, G., 1952. Genetic formulation of gene structure and gene action. Advance. Enzymol. **13**: 121–149.

SADLER, J. R., AND A. NOVICK, 1965. The properties of repressor and kinetics of its action. J. Mol. Biol. **12**: 305–327.

SARABHAI, A. S., O. W. STRETTON, S. BRENNER, AND A. BOLLE, 1964. Colinearity of the gene with the polypeptide chain. Nature **201**: 13–17.

SEKIGUCHI, M., AND S. S. COHEN, 1964. Synthesis of phage induced RNA and sequential enzyme production. J. Mol. Biol. **8**: 638–659.

SMITH, M. A., M. SALAS, W. M. STANLEY, JR., A. J. WAHBA, AND S. OCHOA, 1966. Direction of reading of the genetic message, II. Proc. Nat. Acad. Sci. U.S. **55**: 141–147.

SOMERVILLE, R. L., AND C. YANOFSKY, 1964. On the translation of the *A* gene region of tryptophan messenger RNA. J. Mol. Biol. **8**: 616–619.

SPIEGELMAN, S., AND M. HAYASHI, 1963. The present status of the transfer of genetic information and its control. Cold Spring Harbor Symp. Quant. Biol. **28**: 161–181.

STEERS, E., JR., G. R. CRAVEN, AND C. B. ANFINSEN, 1965. Comparison of β-galactosidases from normal and operator constitutive strains of *E. coli*. Proc. Nat. Acad. Sci. U.S. **54**: 1174–1181.

STENT, G. S., 1964. The operon: On its third anniversary. Science **144**: 816–820.

STREISINGER, G., 1965. Symposium on the mutational process. Prague. In press.

STRETTON, A. O. W., AND S. BRENNER, 1965. Molecular consequences of the amber mutation and its suppression. J. Mol. Biol. **12**: 456–465.

SZILARD, L., 1960. The control of the formation of specific proteins in bacteria and in animal cells. Proc. Nat. Acad. Sci. U.S. **46**: 277–292.

THACH, R. E., M. A. CECERE, T. A. SUNDARARAJAN, AND P. DOTY, 1965. The polarity of messenger translation in protein synthesis. Proc. Nat. Acad. Sci. U.S. 54: 1167–1173.

VOGEL, H. J., 1961. Aspects of repression in the regulation of enzyme synthesis; pathway-wide control and enzyme-specific response. Cold Spring Harbor Symp. Quant. Biol. 26: 163–172.

WILLSON, C., D. PERRIN, M. COHN, F. JACOB, AND J. MONOD, 1964. Non-inducible mutants of the regulator gene in the "lactose" system of *Escherichia coli*. J. Mol. Biol. 8: 582–592.

YANOFSKY, C., B. C. CARLTON, J. R. GUEST, D. R. HELINSKI, AND U. HENNING, 1964. On the colinearity of gene structure and protein structure. Proc. Nat. Acad. Sci. U.S. 51: 266–272.

ZABIN, I., 1963. Proteins of the lactose system. Cold Spring Harbor Symp. Quant. Biol. 28: 431–435.

11

Gene Action
at the Level of the Chromosome

W. Beermann

Since the late nineteenth century, prior to the rediscovery of Mendel's laws of heredity, the study of chromosomes has occupied a peculiar position in the development of genetics. While the importance of chromosome observations for the development of genetic concepts and for the visual illustration of genetic theories can hardly be doubted, one must admit nevertheless that most, if not all, of the actual advances in the analysis of the genetic mechanism could have been and often were accomplished without the help of chromosome cytology. As long ago as 1883, Wilhelm Roux, after reading some of the first descriptions of mitotic chromosome behavior, wrote a small, prophetic paper in which he argued convincingly that the details of mitosis demanded an explanation in terms of linear arrays of particulate genetic determinants. August Weismann, shortly afterward, came to a similar conclusion. Yet, the concept of particulate genes and their arrangement in linear linkage groups was derived later from cross-breeding experiments of the Mendelian type. In the late 1920's and throughout the 1930's cytologists began speculating about the identity of chromosomal subunits and genes, calculating gene sizes, and hopefully localizing mutations in specific chromomeres. But, as we realize now, these attempts at a physical definition of genetic units were doomed to failure, and practically all that we know today about the size, structure, chemistry, and operational behavior of genetic units has resulted from molecular and formal genetic studies on microorganisms, whose chromosomes are almost indiscernible cytologically.

What, then, can be the contribution of direct chromosome studies to modern genetics? In trying to answer this question, I shall choose to discuss gene activity—in the phenogenetic sense. There are many reasons why gene action and gene regulation in terms of present-day molecular models would seem insufficient to describe all aspects of cell

179

differentiation in higher organisms. Nowhere, however, is the lack of information more critically felt than in problems which involve the nucleus and the chromosomes. Everyone acquainted with the basic facts of chromosome cytology will admit that chromosomes of higher organisms possess important organizational and operational features which make them far more complex than bacterial and viral chromosomes. These features may bear significant relationships to the mechanisms of gene regulation and cell differentiation in higher organisms, but to gain the needed information we will have to return to a direct, detailed examination of higher chromosomes in terms of the recent concepts and methods developed by molecular biology. Efforts in this direction have been made in many laboratories over the last 15 years, with two systems which are well known from classical studies: the giant polytene chromosomes of the Diptera and the lampbrush diplotene chromosomes in oocytes and spermatocytes of various organisms.

Chromomeres and Genes

We shall begin the discussion by reviewing some of the pertinent facts of polytene and lampbrush chromosome cytology and reassessing their relation to the concept of the gene. Although strangely ignored in modern speculations on chromosome structure and chromosome model construction, the outstanding feature of chromosomes in operation (both the giant and the lampbrush chromosomes being in a state of maximum metabolic activity) is their chromomeric pattern. This pattern may be described, in terms of the single chromatid, as a sequence of heavily condensed beads of nucleohistone—the chromomeres —which are connected by noncondensed pieces of the same material —the interchromomeres. The presence of DNA in interchromomeres is suggested by fluorescent staining (Wolstenholme 1965) as well as by sensitive Feulgen techniques (Swift 1962). Callan and McGregor (1958) found that deoxyribonuclease breaks the interchromomeres of lampbrush chromosomes, whereas none of the known proteases or ribonuclease is able to do so. Steffensen's (1963) failure to find DNA in interbands may have resulted from mechanical rupture of the interchromomeres by overstretching.

The size of the chromomeres can be determined most precisely in polytene chromosomes by measurement of the thickness and the DNA content of the bands. Band thicknesses (Plate 11.1) may range from 0.05 μ to 0.5 μ. Rudkin (1961) has found from 5×10^{-17} g to 5×10^{-16} g of DNA per individual chromatid. It is interesting to observe, as Rudkin pointed out, that there is an inverse relationship between band size and frequency (Fig. 11.1). Comparable measurements of interchromomeres are less well established. Microscopical data are com-

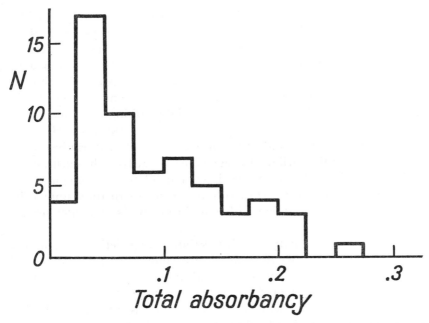

Fig. 11.1.—Histogram showing the distribution of total absorbancies found in 59 single bands of a salivary gland chromosome of *Drosophila melanogaster* (from Rudkin 1961).

patible with the idea that all interchromomeres are more or less of similar length; for example, in giant polytene chromosomes they measure between 0.1 μ and 0.2 μ (see Plate 11.1). Their absolute DNA content would be expected to be lower than that of the smallest size class of chromomeres and, in fact, can be estimated from the photometric data of Swift (1962) to be less than 10^{-17} g for interbands as opposed to 5×10^{-17} g for the smallest bands in *Drosophila* (values calculated for the individual chromatid, corresponding to fewer than 10,000 pairs of nucleotides per interband but at least 50,000 pairs of nucleotides per band).

The significance of the chromomeric organization, in terms of classical cytogenetics, is that it demonstrates the existence of linearly arranged chromosomal subunits in numbers close to estimated gene numbers. This fact has lost none of its validity and intriguing character today. It is true that, as first postulated by Ris (e.g., Ris and Crouse 1945), chromomeres may not exist as "beads" to be set apart from the chromatid axis but that they represent multiple coils or folds of a continuous thread; however, this does not affect their status as real structural entities. Bridges (1935) and others showed long ago that the chromomeric pattern of polytene chromosomes is subject to amazingly little phenotypic variation and can therefore be mapped precisely, provided that cells of comparable type and developmental state are studied. Moreover, at least in polytene chromosomes, the transition between chromomeres and interchromomeres is seen to be very sharp and definite (Plate 11.1), suggesting that if differential coiling causes the chromomeric subdivision of the chromatid, then structural markers must exist which define the limits of the differentially coiling segments. Thus, even though the chromomeric pattern may not express itself at all times in the developmental cycle, for example, not in sperm heads and probably not in the earliest cleavage divisions, at least the euchromatic and the so-called β-heterochromatic sections of the chromosomes may be considered to be genetically subdivided into structural units coinciding in their delimitation with the chromomeres and interchromomeres.

What could be the nature of these subunits in genetic and molecular terms? Regardless of whether such units would have to be considered as "cistrons," "operons," or operational units of a more complex type, evidence has been brought forward in the past 30 years that they do at least in part coextend with Mendelian genes as defined by classical tests. Some of the critical findings may be recalled here. The delimitation of classical "genes" is based on the allelism of mutants as defined by noncomplementation. By comparisons of the mutation frequencies at a specific locus thus defined with the mutation frequencies for the entire chromosome or genome, the number of such loci has been estimated and repeatedly found to be close to, and often nearly identical with, the number of chromomeres counted in polytene chromosomes (e.g., Muller and Altenburg 1919; Alikhanian 1937). The apparent one-to-one relationship between chromomeres and classical genes has been further corroborated by direct gene localization studies. A good example of this (Fig. 11.2) is the analysis of the white-Notch region in the X chromosome of *Drosophila melanogaster* initiated by Demerec (review in Bridges and Brehme 1944; see also Gersh 1965). Through a series of radiation-induced rearrangements, mainly deficiencies and translocations and later duplications also, it has been firmly established that all white mutations are situated within, or closely adjacent to, the two bands 3C1 and 3C2-3 (a doublet). Recently a lethal mutant has been separated from white and been placed in band 3C3, while Lefevre and Wilkins (1966) have argued that 3C1 also represents the locus of a lethal and does not include the white mutant. Thus white would be situated in 3C2, with lethals on either side.

Another widely studied locus near and to the right of the white locus, and in itself comprising a large number of noncomplementing as

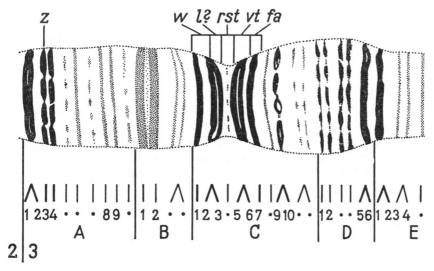

Fig. 11.2.—Localization of Mendelian genes in the white-facet region of the X chromosome of *D. melanogaster.* Symbols from left to right: z = zeste, w = white, l = a probable lethal (see Lefevre and Wilkins 1964), rst = roughest, vt = "verticals" (Gersh 1965), fa = facet-notch.

well as partly complementing mutants, is represented by the facet-split-Notch series (Welshons and von Halle 1962). Deficiencies for band 3C7 invariably give a dominant Notch effect, and none of them apparently complements visible recessive mutants in the same region. Likewise, all known translocations with the Notch effect have breakpoints in the vicinity of 3C7.

The gap existing between bands 3C2-3 and 3C7 has only recently been bridged in an excellent cytogenetic analysis by Gersh (1965). She has found that some of the phenotypic effects usually assigned to the mutant roughest and tentatively localized in band 3C4 are changes in a separate adjacent gene, "verticals," which is localized in 3C4-5 (a doublet). Loss of the faint band 3C4 will produce the roughest eye effect and is nearly lethal in males. Loss of 3C5-6 hardly affects eye structure but leads to the suppression of some vertical bristles. Interestingly, this loss of the heavy double band 3C5-6, in contrast to the loss of 3C4, has no appreciable effect on vitality.

In sum, concerning the white-Notch region, the conclusion seems to be justified that the number of bands as seen under optimum conditions in the light microscope is a maximum rather than a minimum estimate of the number of Mendelian "genes" to be found there. Furthermore, each Mendelian gene seems to occupy a map position cytologically within or around either a single or a double band (when so-called doublets are counted as one). A direct correlation between thickness of a band and genetic complexity of a region does not seem to be indicated.

Simple as the results of the localization work may seem, their interpretation, in the light of modern molecular biology, is by no means so. The cytologist finds himself supported in his view that chromomeres—perhaps including an adjacent interchromomere and sometimes even a further band—are real genetic units. These units must comprise at least one cistron and could, in the manner of microbial operons, contain several operationally linked cistrons, especially where complex cis-trans interactions and polar effects are observed (Lewis 1963). Lewis finds that a rearrangement to the left of the two bands assigned to the bithorax pseudoallelic series will inactivate all five pseudoallelic sites of the locus, whereas a rearrangement between the two bands inactivates only the two sites at the right-hand end of the locus. Another polar effect has been mentioned by Dorn and Burdick (1962), who studied a deficiency at the left end of the miniature-dusky region. The deficiency, which recombines with all mutants of the region, "uncovers" only miniature, not dusky, mutants, thus showing, as do Lewis' data, that the reading of more than one cistron must be involved. Even so, to say that the chromomere, as a rule, is identical with a microbial operon would be entirely unjustified on the basis of the cytogenetic data presented. First, the analogy may be a purely formal one, and second, if operons do exist in chromosomes of higher organisms, they may be only part of more complex operational units. Furthermore, as will be discussed later, there is too much DNA in chromomeres for them to be considered as nothing more than single operons. And, indeed, the cytogenetic data cannot and do not tell us whether the units defined by genetic experiments actually include the entire chromomere or only specific portions of it. They do not even specify, as pointed out long ago by Goldschmidt (1954), how far the subdivision observed on the cytological level is matched by a clear-cut separation of genetic functions between adjacent genes. In order to define operational subunits in chromosomes and in order to check their possible relation to the chromomeres, one must have recourse to a more direct approach—the study of the behavior and metabolism of individual chromomeres at the level of the chromosomes themselves.

Puffs, Loops, and Chromomeres

Some years ago it was discovered that the chromomeric pattern of giant polytene chromosomes is subject to a specific type of local varia-

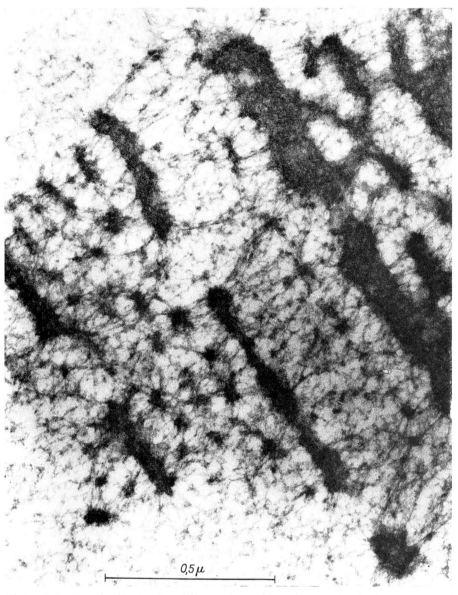

Plate 11.1.—Longitudinal ultra-thin section of a salivary gland chromosome of *Drosophila hydei*. Strands in interband regions are less than 100 Å thick. A number of submicroscopic bands, in the range of 0.1 μ to 0.5 μ, may be seen. Glutaraldehyde, Epon. Courtesy of H. D. Berendes.

Plate 11.2.—Localization of the point of origin of a Balbiani-ring in *Chironomus tentans.* The same chromosomal site develops a Balbiani-ring in the proximal half of the Malpighian tubules (right) but not in the distal half. Homologous bands are connected by lines. The actually puffed region is indicated in the left hand photograph. ×2000.

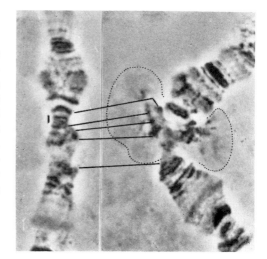

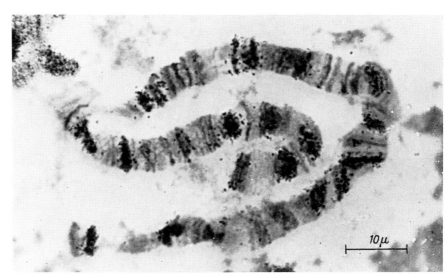

Plate 11.3.—Late replicating bands (late "replicons") in a salivary gland chromosome of *D. funebris,* ^{3}H-thymidine radioautograph (Arcos, in preparation).

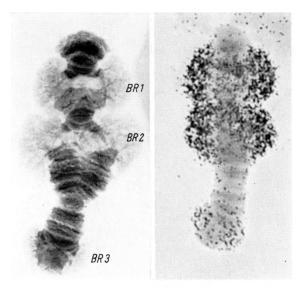

Plate 11.4.—Three large Balbiani-rings in salivary chromosome IV of *Chironomus tentans*. Incorporation of ³H-uridine closely follows the puffing pattern. ×1200.

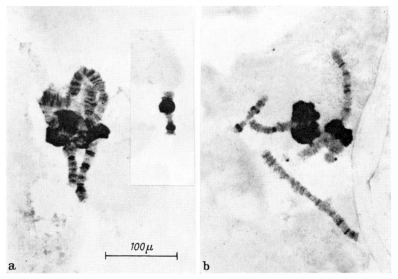

Plate 11.5.—Effect of adenosine on puffing and uridine incorporation in *C. tentans*. Control (*a*) and treated (*b*) cell from the same animal. Treatment: 30 min incubation in 0.1 mg/ml adenosine. Note reduction of overall labeling (but not in the nucleoli) and shrinkage of Balbiani-rings on chromosome IV (chromosome IV is shown in the insert in *a* and opposite to this in *b*).

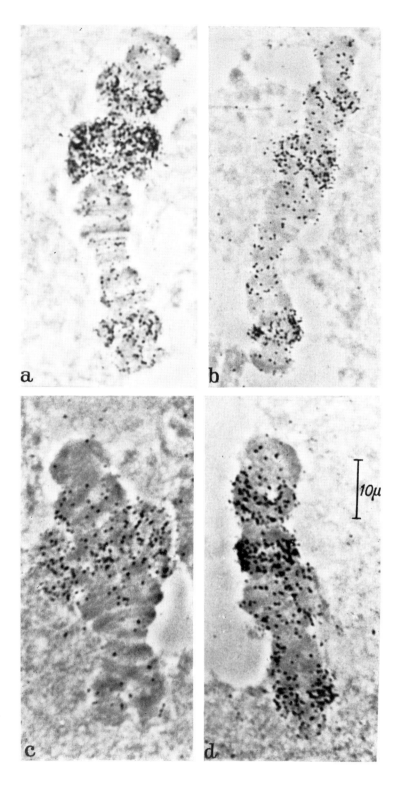

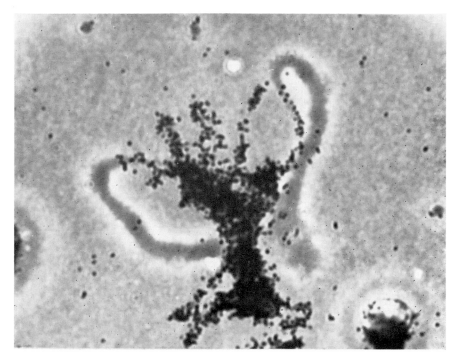

Plate 11.7.—Sequential labeling of a giant loop pair in *Triturus viridescens.* Four days after the injection of ³H-uridine the loops are labeled over approximately one third of their length from the thin insertion (see Fig. 11.3). ×2000.

Plate 11.6.—A comparison of the effects of actinomycin D (*a, b*) and adenosine (*c, d*): (*a*) control and (*b*) treated with actinomycin D for 30 min at a concentration of 0.2 µg/ml; (*c*) control and (*d*) treated with adenosine for 30 min at a concentration of 0.1 mg/ml. The apparent overall increase of uridine incorporation in (*d*) is unexplained.

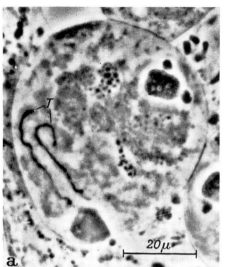
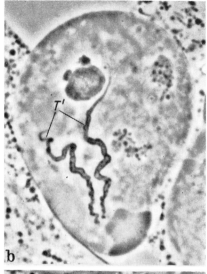
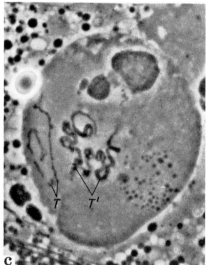

Plate 11.8.—Lampbrush formations of the Y chromosome in spermatocyte nuclei of *D. hydei:* (*a*) wild-type nucleus; (*b*) nucleus of tube-mutant; (*c*) nucleus of XYY male with one mutant Y and one wild-type Y chromosome; *T,* pair of threadlike loops; *T',* mutant form of threads. Note the autonomy of the mutant loop structure in the XYY nucleus (after Hess 1965).

tion which is correlated with the developmental state of the cells under study (Beermann 1952; Breuer and Pavan 1955). It was observed that relatively small sections of the chromosomes give rise to so-called puffs in one type of tissue, or in one stage of development, but not in others. Puffs contain large amounts of higher proteins and RNA; DNA, although certainly present, is hard to identify. Wherever the development of a puff can be traced back to the initial stages, one finds that as a rule it has originated from a defined band. The band swells up, becomes diffuse, and loses staining intensity. However, one could argue that, in the larger puffs, more and more adjacent bands might become secondarily involved in the puffing process as the puff grows so that a one-to-one relation between chromomere and puff would no longer hold true. Careful study of favorable preparations of Balbiani-rings in various chironomids reveals that, apart from two or three of the closest neighbors on either side, all of the adjacent bands can be found in an unpuffed condition, regardless of the size of the puff (Plate 11.2). On the other hand, some of the giant puffs could really represent defined groups of bands, as many as five in number, which would puff in a correlated fashion, either simultaneously or in a fixed order. In *Chironomus tentans,* the zone of origin of a Balbiani-ring can be broken by irradiation into two parts, each of which forms a Balbiani-ring in its new position. It follows that the initial Balbiani-ring actually has two points of origin, and it can be shown that these are separated from each other by a group of three bands. Bauer (1957) has found a similar case and Mechelke (1961) has described a case of correlated, successive puffing of two closely adjacent loci which appears to be an actual migration of the center of puffing along a group of ten bands. The difficulties in interpretation may result only from the limitations of cytological techniques. Some puffs originate and form in what appear to be interbands. This may be caused by puffing of submicroscopic bands. The idea, suggested by incidental observations, that puffing may be initiated, not in the puffed band itself, but in the interband to the right or left of it is interesting but hard to prove or disprove at present.

In accepting, as a first approximation, the view that puffing is an autonomous reaction of single chromomeres (perhaps including adjacent interchromomeres), we arrive at the conclusion that, at least with respect to puffing, the chromomeres are units, not only of structure but also of operation. With more confidence than before, we may also say that it seems to be the entire chromomere which reacts as a unit, for, even if there were a gradient of puffing along the band, the reaction as such always seems to involve the band as a whole. But what kind of change is taking place during puff formation? And how can it be inter-

preted in terms of genetic units? The analysis of puff fine structure as
studied in Balbiani-rings—together with the fact that in typical RNA
puffs there is a progressive dilution of DNA staining—has led to the
concept that during puffing each of the many thousand homologous
chromomeres in a polytene chromosome band unfolds into a long,
loop-like strand up to 10 µ in length, a strand whose axis is less than
100 Å in diameter and probably consists of a single Watson-Crick double helix of DNA or a chain of such helices (Beermann and Bahr
1954). Short fibrous particles extend sideways from the axis in great
numbers and probably represent the additional protein and RNA material which is so characteristic of puffs. This interpretation rests on
the assumption, then, that chromomeres are equivalent to long but
definite sections of a single continuous chain of Watson-Crick helices
running along each individual chromatid. In *Drosophila*, even a
chromomere of low DNA content, equivalent to about 10^5 pairs of nucleotides per chromatid, would represent a length, in terms of free
DNA, of nearly 35 µ. In nonpuffed chromomeres, the entire length
must be folded or coiled into a tiny dot 0.2 µ in diameter. It is clear
that folding and unfolding would both have to be highly ordered processes, probably involving predetermined bends, in order to explain
the coordinated behavior of DNA pieces as long as 100 µ or more.

The interpretation presented here gains more validity from the work
on amphibian oocyte lampbrush chromosomes, mainly by Callan and
co-workers and by Gall (review by Callan 1963). The chromosomes of
lampbrush bivalents are again seen to exhibit the typical chromomeric
subdivision. Interestingly enough, the total number of chromomeres,
about 10,000, is not very far from that found in *Drosophila,* although
the newt chromosome complement contains at least ten times more
DNA than that of *Drosophila.* Correspondingly the chromomeres of
newt chromosomes are relatively large bodies considering that there
are only two chromatids per chromosome. During the lampbrush phase
each chromomere unfolds into a pair of loops with lengths sometimes
greater than 100 µ (Fig. 11.3). As shown convincingly by a study of the
kinetics of deoxyribonuclease-induced fragmentation (Gall 1963), the
axis of each loop is equivalent to just one double helix of DNA, while
the interchromomeric connections, as expected, contain two such double helices in parallel (Fig. 11.4). The rest of the loop consists of ribonucleoprotein which projects radially from the axis and grows in
bulk from one end of the loop to the other.

At this point in the discussion we shall emphasize only the following
facts: Regardless of whether or not the metabolic functions of meiotic
lampbrush chromosomes can be compared to those of polytene somatic

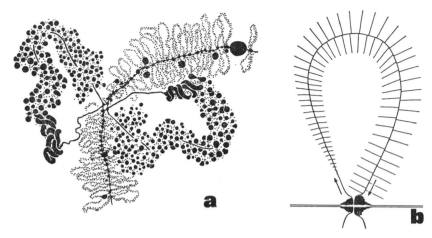

Fig. 11.3.—(a) The left end of chromosome XII from an oocyte of the newt *Triturus cristatus.* A large number of "normal" loop pairs are shown in addition to the "giant granular loops" characteristic of this chromosome region. All loops are asymmetric in the sense that one end is thinner than the other. In the giant granular loops, the thin insertion consists of a fine thread leading to a dense, contorted region. The thick insertion, as well as the bulk of the loop, consists of a coarsely granular matrix surrounding a very delicate axis (from Gall and Callan 1962). (b) Interpretation of chromomere and loop structure in terms of a continuous chromatid (after Callan).

chromosomes, the pattern of subdivision into functional units and the structural changes occurring in these units are basically the same. All the conspicuous changes occur in the chromomeres, none in the interchromomeres. Furthermore, we find that in organisms with large chromosomes the chromomeres represent pieces of DNA with as many as a million or more pairs of nucleotides which react autonomously and as units, depending on unknown conditions, by folding or unfolding themselves. Genetic functional units of these giant dimensions are unheard of from the microbial world. Their size is close to that of entire phage or bacterial chromosomes. DNA-replication studies on polytene chromosomes (Keyl and Pelling 1963; Plaut 1963) have indeed revealed that, like bacterial chromosomes, chromomeres behave as single replicons (Plate 11.3), but in terms of genetic fine structure and function there is a wide gap between the two: The bacterial chromosome with thousands of individual cistrons and perhaps hundreds of operons stands opposed to a unit of DNA which, in spite of similar dimensions, may be equivalent in its information content to no more than a single operon. Elucidation of this apparent paradox requires analysis of the actual chemical activities of chromomeres.

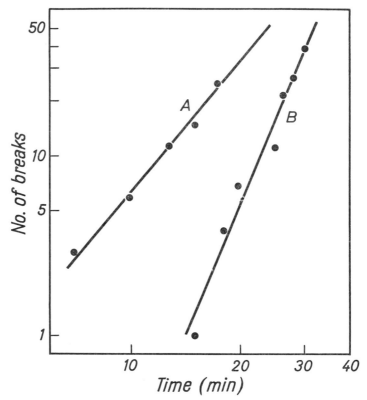

Fig. 11.4.—Log-log plots of the number of lampbrush chromosome breaks as a function of time of deoxyribonuclease action. *A,* breaks in a loop; *B,* breaks along the main chromosome axis. The slopes of the two curves (2.6 in *A* and 4.8 in *B*) are consistent with a model of the chromatid containing only one very long DNA double helix (from Gall 1963).

Puffing and RNA Synthesis

The observations on tissue and stage specificity of puffing patterns strongly suggest that chromomeres behave as units in the transfer of information from the nucleus to the cytoplasm. In other words, differential puffing of the individual chromomeres may be an expression of differential activation of the individual genes. Consequently, one would predict that, when a chromomere is found puffed in a specific type of cell and not in others, this chromomere should contain a gene of specific relevance to the functions of that cell. For one of the Balbiani-rings of the salivary gland chromosomes of *Chironomus* such a correlation between gland function and chromomere puffing has been established by cytogenetic tests (Beermann 1961). The secretion of a genetic variant in which this chromomere does not puff lacks a specific component, electrophoretically characterized as a single protein fraction (Grossbach, in preparation) which presumably is synthesized by the gland cells. Other less direct relations between puffs and cell functions are conceivable (e.g., Laufer and Nakase 1965) and, indeed, likely; nevertheless, the primary functions in information transfer would be expected to be the same in the genetic variant described as in other mutants. They involve the transcription of DNA nucleotide sequences into those of RNA molecules and their subsequent translation into the amino acid sequences of specific proteins. Therefore, at the level of the chromosome we would expect primarily that the chemical equivalent of transcription, DNA-dependent RNA synthesis, takes place and is correlated, in some fashion, to the chromomeres and their puffing behavior.

Radioautographic studies by Pelling (1959, 1964) on *Chironomus* and by Rudkin and Woods (1959) on *Drosophila* confirmed early that the chromosomes are the only sites of intense RNA synthesis in the cell. And, on closer examination, the pattern of incorporation of labeled RNA-precursors was found to coincide perfectly with the puffing pattern of the chromosomes, both topographically and quantitatively (Plate 11.4). Large puffs, such as the Balbiani-rings, incorporate more than a thousand times as much per unit time as do small ones, while the incorporation rate of nonpuffed chromomeres remains practically zero. Of course, different rates of incorporation do not necessarily reflect different rates of synthesis. However, the possibility is remote that the observed labeling patterns result entirely from the differential collection and accumulation, according to puff size, of newly synthesized nuclear RNA. The relative distribution of label along the chromosomes does not change even in the shortest possible pulse experiments. Thus, if large-scale migration of RNA from nonpuffed to puffed regions occurred, it would have to be extremely rapid; if, on the other hand, no such migration took place and equal rates of synthesis were still assumed for all chromomeres, then one would have to postulate fantastic rates of RNA turnover in most chromomeres to explain the nonappearance of label. Unspecific accumulation of RNA is also improbable; direct analyses of the base composition of the RNA from different puffs (Edström and Beermann 1962) show that, although general characteristics of chromosomal RNA molecules, such as high adenine and low uracil content, distinguish them as a group from nucleolar and cytoplasmic RNA molecules, their actual base composition varies significantly from puff to puff.

Thus, none of the data from RNA turnover studies on polytene chromosomes is in conflict with our basic idea that differential puffing is an expression of differential *in situ* transcription and that the chromomeres are therefore units of genetic transcription. Unfortunately, however, this statement raises more questions than it answers. Knowing that the DNA of each chromomere corresponds to a length of 10^5 to 10^6 nucleotides (i.e., to molecular weights between 10^8 and 10^9), we are led to ask whether all of this length is really participating in transcription when a chromomere becomes puffed, whether transcription is in one piece or in several, and whether all of the RNA will serve as messenger in protein synthesis. To begin with, let us consider the last of these questions: The base composition studies just mentioned have demonstrated that puff RNA, in contrast to nucleolar and cytoplasmic RNA, has at least some of the characteristics which are expected from messenger RNA. Its unique base asymmetry, with A/U ratios approaching a value of 2, argues for its having been copied from only one of the two strands of the DNA template. Why that DNA strand must be rich in thymine in all puffs, as indicated by the data, is not clear. Further information on the nature of puff RNA is not available at present. The question of its molecular weight and whether each puff produces only a single species of molecule will have to await an answer from ultracentrifugation studies on RNA extracted from *Chironomus* Balbiani-rings. These studies are now being conducted in our laboratory by Pelling. Whether the chromomere behaves as a unit in the processes of information transfer may be ascertained by a consideration of the mechanics of puffing itself.

To the naive observer the correlation between puffing and synthetic activity would seem to be quite a natural one. He would assume, as we did for a long time, that puffing somehow creates the conditions for uninhibited synthesis of RNA to go on. Activating agents would unfold the DNA, hold it in place, and make it available to the action of RNA polymerases. Such a view seemed supported by the fact that, in *Chironomus*, nuclear incorporation of uridine is regularly found to be suppressed in some individuals without an appreciable reduction in puff size. Thus, RNA synthesis seemed to depend on puffing, but puffing not on RNA synthesis. However, it is difficult to see why RNA synthesis, as such, would require unfolding of the template if DNA synthesis does not do so. Furthermore, uridine could fail to be incorporated for many reasons, in spite of continued RNA synthesis, and recent experiments suggest that the causal relation between RNA synthesis and puffing may be the reverse of that previously considered.

In these experiments we tested several antimetabolites for their ability to suppress RNA synthesis and puffing in explanted salivary glands of *Chironomus*. Some of the agents tested were actinomycin D, 2,4-dinitrophenol, and several nucleosides and deoxynucleosides (Beermann, in preparation). The main results can be summarized as follows: If glands are treated, either *in vivo* or *in vitro*, with actinomycin at concentrations between 0.1 and 2 μg per ml at 20°C, a rapid shrinkage of all puffs invariably occurs and is paralleled by a drastic inhibition of uridine incorporation (Plate 11.6 *a,b*). Shrinkage becomes apparent within 5 minutes and is nearly complete within 40 minutes. Incorporation of uridine is completely stopped after 2 to 3 hours. Under the same conditions shrinkage also occurs in a sister gland, used as a control, which is not incorporating uridine. Shrinkage does not occur, however, in spite of inhibited uridine incorporation, if the experiment is performed at 4°C or if dinitrophenol at concentrations of 10⁻⁴ M is added to the actinomycin. If glands treated with actinomycin at low temperature are thoroughly washed in sucrose medium and then transferred into sucrose medium at room temperature, shrinkage of the puffs will subsequently occur. These experiments show that actinomycin binds to the chromosomes and inhibits RNA synthesis but that it does not in itself shrink the puffs. Shrinkage of the puffs seems to depend on a second factor or process which is inhibited by low temperature and which requires ATP. A direct structural effect of the actinomycin is indicated only at much higher concentrations of the drug (i.e., 20 μg per ml), but this effect is quite different from shrinkage: RNA synthesis is blocked instantaneously and there is a general condensation of the chromosomes, but the puffs do not change at all.

What could be the nature of the second factor involved in puff shrinkage? One could assume that, at low concentrations, the actinomycin binds to the DNA in the puffs and, quite apart from its possible effect on RNA synthesis, activates an enzymatic reaction whose function would be to fold the DNA back into a compact chromomere. Indeed, in accordance with our earlier views on the causal relation between puffing and RNA synthesis, this could be the very cause of the inhibition of RNA synthesis by actinomycin, at least at low concentrations. Checking these assumptions requires the study of antimetabolites other than actinomycin, specifically those which do not inhibit RNA synthesis by directly binding to DNA. That dinitrophenol, which is supposed to be such an agent, would not be useful in this respect is indicated by its inhibitory effect on actinomycin-induced puff shrinkage. We were surprised to find, however, that two of the natural precursors of RNA synthesis, if given in overdoses, mimic the action of actinomycin on giant chromosome puffs. Glands were incubated in sucrose medium containing one of the following nucleosides in concentrations between 10^{-4} and 10^{-3} M: uridine, cytidine, adenosine, guanosine, deoxyadenosine, xanthosine, inosine. Of these, only adenosine and, to a much lesser extent, guanosine were found to be effective. With adenosine a rapid shrinkage of the puffs and a parallel reduction of uridine incorporation can be observed within 30 minutes (Plates 11.5 and 11.6), whereas in control experiments with cytidine, for example, there was no reduction of puff size within 60 minutes and no reduction of RNA synthesis, as measured by the incorporation of ^{3}H-adenosine. Interestingly, nucleolar incorporation was found to be definitely less sensitive to adenosine treatment.

An interpretation of the effect of adenosine overdoses on puffing depends upon the nature of its effect on RNA synthesis. Studies on mouse L cells have confirmed the inhibitory action of adenosine on RNA synthesis (Hausen, unpublished). It was found that the rate of RNA synthesis in treated cells drops within 30 minutes to a minimum of about 15 to 20 per cent of the rate in controls. If such cells had been previously infected with an RNA virus, viral RNA synthesis was found to be inhibited to the same degree, thus suggesting that the point of attack of adenosine is not on the level of RNA polymerase but at some step prior to the polymerization of nucleotides. Moreover, preliminary biochemical studies have indicated that overdoses of adenosine specifically inhibit the phosphorylation of uridine and possibly other nucleosides. These concordant observations make our previous contentions appear doubtful. Puffing seems to be an effect of and not a condition for RNA synthesis, since shrinkage of puffs can be produced by what appears to be a specific depletion of the RNA precursor pool. The possibility that adenosine directly affects puffing still remains to be tested, but such a possibility seems remote. Almost certainly the effect of actinomycin is also produced through its effect on RNA synthesis as postulated by Izawa, Allfrey, and Mirsky (1963) in a study of actinomycin effects on lampbrush chromosomes.

We are now in a position to re-interpret our findings on the effects of low temperature and ATP depletion in combination with actinomycin. Our experiments, described above, have shown that puffing is not controlled by the level of RNA synthesis alone. Puffing must be under the control of at least one other factor, and it is the nature of this second factor or process which may give a clue to other possible functions of the chromomere, aside from transcription. Electron microscopy has provided ample evidence for the formation of ribonucleoprotein particles of various sizes and shapes within different puffs and for a subsequent migration of these particles into the cytoplasm (Beermann and Bahr 1954; Swift 1962; Beermann 1964; Berendes, unpublished). If it is assumed that the newly made RNA must be packaged in protein before it can leave the chromomere, puffing might be postulated actually to depend upon an equilibrium between the two processes, RNA synthesis and RNA packaging with subsequent removal. If RNA synthesis is slowed down and the packaging process is also inhibited, shrinkage of the puff would not occur. If packaging and removal go on at full speed while RNA synthesis slows down, the stripped DNA sections would fold and the puff as a whole would shrink. This model is almost certainly too simple. Nevertheless, it offers a clue not only to the causes but also to the possible biological functions of puffing. If packaging is an obligatory link in the transfer of messenger molecules from the chromosomes to the cytoplasm, then a large part of the chromomeric DNA might have no other function than to provide a substrate for this process—in other words, to bind and stabilize the messengers until their complex formation with transport protein is complete. Puffing would be the visible expression of this activity. The view that a large part of the chromomeric DNA may not regularly function in the transcription of RNA, and that in fact it may be only the initial section of the chromomere which functions like an operon, is further strengthened by other independent cytological and cytogenetic data, mainly from lampbrush chromosomes.

Chromomeres: Operational Units of Higher Order

In studying the incorporation of uridine into the loops of lampbrush chromosomes, Gall and Callan (1962) discovered a striking phenomenon. Some of the largest loops incorporate uridine in a sequential fashion such that, regardless of the developmental stage of the individual oocytes in an ovary, the labeling always starts at one end of the loop and ends, in all oocytes, at some definite point further along the loop; the position of this point moves closer and closer to the other end as the time of incubation increases (Plate 11.7). The polarity expressed by this behavior had long been apparent from studies of loop morphology: It manifests itself by an increased diameter of the ribonucleoprotein matrix of the loops from one end to the other (Fig. 11.3). But, aside from polarity, the first important conclusion to be drawn from the sequential labeling experiment is that the RNA, long after its synthesis has been completed, remains attached to the chromomeric loop and associates, *in situ,* with protein. Gall and Callan have interpreted the movement of label around the loop as the result of an actual movement of the DNA axis of the loop by continuous unfolding of loop DNA at the anterior half of the chromomere and a more or less synchronous folding back at the posterior half-chromomere. The fact that labeling always starts at "zero" position is then interpreted to mean that at one end of the loop a fixed polymerase site exists, through which all of the DNA will pass in opening out into the loop. Thus, all portions of the loop DNA are thought to be active as templates. However, the data can be interpreted in a less complicated way by our view that only an initial section of the chromomeric DNA is being transcribed. The moving boundary of label would then easily be explained as a movement around the loop by the RNA copied from the initial section, in association with the synthetically inactive posterior sections. Movement could be attributed either to actual transport of the RNA relative to the loop axis or to a sequential pick-up of RNA copies while the DNA unfolds.

A second set of data, again from studies on lampbrush chromosomes, lends further support to our view. Hess and Meyer (1963) in our laboratory found that the Y chromosome of *Drosophila hydei,* during the growth phase of the spermatocytes, forms several pairs of lampbrush loops of giant dimensions, each with a characteristic morphology and fine structure. Although chromomeres cannot be seen in the Y chromosome, the loop pairs on the Y chromosome have been located by cytogenetic methods (Hess 1965a) and have each been found to occupy a small segment of the Y chromosome, less than one tenth of its length, either at the tip or at the base of the chromosome arms. Males with Y chromosomes deficient for segments containing any one of the five or six giant loop pairs seem to be sterile.

Hess (1965b) has found in irradiated males several mutations affecting loop morphology, two of which are of particular interest in this connection (Plate 11.8). One of the most conspicuous loop pairs is the one called "compact threads"; it is immediately adjacent to, and practically continuous with, a second one, called "diffuse threads." Both are more than 40 μ long, and in both of them—independent from each other, as would be expected—mutations have occurred which dramatically change the microscopic appearance and fine structure of the loop matrix along the entire length of the loop. Cytogenetic tests show that the mutations must indeed have occurred either within or very near the affected loops themselves. Furthermore, there is no indication of a gross structural change, either deficiency or duplication, in the Y chromosome, and males carrying these mutant Y chromosomes are completely fertile. Similar variants of Y chromosome loops have been detected in wild stocks of *D. hydei*. For all practical purposes, therefore, we may classify these mutations as point-like. How could a point mutation which is localized within a loop change the morphology of the loop as a whole? One possibility would be that the mutant section of the loop codes for a protein component of the loop matrix which, after having been synthesized somewhere else in the cell, attaches itself to the entire loop and determines its characteristic appearance. However, this cannot be true because, as Hess has shown, the mutant appearance of the loops is expressed autonomously even in the presence of a second, nonmutant Y chromosome (Plate 11.8c). It appears, then, that the effects of some point mutations can directly spread along the loops. The only reasonable explanation of this behavior would seem to be that there is a functional subdivision within the chromomeric DNA so that an initial "master" segment, which is active in transcription, would be followed by a long segment with other, auxiliary functions, predominantly that of permitting the sequential attachment of RNA copies from the master segment. A mutation in the master segment could then be expressed as a change of the loop as a whole; however, the possible molecular basis of such changes remains to be clarified. Functional subdivision into transcribing and stabilizing or "packaging" segments, as proposed here, could also account for the transvection effects described by Lewis (1963) and for other complex interactions between related loci such as zeste and white in *Drosophila*—effects which seem to involve an intranuclear interaction between genes. These effects may be caused by errors in the attachment of closely related messengers to their mutual packaging segments.

In postulating "auxiliary" functions for the major portion of the chromomeric DNA, I do not wish to imply that its only functions are those of messenger stabilization and packaging. It is also conceivable that in some phase of chromosomal activity the same sections of the chromomere are synthetically active, perhaps in producing the raw material for specific transfer RNA molecules. Both of these auxiliary functions, however, could be used by the cell as a means specifically to amplify and canalize the genetic information—in other words, to control its availability in the final process of translation. The only evidence we have for such a view is of a very general nature: Closely related species of higher organisms often show widely divergent chromosome sizes and DNA contents, presumably owing to different chromomere sizes. The only phenotypic characters known to be correlated with such differences are quantitative, notably cell size.

In our attempt to push speculation concerning the chromomere be-

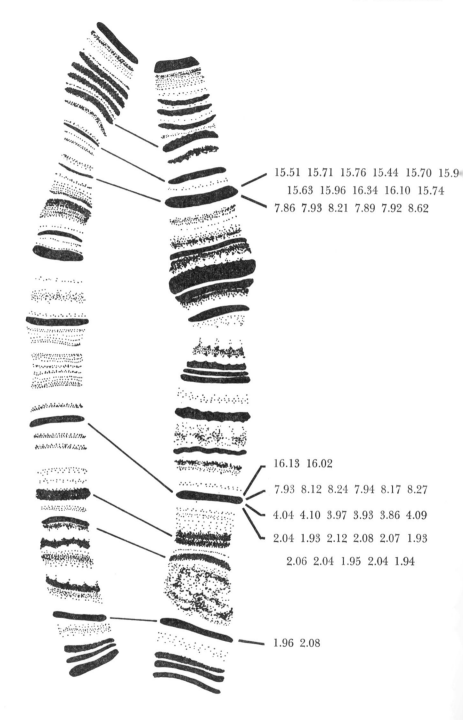

15.51 15.71 15.76 15.44 15.70 15.9◄
15.63 15.96 16.34 16.10 15.74
7.86 7.93 8.21 7.89 7.92 8.62

16.13 16.02

7.93 8.12 8.24 7.94 8.17 8.27

4.04 4.10 3.97 3.93 3.86 4.09

2.04 1.93 2.12 2.08 2.07 1.93
2.06 2.04 1.95 2.04 1.94

1.96 2.08

yond the level of present knowledge, we may now raise a final question: What could be the genetic relation between the postulated components of the chromomeric DNA, namely, the initial transcribing segment and the posterior auxiliary sections? If the function of the auxiliary sections is assumed to be that of vehicle for sequential attachment of RNA molecules, then, as our observations require, the attachment must be highly specific in the sense that a given packaging segment will pick up copies only from its own initial transcribing segment. Such a specificity could result from partial base-sequence homology between the two segments; thus the packaging section might represent a multiple redundant portion of the initial master segment. The growth of chromomeres and chromosomes in evolution would be easily understood, on this basis, as the result of intrachromomeric duplications. Intrachromomeric replications have recently been found to occur in *Chironomus*. Keyl (1965) observed that the total DNA content of the haploid chromosome complement of the two subspecies, *Chironomus thummi thummi* and *C. thummi piger*, differs by about 25 per cent. He was able, by Feulgen spectrophotometry of the giant salivary chromosomes, to trace this difference back to increases in the DNA content of a large number of individual bands in specific chromosome sections of *C. thummi thummi*. These increases, however, are of a very peculiar kind: Regardless of the absolute amount of DNA present in each individual chromomere, the DNA value in any chromomere of *C. thummi thummi* is always precisely either 2, 4, 8, or 16 times higher than that in the homologous chromomere of *C. thummi piger* (Fig. 11.5).

Such a geometric progression, besides showing that intrachromomeric duplications do occur, may be a reflection of the fact, pointed out earlier, that chromomeres are units of DNA replication. If the duplication events are considered as errors in replication, the geometric progression indicates a type of repeated replication which does not include the starting point of the replicon, perhaps not even the "master" segment as a whole. Repeated replication in itself requires either a back and forth type of copying or, more probably, a contact between initial and terminal segments in a ring-like fashion. Viewing the chromomere as a potential ring which is capable of repeated replica-

Fig. 11.5.—The median, unpaired section of chromosome III of a hybrid between *C. thummi thummi* and *C. thummi piger* showing the increased DNA content of many bands in *C. thummi thummi*. For three bands the observed proportional increases in Feulgen absorbancy are given. Courtesy of H. G. Keyl (see Keyl 1965).

tion has many attractive operational aspects: Not only does a ring duplicate easily to form a double-sized ring, but it also may detach itself from a larger continuous DNA chain without breaking it or may re-insert itself into an old or new position, as evidenced by the behavior of prophages in bacteria. Recent cytological data lend further support to the concept of repeated replication in rings. Students of amphibian lampbrush chromosome cytology (see Callan 1966) have discovered that the nucleolus organizer regions in the lampbrush stage bud off large numbers of DNA rings, each of which forms a free nucleolus, thus amplifying by extravagant means the flow of genetic information from a specific locus. Repeated replication may also account for the phenomenon of DNA puffs in Diptera as described by Pavan and Breuer (1952) and others (Rudkin and Corlette 1957) and for the extra DNA-containing bodies formed in the nuclei of oogonia in several insects (Giardina 1901; Bayreuther 1952). Finally, the interstitial loss of large amounts of DNA from the chromosomes of Cyclops furcifer during certain phases of development, as found in our laboratory (S. Beerman 1966), would become understandable as a detachment of ring-like loops from a potentially continuous chain of interchromomeres.

Conclusions

In higher organisms the primary function of the genes, transcription, seems to be coordinated with other activities which control the flow of information from the nucleus into the cytoplasm. The elements of coordination seem to be the chromomeric subdivisions within the chromosome. Chromomeres, the physical equivalents of Mendelian genes, are thought to be giant operational units combining the functions of transcription with those of messenger stabilization and packaging and perhaps with other modulating functions in the subsequent translation process. This model would explain the evolution of large chromosomes. It may also help the elucidation of gene regulation and cell differentiation in higher organisms.

Literature Cited

ALIKHANIAN, S. J., 1937. A study of the lethal mutations in the left end of the sex chromosome in Drosophila melanogaster. Zool. Zh. 16.

BAUER, H., 1957. Chromosomenstruktur und -funktion. Jahrbuch Max-Planck-Ges. (1957): 23–39.

BAYREUTHER, K., 1952. Extrachromosomale feulgenpositive Körper (Nukleinkörper) in der Oogenese der Tipuliden. Naturwissenschaften 39: 71.

BEERMANN, S., 1966. A quantitative study of chromatin diminution in embryonic mitoses of Cyclops furcifer. Genetics 54: 567–576.

Beermann, W., 1952. Chromomerenkonstanz und spezifische Modifikationen der Chromosomenstruktur in der Entwicklung und Organdifferenzierung von *Chironomus tentans*. Chromosoma 5: 139–198.

———, 1961. Ein Balbianiring als Locus einer Speicheldrüsen-Mutation. Chromosoma 12: 1–25.

———, 1964. Control of differentiation at the chromosomal level. J. Exp. Zool. 157: 49–62.

Beermann, W., and G. F. Bahr, 1954. The submicroscopic structure of the Balbiani-ring. Exp. Cell Res. 6: 195–201.

Breuer, M. E., and C. Pavan, 1955. Behavior of polytene chromosomes of *Rhynchosciara angelae* at different stages of larval development. Chromosoma 7: 371–386.

Bridges, C. B., 1935. Salivary chromosome maps. J. Hered. 26: 60–64.

Bridges, C. B., and K. S. Brehme, 1944. The mutants of *Drosophila melanogaster*. Carnegie Inst. Washington Publ. No. 552.

Callan, H. G., 1963. The nature of lampbrush chromosomes. Int. Rev. Cytol. 15: 1–34.

———, 1966. Chromosomes and nucleoli of the axolotl, *Ambystoma mexicanum*. J. Cell. Sci. 1: 85–108.

Callan, H. G., and H. C. McGregor, 1958. Action of deoxyribonuclease on lampbrush chromosomes. Nature 181: 1479–1481.

Dorn, G. L., and A. B. Burdick, 1962. On the recombination structure and complementation relationships in the *m-dy* complex of *Drosophila melanogaster*. Genetics 47: 503–518.

Edström, J. E., and W. Beermann, 1962. The base composition of nucleic acids in chromosomes, puffs, nucleoli, and cytoplasm of *Chironomus* salivary gland cells. J. Cell Biol. 14: 371–380.

Gall, J. G., 1963. Kinetics of deoxyribonuclease action on chromosomes, Nature 198: 36–38.

Gall, J. G., and H. G. Callan, 1962. ^{3}H-uridine incorporation in lampbrush chromosomes. Proc. Nat. Acad. Sci. U.S. 48: 562–570.

Gersh, E. S., 1965. A new locus in the white-notch region of the *Drosophila melanogaster* X chromosome. Genetics 51: 477–480.

Giardina, A., 1901. Origine d'ell'oocite e delle cellule nutrici nel *Dytiscus*. Int. Monatsschr. Anat. Physiol. 18: 1–68.

Goldschmidt, R., 1954. Different philosophies of genetics. Proc. IX Int. Congr. Genet., Caryologia 4 Suppl.: 83–99.

Hess, O., 1965a. Struktur-Differenzierungen im Y-Chromosom von *Drosophila hydei* und ihre Beziehungen zu Gen-Aktivitäten. III. Sequenz und Lokalisation der Schleifen-Bildungsorte. Chromosoma 16: 222–248.

———, 1965b. Struktur-Differenzierungen im Y-Chromosom von *Drosophila hydei* und ihre Beziehungen zu Gen-Aktivitäten. I. Mutanten der Funktionsstrukturen. Verhandl. Deutsch. Zool. Ges., Zool. Anz. Suppl. 28: 156–163.

Hess, O., and G. F. Meyer, 1963. Chromosomal differentiation of the lampbrush type formed by the Y chromosome in *Drosophila hydei* and *Drosophila neohydei*. J. Cell Biol. **16**: 527–540.

Izawa, M., V. G. Allfrey, and A. E. Mirsky, 1963. The relationship between RNA synthesis and loop structure in lampbrush chromosomes. Proc. Nat. Acad. Sci. U.S. **49**: 544–550.

Keyl, H. G., 1965. A demonstrable local and geometric increase in the chromosomal DNA of *Chironomus*. Experientia **21**: 191–193.

Keyl, H. G., and C. Pelling, 1963. Differentielle DNS-Replikation in den Speicheldrüsenchromosomen von *Chironomus thummi*. Chromosoma **14**: 347–359.

Laufer, H., and Y. Nakase, 1965. Salivary gland secretion and its relation to chromosomal puffing in the dipteran, *Chironomus thummi*. Proc. Nat. Acad. Sci. U.S. **53**: 511–516.

Lefevre, G., Jr., and M. D. Wilkins, 1964. The salivary chromosome position of the white locus. Genetics **50**: 264.

———, 1966. Cytogenetic studies on the white locus in *Drosophila melanogaster*. Genetics **53**: 175–187.

Lewis, E. B., 1963. Genes and developmental pathways. Amer. Zool. **3**: 33–56.

Mechelke, F., 1961. Das Wandern des Aktivitätsmaximums in BR_4-Locus von *Acricotopus lucidus* als Modell für die Wirkungsweise eines komplexen Locus. Naturwiss. **48**: 29.

Muller, H. J., and E. Altenburg, 1919. The rate of change of hereditary factors in *Drosophila*. Proc. Soc. Exp. Biol. Med. **17**: 10–14.

Pavan, C., and M. E. Breuer, 1952. Polytene chromosomes in different tissues of *Rhyncosciara*. J. Hered. **43**: 151–157.

Pelling, C., 1959. Chromosomal synthesis of ribonucleic acid as shown by the incorporation of uridine labeled with tritium. Nature **184**: 655–656.

———, 1964. Ribonukleinsäure-Synthese der Riesenchromosomen. Autoradiographische Untersuchungen an *Chironomus tentans*. Chromosoma **15**: 71–122.

Plaut, W., 1963. On the replicative organization of DNA in the polytene chromosomes of *Drosophila melanogaster*. J. Mol. Biol. **7**: 632–635.

Ris, H., and H. Crouse, 1945. Structure of the salivary gland chromosomes of Diptera. Proc. Nat. Acad. Sci. U.S. **31**: 321–327.

Roux, W., 1883. *Über die Bedeutung der Kernteilungsfiguren*. Engelmann, Leipzig.

Rudkin, G. T., 1961. Cytochemistry in the ultraviolet. Microchem. J., Symp. Ser. **1**: 261–276.

Rudkin, G. T., and S. L. Corlette, 1957. Disproportionate synthesis of DNA in a polytene chromosome region. Proc. Nat. Acad. Sci. U.S. **43**: 964–968.

Rudkin, G. T., and P. S. Woods, 1959. Incorporation of H³-cytidine and H³-thymidine into giant chromosomes of *Drosophila* during puff formation. Proc. Nat. Acad. Sci. U.S. **45**: 997–1003.

Steffensen, D. M., 1963. Localization of deoxyribonucleic acid exclusively in the bands of *Drosophila* salivary chromosomes. *Genetics Today*, vol. I,

p. 109. Edited by S. J. Geerts. Proc. XI Int. Congr. Genet., The Hague, The Netherlands. Pergamon Press, New York.

SWIFT, H., 1962. Nucleic acids and cell morphology in dipteran salivary glands. *The Molecular Control of Cellular Activity,* pp. 73–126. Edited by J. M. Allen. McGraw-Hill, New York.

WELSHONS, W. J., AND E. S. VON HALLE, 1962. Pseudoallelism at the Notch locus of *Drosophila.* Genetics 47: 743–759.

WOLSTENHOLME, D. R., 1965. The distribution of DNA and RNA in salivary gland chromosomes of *Chironomus tetans* as revealed by fluorescence microscopy. Chromosoma 17: 219–229.

12

Control of Gene Activity during the Early Development of *Xenopus laevis*

J. B. Gurdon

The identification of a genetic locus is largely dependent upon the existence of variations, such as mutations, in the expression of that locus. In the same way, the control of gene activity is best studied under conditions in which the extent of that activity varies. Just such conditions are provided by the early developmental stages of many plants and animals. During the first few days of embryogenesis, the great majority of adult cell types differentiate from undetermined embryonic cells, and, as we shall see, different classes of genes show greater changes in activity at this time than can be observed in other stages of life.

Particular attention is devoted in this chapter to a species of frog (*Xenopus laevis*) which has proved especially favorable for the study of gene activity during development. The eggs and embryos of Amphibia are large and easily subjected to surgical manipulations. They are also suitable for work on nucleic acids since many embryos at the same developmental stage can be obtained, radioactivity can be introduced at any desired stage, and endogenous nuclease activity in homogenized material is low. Lastly, the time between fertilization and puberty in this species of frog is brief enough, in relation to our own working lifetime, that the species is reasonably tractable for some kinds of genetic experiments.

Methods of Determining Rates of Gene Activity in Early Development

Of the methods available for detecting gene activity, rather few are suitable for investigating changes in the *rate* of gene activity. As far as is known, proteins are always the indirect products of genes in multicellular organisms, and variations in the activity and abundance of an enzyme or protein may therefore result from control at a number of steps in the information transfer process other than at the level of gene transcription. Thus studies on the appearance of proteins during de-

203

velopment (Herrmann and Tootle 1964), as well as work on the developmental effects of mutations which are usually recognized by their effect on protein structure (Hadorn 1955), do not provide direct information on the rate of gene activity.

Methods used so far to give information on the rate of gene activity include cytological analysis of chromosomes and studies on nucleic acid synthesis. The application of cytological studies to the present problem is limited to cells with easily visible interphase chromosomes, such as lampbrush and polytene chromosomes. For the following reasons the direct measurement of nucleic acid synthesis is at present the most satisfactory method of determining the rates of gene activity during early development: (1) DNA and RNA are both direct gene products. In higher organisms they are probably the only direct gene products. (2) The amounts of these nucleic acids can be measured independently of their activity. (3) These molecules can be quantitatively extracted from embryos whether they are free or integrated into some cell structure. (4) It is possible to distinguish newly synthesized nucleic acids from the total content of nucleic acids accumulated as a result of their stability.

The main disadvantage of this means of measuring gene activity is that one may be dealing with a heterogeneous population of molecules within each class of nucleic acid. Since this difficulty applies especially to messenger RNA (mRNA) only soluble RNA (sRNA), ribosomal RNA (rRNA), and DNA are discussed here. The greater part of this chapter is devoted to the synthesis of nucleic acids *in vivo,* although nucleic acid synthesis can also be studied *in vitro,* as is mentioned in the discussion.

Rates of Nucleic Acid Synthesis During the Early Development of *X. laevis*

Before attempting to identify factors which may control the rates of nucleic acid synthesis, we must first know what the rates of synthesis are for sRNA, rRNA, and DNA. Three kinds of measurements are useful: the total content of each class of nucleic acid present in an egg or embryo; the amount of each class of nucleic acid that has accumulated since the beginning of development; the amount of each class of nucleic acid synthesized in a short period of time at each stage in development.

Total content

A measure of the total content of a class of nucleic acid is provided by its optical density or ultraviolet absorption at 260 mμ. The values obtained for embryos will include molecules present in the egg before fertilization (inherited from oogenesis or egg maturation), as well as any molecules which have been synthesized but not broken down since fertilization. The content of rRNA and sRNA present in mature unfertilized *Xenopus* eggs has been measured by Brown and Littna (1964a) and Brown (1965). Each unfertilized egg has a wet weight of about 1 mg and contains about 4 µg of RNA, of which 40 mµg are free sRNA and nearly all the rest is rRNA. Dawid (1965) has found about 3 mµg of high molecular weight DNA in each unfertilized egg along with a similar amount of low molecular weight diphenylamine-reacting material. The synthesis of nucleic acids during development is better measured by the incorporation of labeled substances than by increases in the total content of nucleic acids.

Accumulated content

The amount of nucleic acid which has been synthesized, but not broken down, since the beginning of development will be called the accumulated content. The total content therefore includes both the accumulated content and the content of nucleic acids in the unfertilized egg. The accumulated content can be measured in *Xenopus* embryos by injection of inorganic ^{32}P-phosphate into a female frog a few hours before she starts to lay eggs (Kutsky 1950). The eggs that are laid then contain a pool of acid-soluble ^{32}P-phosphate, which, as shown by Brown and Littna (1964a), does not become substantially depleted until after the heartbeat stage (see also Fig. 12.2). The effect of the persistence of this ^{32}PO$_4$-labeled pool is that, up to the heartbeat stage, the accumulated ^{32}P-labeled nucleic acids will include stable molecules synthesized early in development as well as both stable *and unstable* molecules synthesized just before the stage under analysis. Using sucrose-gradient distributions of RNA labeled by this method, Brown and Littna (1964a) and Brown (1964) have noted that sRNA and rRNA are not synthesized at a detectable rate until the end of cleavage and that, during the first few days of development, rRNA accumulates in a way quite different from that of sRNA and DNA. Recently Brown (1965) estimated the actual rates of accumulation of sRNA and rRNA by determining the specific activity of the alpha-phosphates of the ^{32}P-nucleotides (the only one of the three nucleotide phosphates to be incorporated into nucleic acids). Knowing the specific activity of the alpha-phosphates of the RNA precursor nucleotides and the amount of radioactivity contained in a class of RNA, he was able to calculate the amount of that class of RNA which had accumulated between the beginning of development and the stage at which embryos were collected

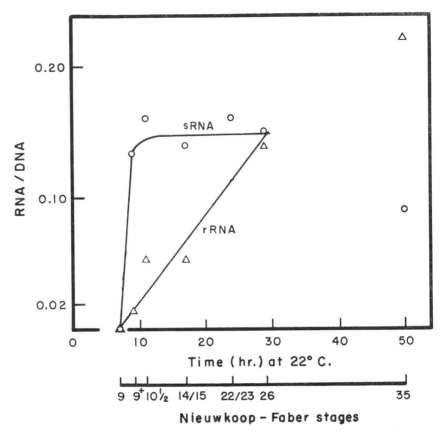

Fig. 12.1.—The accumulated content of ^{32}P-labeled sRNA and rRNA expressed as a proportion of DNA content at different developmental stages. Reprinted from Brown (1965) by kind permission of the author.

for analysis. The sRNA could be separated from other RNA types by virtue of its retardation in a Sephadex G 100 column. The amounts of rRNA and DNA-like RNA present in the first peak of the Sephadex elution could be estimated from the average base composition of the peak, since these two classes of RNA have very different average contents of cytidylic acid plus guanylic acid. Using this kind of analysis, Brown (1965) concluded that, between early gastrulation and the tailbud stage, the rate of accumulation of sRNA is similar to that of DNA, as shown by Grant (1960) and Dawid (1965), but is different from that of rRNA (Fig. 12.1).

The rate of accumulation of a class of molecules can provide a measure of their rate of synthesis during a particular period in development only if the molecules are stable. If they are broken down or undergo turnover, then their rate of accumulation will reflect the balance between synthesis and turnover. As an attempt to determine the rate of RNA synthesis rather than of accumulation, the following short-term labeling experiments have been carried out.

New synthesis

For the measurement of a rate of synthesis over a short period of time, it is necessary to use a labeled substance which will enter the nucleic acid precursor pool rapidly and in sufficient amounts to be incorporated efficiently within one to two hours. During such short periods of time any breakdown of sRNA, rRNA, or DNA that may take place is likely to be small enough to be disregarded. The only substance known to penetrate intact *Xenopus* embryos effectively in one- to two-hour periods is CO_2 (Cohen 1954). CO_2 has the disadvantage, like phosphate, of being a very unspecific precursor for nucleic acids, and, therefore, much of its radioactivity will enter substances other than nucleic acids. Nucleosides do not penetrate *Xenopus* embryos satisfactorily by diffusion (Loeffler and Johnston 1964), but rapid and efficient incorporation of ^{3}H-nucleosides has been obtained when they have been injected into eggs and embryos (Gurdon and Graham, unpublished). Owing to the high specific activity of commercially available ^{3}H-nucleosides and to the fact that they are incorporated primarily into nucleic acids, we have been able to obtain in one hour sufficient labeling of the RNA and DNA for subsequent analysis of the nucleic acids of only ten embryos.

In the experiments to be described two types of nucleic acid precursors have been used. [32]PO_4 enters the egg before fertilization, and its measurement serves a similar function to the measurement of optical density; that is, in such experiments it shows, independently of ^{3}H-labeling, that the RNA and DNA have not been substantially lost or degraded. Optical density measurements are too low for detection except in experiments involving rRNA. ^{3}H-uridine has been used for continuous labeling over periods as long as eight hours. Although acid-soluble ^{3}H substances derived from ^{3}H-uridine disappear much more quickly than does the acid-soluble ^{32}P-pool (Fig. 12.2), they nevertheless persist for several hours, even in late stages. ^{3}H-guanosine, on the other hand, appears to enter a smaller and more rapidly turning over pool than does ^{3}H-uridine, since acid-soluble ^{3}H compounds decrease very quickly after ^{3}H-guanosine injection (Fig. 12.2).

In short-term labeling experiments it is impracticable to calculate the amount of synthesis from the specific activity of the nucleic acid

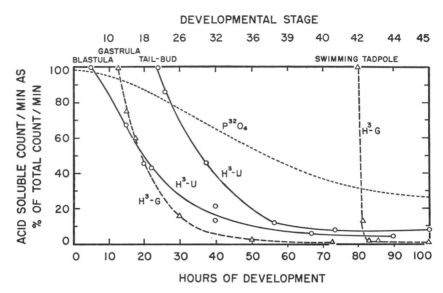

Fig. 12.2.—Rates of disappearance of radioactive substances from acid-soluble pools after introduction of different labeled precursors. $^{32}PO_4$ was injected into the mother frog a few hours before egg deposition; ^{3}H-uridine (H^3-U) and ^{3}H-guanosine (H^3-G) were injected into embryos at different stages. For each of the values given, two 0.1 ml aliquots were taken from the aqueous supernatant fluid after phenol extraction. One aliquot was precipitated with 5 per cent trichloroacetic acid and caught on a filter to show acid-insoluble counts per min; the other was adsorbed directly onto a filter to give total counts per min. The excess of the total counts over the acid-insoluble counts was expressed as a percentage of the total counts and plotted as acid-soluble counts per min. The curve for $^{32}PO_4$ is the average of many different experiments and resembles the comparable curve published by Brown and Littna (1964*a*).

precursors, because any substance which gives *efficient* short-term labeling will necessarily be present in the precursor pool at rapidly changing concentrations, for which an average value would be difficult to determine. Gurdon and Brown have attempted to overcome this difficulty by using the *same* procedure for the extraction, purification, and separation of sRNA, rRNA, and DNA so that the synthesis of DNA and of the different classes of RNA may be directly compared. Embryos are homogenized at an alkaline *p*H in the presence of sodium dodecyl sulfate (sds), and as a result, DNA as well as RNA enters the aqueous phase in the subsequent phenol extraction. The solution of nucleic acids is then adsorbed onto a methylated serum albumin kieselguhr (MAK) column and eluted by a salt gradient (Mandell and Hershey 1960). Nucleic acids are eluted in the following order: sRNA at about 0.4 M NaCl, DNA at about 0.6 M, and rRNA at about 0.7 M. The radioactivity counts, marked on the ordinate, under each main peak of the MAK chromatogram are then summed, and the values obtained are considered to represent the relative amount of synthesis of each class of nucleic acid during the period of labeling. Fractionation by an MAK column has several special advantages for our material: DNA, sRNA and rRNA elute from the column in peaks, whereas mRNA, which is also present, elutes in a dispersed way throughout the gradient and therefore does not obscure the main peaks; rRNA of different molecular weights is all eluted in the same region of the gradient, facilitating an estimation of its quantity; an MAK column works well, if not best, with small amounts of material.

Since this procedure has not been regularly used for estimating rates of synthesis, some justification of its application is required. Three sources of error are likely to be introduced by this procedure.

(1) DNA, sRNA, and rRNA might be unequally affected by loss during extraction and purification or by nonrecovery from an MAK column. The efficiency of extraction of RNA and DNA has been tested in embryos injected with ^{3}H-guanosine, about 10 per cent of which was incorporated into DNA and the rest into RNA. Aliquots were taken at each stage of the procedure and the acid-insoluble radioactivity counted. Table 12.1*A* shows that no loss of the ^{3}H radioactivity occurred but that the ^{32}P radioactivity is much reduced after the phenol extraction, as would be expected since it is incorporated into many substances other than nucleic acids. It can be seen from Table 12.1*B* that, when RNA and DNA are eluted from an MAK column, the total acid-insoluble radioactivity recovered from the column is close to the amount thought to have been added. These experiments show that no substantial loss of DNA or RNA generally takes place during the extraction, purification, and separation procedures.

(2) The three main peaks on the MAK profile might not provide a quantitative estimate of the amounts of sRNA, DNA, and rRNA in the preparation. The identity of the three main peaks in MAK chromatograms has been extensively documented in the literature (e.g., Otaka, Mitsui, and Osawa 1962). Figure 12.3*A* shows the position of the three main peaks in MAK profiles of our material. Two of the three main peaks are removed by ribonuclease treatment (Fig. 12.3*B*), confirming the identity of the DNA peak in the profile. Precursor rRNA sediments faster in a sucrose gradient than 28S rRNA, and Yoshikawa, Fukuda, and Kawade (1964) have identified the two peaks that sediment faster than 28S rRNA in a sucrose density gradient with

Table 12.1

Loss of RNA and DNA during extraction and purification and during separation by MAK chromatography. Experiment *A*: 12 stage-15 neurulae obtained from $^{32}PO_4$-labeled eggs were injected with ^{3}H-guanosine and frozen for processing after 8 hours at 24° C. Experiment *B*: Between 12 and 22 embryos were used for each experiment which was terminated 2–8 hours after label injection. The percentage recovery from MAK columns is variable but is rather consistent for all parts of the same experiment, perhaps because they were all carried out on the same set of columns. The figures given here are from ^{3}H-uridine injection experiments, some of which are shown in Figure 12.6. The expected counts in the whole sample were estimated from the counts in the 0.1-ml aliquot which was taken from the 3-ml to 4-ml total of aqueous supernatant fluid remaining after phenol extraction. This is therefore an imprecise measurement, thus accounting for the variation, as well as for the apparent cases of gain, seen in the last column of the table.

A. Loss during extraction and purification

Aliquot taken	Acid-insoluble counts/min as % of posthomogenization value	
	^{3}H	^{32}P
After homogenization in 2 ml	100.0	100.0
After sodium dodecyl sulfate treatment	100.1	104.5
After second phenol extraction	102.8	41.4

B. Loss during MAK chromatography

Developmental stage reached	Acid-insoluble ^{3}H counts/min in 0.1 ml	Recovered counts/min / Expected counts/min
9	1016	111%
11	1129	104%
13	1911	81%
18	1338	97%
20	2755	94%
26	1485	101%
32	3860	90%
37	3812	95%
39	5805	102%
43	5398	121%

the two peaks which elute at the highest salt molarity on an MAK column. Brown and Gurdon (1964) have shown that both these heavy RNA peaks are absent in *Xenopus* embryos unable to synthesize rRNA and are therefore composed mainly of precursor rRNA. Hence, it has been assumed in the experiments described here that these "high mo-

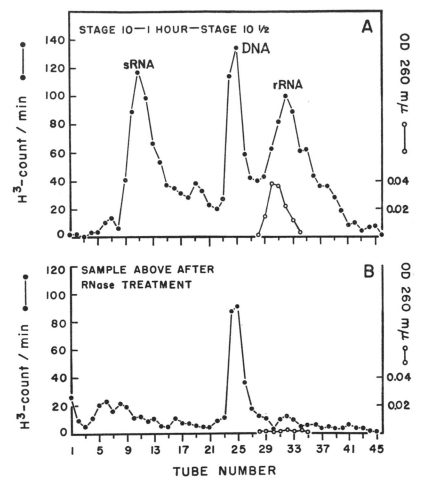

Fig. 12.3.—MAK profiles of ^{3}H-labeled RNA and DNA synthesized during 1 hour at 24° C after ^{3}H-guanosine injection at stage 10 (early gastrula). After extraction of 20 embryos as described in the text, the sample was divided into two equal parts, of which one (*A*) was applied directly to the column and the other (*B*) was first treated with 5 µg/ml ribonuclease for 10 minutes at 24° C. Most of the radioactive material present between tubes 5 and 9 in *B* is probably incompletely digested RNA since it is absent from the same region in *A*.

In this and all following experiments, about 40 mµl of ^{3}H-nucleosides at 4–8 mc/ml were injected. The MAK columns were eluted with a 0.2–0.9 M or 0.2–1.0 M gradient of NaCl, buffered to *p*H 7.2 with 0.05 M tris (hydroxymethyl) amino methane.

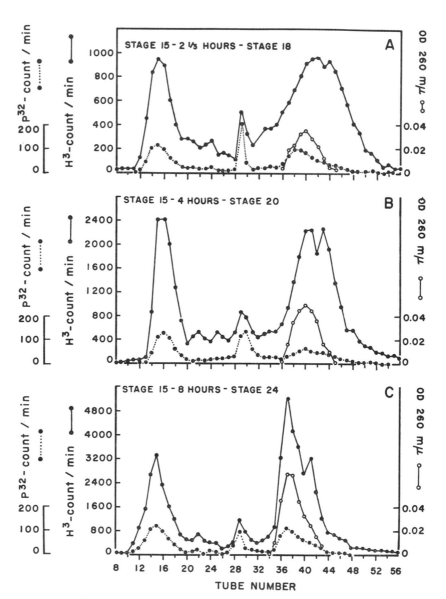

Fig. 12.4.—MAK profiles of RNA and DNA extracted from 17 embryos in each experiment. Embryos from ³²P-labeled eggs were injected with ³H-uridine at stage 15 and incubated at 24° C for the lengths of time indicated.

larity" peaks, seen in Figure 12.4*A* as ³H peaks at tubes 42 and 44 (cf. the OD peak of mature rRNA at tube 40), contain mainly precursor rRNA. This assumption is further justified by the fact that the peaks eluting at high salt concentrations gradually disappear with increasing length of labeling period (Fig. 12.4*A*, *B*, and *C*). Such a disappearance would be expected if the RNA the peaks contain matures into rRNA, which then obscures the smaller amount of newly synthesized rRNA precursor. RNA which elutes diffusely throughout the MAK gradient, and which might be mRNA, can be clearly seen at late cleavage stages before appreciable sRNA and rRNA synthesis has commenced (Fig 12.5*D*). It is believed that a significant amount of this RNA is present in all of the MAK profiles of nucleic acids labeled for short periods of time; thus two small RNA peaks are consistently seen in the MAK profiles between sRNA and DNA regions (Figs. 12.4, 12.6, 12.7). When the relative amounts of labeled sRNA, DNA, and rRNA are estimated from these MAK profiles, it is assumed that the peaks are superimposed upon a base of heterogeneous RNA. When a line has been drawn between the points where each main peak starts to spread at its base, the total radioactivity within each "true" peak may be summed.

(3) The relative sizes and rates of labeling of the precursor pools for sRNA, DNA, and rRNA might not be the same at different stages of development. There is no evidence that the sRNA and rRNA precursor pools are separate, and the contents of the DNA precursor pool are related to those of the RNA precursor pool at least insofar as the former are chemically derived from the latter. If the sRNA, DNA, and rRNA precursor pools were separate and their specific activities were to change independently following label injection, then the relative amounts of these kinds of molecules synthesized would vary for different periods of time after label injection. In fact, we have found that at one developmental stage the relative amounts of sRNA, DNA, and rRNA are the same at two, four, and eight hours after ³H-uridine injection (Table 12.2).

The results with ³H-guanosine for one-hour labeling periods during cleavage are shown in Figure 12.5. DNA synthesis can be clearly seen (tube 28) at all stages in cleavage. Synthesis of sRNA cannot be clearly seen until stage 9 (Fig. 12.5*D*) and does not occur at a substantial rate until stage 10 (Fig. 12.3*A*). Very little if any rRNA synthesis has taken place by stage 9½, but its synthesis has clearly commenced by stage 10½ (Fig. 12.3*A*). Some heterogeneous RNA which elutes throughout the gradient can be seen in Figure 12.5 at all stages of cleavage. This RNA, which probably includes mRNA, increases very greatly just before gas-

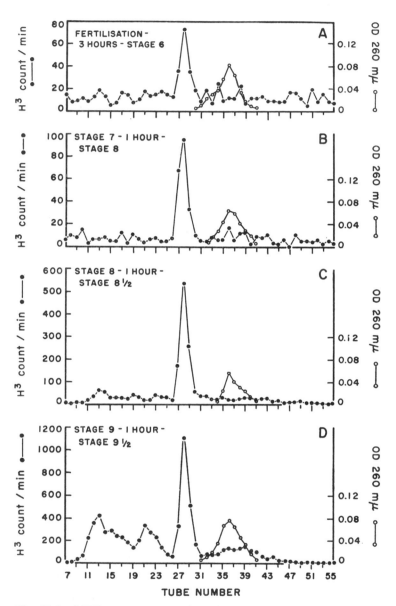

Fig. 12.5.—MAK profiles of RNA and DNA labeled by injection of
³H-guanosine into ³²P-labeled eggs at the cleavage stages indicated.
For each experiment 25 embryos, reared at 24° C, were used.

Table 12.2

[3]H-incorporation into sRNA, DNA, and rRNA following the injection of ^{3}H-uridine into embryos at different stages of development. The counts per minute values were calculated as the sums of the radioactivity under each main peak in the MAK profiles as described in the text and as shown in Figure 12.6. Between 12 and 22 embryos were used for each experiment. The developmental stages are those of Nieuwkoop and Faber (1956).

Duration of labeling period in hours	Developmental stages passed during labeling	DNA counts/min per embryo	sRNA counts/min / DNA counts/min	rRNA counts/min / DNA counts/min
2	8–9	71	3.6	1.1
4 (Fig. 12.6*A*)	8–11	153	3.1	1.1
2	10–11½	97	5.1	1.4
8	10–19	158	6.5	1.9
2	15–18	30	7.4	13.5
4 (Fig. 12.6*B*)	15–20	57	8.35	12.95
8	15–24	91	8.3	15.0
2	24–26	68	5.8	24.1
4 (Fig. 12.6*D*)	34–37	100	2.44	33.3
8	34–39	176	3.1	31.2
4 (Fig. 12.6*E*)	42–43	172	2.1	34.0

trulation (Fig. 12.5*D*) and constitutes the main part of total RNA synthesis at stage 9. Bachvarova and his co-workers (1966) have confirmed and to some degree extended these results.

The relative rates of synthesis of sRNA, DNA, and rRNA from gastrulation onward have been investigated with ^{3}H-uridine and ^{3}H-guanosine. The results with ^{3}H-uridine for four-hour labeling periods from late cleavage to advanced tadpole stages are shown in Figure 12.6. When gastrulation starts at stage 10, sRNA is being synthesized at a rapid rate. During gastrulation and neurulation (stages 10-20), ^{3}H incorporation is several times greater into sRNA than into DNA. During the tail-bud and tadpole stages, the incorporation into sRNA decreases compared to that into DNA. Synthesis of rRNA shows a different pattern; it takes place slowly during gastrulation (Fig. 12.6*A*), but its rate increases enormously compared to DNA synthesis during neurula and

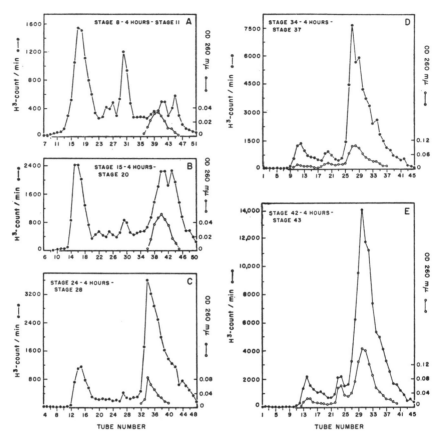

Fig. 12.6.—MAK profiles of RNA and DNA labeled by injection of ³H-uridine. In each experiment embryos were reared at 24° C, and the following numbers of embryos were used: *A,* 22 late-cleavage embryos; *B,* 18 neurulae; *C,* 12 tail-buds; *D,* 12 hatching tadpoles; *E,* 12 advanced swimming tadpoles.

tail-bud stages (Fig. 12.6*B* and *C*). After the tadpole has hatched (Fig. 12.6*D* and *E*), the rates of sRNA and rRNA synthesis maintain a rather constant relationship to that of DNA. These conclusions have been confirmed for one- and four-hour periods with ³H-guanosine labeling (Figs. 12.3*A* and 12.7*A, B,* and *C*). In the ³H-guanosine experiments, ³H incorporation into DNA relative to that into sRNA and rRNA is greater than in the ³H-uridine experiments, but the same general patterns of synthesis are observed. Incorporation into sRNA is very high compared to that into DNA during gastrulation, after which it decreases until late tadpole stages. Synthesis of rRNA increases fast be-

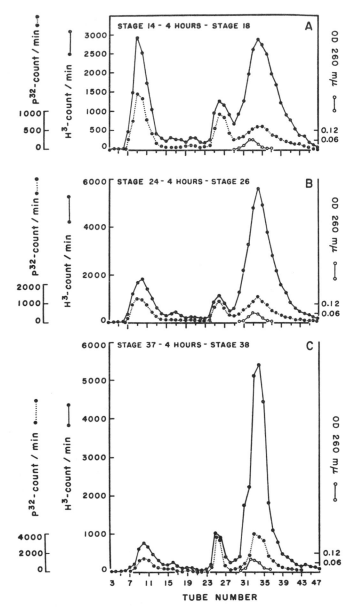

Fig. 12.7.—MAK profiles of RNA and DNA after ³H-guanosine injection into ³²P-labeled embryos: *A,* 25 neurulae; *B,* 25 tail-buds; *C,* 25 hatching tadpoles.

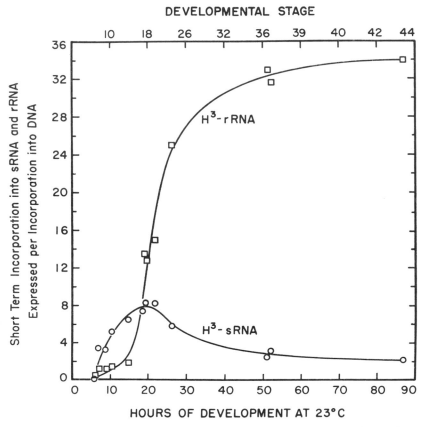

Fig. 12.8.—Summary of rates of ³H-incorporation into rRNA and sRNA expressed as a proportion of ³H-incorporation into DNA in the same embryos. The points in the graph represent the sum of the radioactivity under each main peak of MAK profiles, and all were obtained from short-term ³H-uridine experiments of the kind listed in Table 12.2 and shown in Figure 12.6.

tween neurula and tail-bud stages (Fig. 12.7*A* and *B*) and has reached a very high level by hatching time (Fig. 12.7*C*).

Conclusions on rates of synthesis

The amount of radioactivity incorporated into sRNA, DNA, and rRNA at different developmental stages is listed in Table 12.2. The results are presented in two ways, by comparisons of sRNA and rRNA synthesis (1) to DNA synthesis and (2) to DNA content. Incorporation into RNA is compared with incorporation into DNA in Figure 12.8, from which we may conclude that (1) sRNA synthesis first starts during

Table 12.3

Changes in the amount of stable sRNA and DNA under chase conditions after injection of ³H-guanosine. Thirty-nine embryos were injected with ³H-guanosine at stage 12 and were collected for freezing at 2, 32, and 55 hours later. The second line of the table is from another series of ³H-guanosine experiments and shows that the ratio of new sRNA to DNA is still high at stage 18, after which the amount of acid-soluble ³H-guanosine becomes substantially reduced (Fig. 12.2).

Stage of injection	Duration of labeling (hrs at 24° C)	Stage at analysis	Total sRNA counts/min	Total DNA counts/min	sRNA counts/min ——————— DNA counts/min
12	2	14	1980	630	3.2
14	4	18	9850	1200	4.1
12	32	36	11400	6300	1.8
12	55	41	9800	7100	1.4

late cleavage and takes place at an increasing rate compared to DNA synthesis until the end of neurulation; its rate of synthesis then declines and reaches a constant rate relative to DNA by hatching. And (2) rRNA synthesis proceeds slowly during gastrulation, increases very rapidly during neurula stages, and gradually reaches a nearly constant rate relative to DNA after the tadpole hatches.

The results obtained after the injection of ³H-uridine have been confirmed by the use of ³H-guanosine. However, this method is intended to show only the differences in *relative* incorporation at different developmental stages; it does not necessarily show the true ratios among sRNA, DNA, and rRNA synthesis at any one stage of development.

The accumulation of ³²P-labeled sRNA and rRNA has been studied by Brown (1965), and the conclusion has been reached that the accumulation of sRNA bears a constant relationship to that of DNA between the gastrula and tail-bud stages. This conclusion is not necessarily inconsistent with the results of the short-term labeling experiments, since the rate of synthesis may be greater than that of accumulation if turnover takes place. Evidence that sRNA may undergo turnover during early development is suggested by experiments with ³H-guanosine which creates partial chase conditions owing to its rapid disappearance from the acid-soluble pool (Table 12.3). Both short-term and cumulative experiments are qualitatively in agreement with respect to rRNA synthesis. The main discrepancy concerns the relative amounts of sRNA and DNA synthesis. The values from nucleoside injection experiments would be artificially low for DNA if the labeled nucleosides were to enter the DNA precursor pool less efficiently than they do the

RNA precursor pool. However, judged from optical density measurements (see Fig. 12.6E), the values obtained from ^{32}P accumulation experiments are probably too low for sRNA.

Another way of presenting the results of short-term labeling experiments is to relate incorporation into RNA and DNA to DNA content, a procedure which therefore shows developmental changes in the rate of certain kinds of gene activity. Measurements of total DNA in embryos (Dawid 1965) show that the rate of DNA accumulation in *Xenopus* decreases as development progresses. This trend is intimated from the short-term labeling experiments by a comparison of the actual radioactivity incorporated in a given time to the amount of DNA present (Fig. 12.9). The rate of gene activity with respect to DNA and sRNA synthesis evidently decreases progressively from the end of cleavage, whereas this is not true of rRNA synthesis.

In conclusion, the details of the relative rates of synthesis of sRNA, DNA, and rRNA are not yet fully understood. However, all relevant experiments agree that in *X. laevis* sRNA synthesis commences at stages 8–9 and then accelerates rapidly; that the rate of rRNA synthesis accelerates later than that of sRNA synthesis; and that sRNA and DNA are synthesized at a decreasing rate per DNA content after the end of cleavage but that this is not true of rRNA.

Explanations of Changing Rates of Synthesis

The pronounced changes in the relative rates of RNA and DNA synthesis described above can be considered to demonstrate changes in the rate of gene activity only if other explanations for these results are first excluded. The simple explanations for these changing rates of synthesis fall into the following three general categories: (1) Genes of any one kind constitute a changing proportion of the whole genome by loss or gain during development, but the activity of each gene remains the same. (2) Embryonic cells are either fully active or wholly inactive with respect to sRNA, rRNA, or DNA synthesis, and changes in the average rates of synthesis in a whole embryo reflect only the proportion of cells which are active or inactive. (3) Genes are intermittently active in *all* cells of an embryo, and changes in the average rate of synthesis in a whole embryo reflect changes in the frequency with which genes are transcribed.

Changes in the composition of the genome

Loss or permanent inactivation of genes.—The extraordinary capacity of plants to achieve complete regeneration from single somatic cells (Braun 1959; Sinnott 1960) demonstrates that essential genes are not

DEVELOPMENTAL STAGE

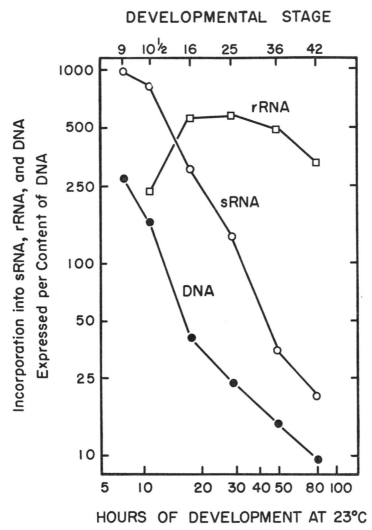

Fig. 12.9.—The relative rates of rRNA, sRNA, and DNA synthesis expressed in terms of the DNA content of embryos at different stages. The values for radioactivity were obtained from ³H-uridine injection experiments. The actual number of ³H counts per min incorporated at each stage per hour per embryo was divided by the number of mµg of DNA present in each embryo at the same stage. The values for DNA content are taken from Dawid (1965). Both abscissa and ordinate are plotted on log scales, giving a nearly straight line for DNA. The values for incorporation are likely to be inaccurate since no account has been taken of possible changes in the size or rate of labeling of the precursor pools during development or of variation in the amount of label injected.

lost in the course of normal plant cell differentiation. In animal development, however, there are clear cytological examples of the loss of chromosomes both by elimination, especially in certain insect families (described in White 1954), and by diminution followed by elimination in *Ascaris* (Boveri 1899). Probably the most direct evidence concerning genetic losses in differentiating animal cells is provided by nuclear transplantation experiments in Amphibia. In all such experiments it is found that nuclei transplanted from differentiating cells support normal development less often than do nuclei from embryonic cells. There are many possible explanations for this effect (Gurdon 1963), and the experiments have not yet shown that genes are actually lost in the course of normal cell differentiation. On the contrary, nuclear transfer experiments have given definite evidence that in many cases the nuclei of differentiating cells can support normal development and therefore have not lost any essential genes. Table 12.4 summarizes the extent to which nuclei transplanted from differentiating cells have been shown to retain the capacity to support the normal differentiation of other cell types. Gurdon and Uehlinger (1966) have shown that differentiated cells of *Xenopus* sometimes contain nuclei genetically equivalent to germ-cells, since a few nuclei of tadpole intestine cells transplanted into enucleated eggs have permitted development of these eggs into fertile male and female frogs. It seems evident that essential genes are not lost in the course of normal cell differentiation, though the possibility has not yet been excluded that a cell may contain many copies of certain genes and that the number of these might be reduced during development. However, reduction in the number of genes per genome could not possibly account for the total absence of sRNA and rRNA synthesis during most of cleavage.

Gain of parts of the genome.—It is conceivable that the proportion of certain genes in the genome could increase during embryogenesis. A few examples are known in which certain parts of the genome may increase during cell differentiation. In the polytene chromosomes of certain insects, localized regions of DNA synthesis have been identified (Pavan 1965). It seems likely that the multiple nucleoli in the germinal vesicle of amphibian oocytes may contain DNA predominantly transcribing rRNA (Miller 1964; Davidson, Allfrey, and Mirsky 1964). Although egg cytoplasm and other intranuclear cell components appear to contain small amounts of DNA (Kirk 1963; Rabinowitz *et al.* 1965), changes in the amount of non-nuclear DNA probably do not account for overall changes in rates of sRNA and rRNA synthesis. A direct test for increases in parts of the genome during embryogenesis could be provided by the specific "hybridizing" of a class of RNA with the DNA

The capacity of somatic cell nuclei to support normal cell differentiation after transplantation to enucleated unfertilized eggs

Species	Type of cell providing transplanted nucleus	Total number of nuclear transfers	Number of complete blastulae	% of complete blastulae attaining differentiation indicated		Reference
				Muscular response or tail-bud (muscle and nerve cells)	Normal swimming tadpole (all main cell-types)	
Pleurodeles Waltlii	Neurula endoderm	201	50	10%	2%	Picheral 1962
	Tail-bud endoderm	207	65	4.5%	3%	Picheral 1962
Ambystoma mexicanum	Neurula notochord	1021	434	4%	0.6%	Briggs, Signoret, & Humphrey 1964
Xenopus laevis	Intestinal epithelium of feeding tadpoles	726	48	35%	22%	Gurdon 1962
	Same; 1st & serial transfers	726	48	81%	37%	Gurdon 1962
	Tail-bud endoderm	152	53	60%	47%	Gurdon 1960
Bufo bufo	Eye primordium of neurula	76	13	15%	15%	Nikitina 1964
	Eye cup and lens primordium of tail-bud	57	10	20%	10%	Nikitina 1964
Rana arvalis	Eye cup and lens primordium of tail-bud	91	8	13%	13%	Nikitina 1964
Rana temporaria	Eye cup and lens primordium of tail bud	91	7	14%	14%	Nikitina 1964
Rana pipiens	Mid-neurula endoderm	130	16	19%	6%	Briggs & King 1957
	Tail-bud endoderm	130	9	22%	0%	Briggs & King 1957
	Swimming-tadpole germ cells	410	77	—	40%	Smith 1965
	Adenocarcinoma (intraocular, organ, or cell culture); 1st & serial transfers	?200	3	33%	33%	DiBerardino & King 1965

of embryos at different developmental stages. No one has performed such tests for different embryonic cell types, but McCarthy and Hoyer (1964) have found no detectable differences between the DNA from various adult mouse organs and that from whole mouse embryos in the capacity to compete with the specific attachment to DNA of DNA fragments isolated from mouse L-cells or, in other experiments, from mouse embryos. Lastly, an increase in certain parts of the genome during early development could not account for the predominantly *decreasing* rate of DNA and sRNA synthesis.

Cell heterogeneity

The experiments discussed so far have established that the rates at which gene products are synthesized during early *Xenopus* development change in a way that cannot be wholly accounted for by alterations in the composition of the genome. The evidence for these changing rates of synthesis rests entirely upon experiments with whole embryos. During embryogenesis the number of cells and diversity of cell types increase, and it is theoretically possible that an embryo might consist of a mixed population of cells each of which can synthesize sRNA and rRNA only at a maximal rate or not at all. It would then be possible to account for the observed gradual changes in sRNA or rRNA synthesis as alterations in the proportion of cells which are active in synthesis. If this explanation were true, the problem in the control of synthesis would be to determine what controls the proportion of active to inactive cells at each stage of development. This hypothesis can be excluded if it can be shown that every cell in an embryo synthesizes DNA and RNA intermittently if not continuously. In early *Xenopus* embryos the great majority of cells must synthesize DNA at frequent intervals, since ^{3}H-thymidine is incorporated into nearly all nuclei within 24 hours of its injection (Graham and Morgan 1966). All active cells require sRNA and rRNA, and the large size of these molecules makes it likely that they are synthesized in each cell and not transferred from one to another. More directly, nucleolus size provides a visible indication that rRNA is being synthesized in any given cell, both in *Xenopus* embryos (Gurdon and Brown 1965) and in other organisms (Perry 1962; Ritossa and Spiegelman 1965). In *Xenopus* the size of the nucleolus increases with the amount of rRNA synthesis, as has been shown by the rapid increase in nucleolar size and rRNA synthesis in epidermal cells of a regenerating tail (Gurdon, unpublished) as well as by the correlation between the size of the nucleolus (Barr and Esper 1963) and the amount of rRNA synthesis (Brown and Gurdon 1964) in 1-*nu* mutant embryos. A nucleolus is seen in nearly all interphase cells of post-blastula *Xenopus* embryos; furthermore, some cells, such as those in somites, have very large nucleoli compared to others, like epidermal cells, with very small nucleoli. Therefore rRNA appears to be synthesized at some time by all post-blastula embryonic cells, and at a much faster rate in some cells than in others.

We can conclude that the changing rates of synthesis observed in whole embryos apply to the majority of individual cells and cannot be entirely accounted for by changes in the genome during development. The changing rates of nucleic acid synthesis must therefore represent to some extent changes in gene activity during development.

Conditions Affecting the Regulation of RNA and DNA Synthesis During Early Development in *X. laevis*

We have now reached the point at which we may inquire by what means RNA and DNA synthesis might be regulated. We have no knowledge of any actual mechanism by which genes are regulated in higher organisms. We are, however, able to relate the synthetic activities of cells to certain other features of their behavior and to describe experimental conditions under which RNA and DNA synthesis is altered. The following three parts of this section are therefore best regarded as possible approaches to the problem of the regulation of gene activity.

Genetic demonstration of gene regulation

An apparent opportunity to observe the control of gene activity is presented whenever it is possible to compare individuals heterozygous for a deletion or for total inactivation of a locus with homozygotes which differ only by having two normal alleles at that locus. In plants and animals many alleles appear to be completely dominant or wholly recessive in heterozygous condition, as with the gene for tall growth in peas (Mendel 1866). In other cases, the phenotypic expression of the heterozygote is intermediate between the two homozygotes, as in red (RR) and roan (Rr) in Shorthorn cattle (examples in Snyder and David 1957). Complete dominance of the type observed in tall peas can be achieved by regulation of the activity of genes in such a way that they are twice as active when present in one dose as when present in two doses. It can also be achieved without any change in gene activity, as happens in the gene for round (R) in peas. This appears completely dominant to wrinkled (r) as judged by seed morphology (Mendel 1866), but in fact much less of the eventual gene product, the enzyme converting sugar to starch, is present in Rr than in RR. The amount of enzyme produced by the heterozygote is sufficient to give the same phenotypic effect as the dominant homozygote. Since nearly all genes in higher organisms are recognized by some effect of their indirect (protein) product, known examples of complete dominance do not necessarily reveal changes in the regulation of gene activity.

The discovery of the anucleolate mutation in X. laevis (Elsdale, Fischberg, and Smith 1958) has permitted the demonstration that in this case dominance does involve a change in gene activity. Individuals heterozygous for this mutation (1-nu) contain only one nucleolus in each diploid cell and are indistinguishable in function and viability from wild-type animals (2-nu). Embryos homozygous for the mutation (0-nu) possess no normal nucleoli and die shortly before feeding commences, though they develop normally up to that point. The homozygous mutants have been shown by Brown and Gurdon (1964) never to synthesize rRNA, and Wallace and Birnstiel (1966) have shown that the mutant genome lacks most of that portion which is complementary to rRNA. It can be deduced that the 1-nu heterozygotes have little more than half as many rRNA genes as the 2-nu wild type, a deduction confirmed by the finding that only 57 per cent as much rRNA is required to saturate 1-nu DNA as is required for 2-nu DNA (Wallace and Birnstiel 1966). The question of whether the 1-nu embryos synthesize only half as much rRNA as 2-nu embryos, or whether the activity of their genes can be regulated so that each rRNA gene in the 1-nu heterozygote synthesizes twice as much rRNA as does the same gene in the 2-nu wild type, has been approached in the following way (Brown and Gurdon 1964): 1-nu and 2-nu embryos were separated by phase-contrast microscopy, a small piece of tissue from the tail region of the embryos being used, and each group was incubated with $^{14}CO_2$. The subsequent extraction and sucrose-gradient distribution of newly synthesized rRNA showed that the 1-nu and 2-nu embryos had synthesized similar quantities of rRNA. This finding has been confirmed by an MAK fractionation of RNA and DNA as described previously. Figure 12.10 shows that the amount of sRNA and DNA as well as rRNA synthesized by 1-nu embryos is within a few per cent of the amount synthesized under the same conditions by 2-nu embryos. The 1-nu and 2-nu embryos appear not to differ in any other respect than that of a reduction in the number of rRNA genes. These experiments therefore show that the activity of rRNA genes is much greater when they are present in 1-nu embryos than when many more of the same genes are present in 2-nu embryos. The amount of rRNA synthesized is apparently kept constant in relation to other cell properties by regulation of the activity of each set of rRNA genes. This situation does not necessarily prove that *each* rRNA gene synthesizes rRNA faster in 1-nu cells than in 2-

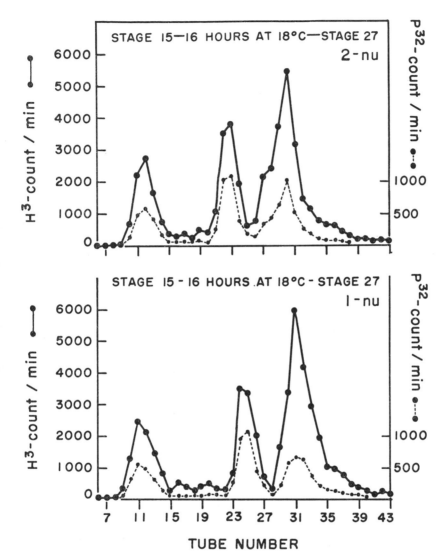

Fig. 12.10.—MAK profiles of RNA and DNA synthesized after the injection of ³H-guanosine into ³²P-labeled embryos which were reared at 18° C for 16 hours: lower figure, 12 embryos heterozygous (1-*nu*) for the anucleolate mutation; upper figure, 12 wild-type embryos (2-*nu*) from the same mating.

nu cells. The activity of all rRNA genes might be increased in the 1-*nu* by a doubling of the proportion of rRNA genes which are active rather than by a doubling of the activity of each of these genes. This possibility does not, however, detract from the value of this example as a demonstration of gene regulation. A simple, but not unique, explanation of these phenomena would be provided if, on reaching a certain concentration within the cell or nucleus, a direct or indirect product of the rRNA genes were to repress further rRNA synthesis.

This conclusion has recently been confirmed by Schultz and Travaglini (1965) in *Drosophila melanogaster*. Eggs of this species which contained one, two, or three nucleolar organizers because of extra sex chromosomes nevertheless synthesized the same amount of rRNA. Some older cytological work becomes relevant to the present discussion if we accept the size of the nucleolus as a cytological indicator of rRNA synthesis (see page 224). We would expect the amount of nucleolar material in a nucleus to remain the same, irrespective of the number of nucleolus organizers present, since it remains the same in 1-*nu* and 2-*nu* *Xenopus* embryos. However, this may not always be so. Lin (1955) has reported an increase in the total content of nucleolar RNA per cell in maize after extra chromosomes carrying a translocated portion (about half) of the nucleolus organizer had been added to a diploid chromosome set. The increase in total nucleolar RNA per nucleus was about 10 per cent for each extra portion of nucleolus organizer added. Unfortunately, it is not known whether the volume of the nucleus increased in proportion to the extra content of nucleolar RNA. If a proportionate nuclear increase did occur, Lin's results would be consistent with those described in *Xenopus*, as well as with the work of Schrader and Leuchtenberger (1950) who found that the nucleolar RNA content of spermatocytes in a hemipteran insect was directly related to increases in nuclear volume.

Cytoplasmic demonstration of gene regulation

It has long been thought that the different kinds of cytoplasm in which nuclei come to lie, for example during early embryogenesis, may help to determine which genes are active in nuclei with presumably identical genomes (e.g., Morgan 1934). Nuclear transplantation in Amphibia provides a means for investigation of the nature of the interaction between nucleus and cytoplasm in higher organisms. When a nucleus is transplanted to an enucleated unfertilized egg, it often undergoes remarkable changes in function which have been demonstrated by morphological, cytological, and biochemical criteria.

The morphological evidence for a change in nuclear function is that, when a nucleus is taken from one kind of cell and transplanted, its mitotic products will support the normal differentiation of other quite different cell types. The percentage of transplanted nuclei in which this has been demonstrated varies according to the species and the stage of differentiation reached by the cell providing the nucleus for transplantation. Examples of the extent to which transplanted nuclei can support normal cell differentiation are given in Table 12.4. Nuclei from *X. laevis* have proved more responsive in this respect than nuclei from other genera, and it has been shown that many nuclei from cytologically differentiated intestinal epithelium cells of feeding *Xenopus* tadpoles can support, after transplantation, the normal differentiation of muscle and nerve cells (Gurdon 1962).

Successfully transplanted nuclei undergo pronounced cytological changes—the disappearance of definitive nucleoli and a rapid increase in nuclear volume up to the size normal for a zygote nucleus. In *Rana pipiens*, blastula nuclei increase their volume about three times in 30 minutes (Subtelny and Bradt 1963), and in *X. laevis* intestinal epithelium nuclei can increase their volume 30 times and lose their nucleoli within 40 minutes after transplantation (Gurdon 1964; Gurdon and Brown 1965).

Biochemical changes induced by nuclear transplantation have been demonstrated in *X. laevis* with respect to RNA and DNA synthesis. Gurdon and Brown (1965) have shown that the kind of RNA synthesized by the mitotic products of a transplanted nucleus is quite different from that synthesized by the same nucleus before its transplantation. Use was made of the fact that rRNA is not synthesized until late cleavage or gastrulation but is made in large amounts by tadpole endoderm cells. Nuclei from such cells were transplanted to enucleated eggs containing $^{32}PO_4$, and the resulting nuclear-transplant embryos were collected at the mid-late blastula stage. The embryos had synthesized no detectable amounts of rRNA, a result expected if the transplanted nuclei had reverted to the synthetic behavior typical of cleavage nuclei. When similar nuclear-transplant embryos were allowed to develop to the neurula stage, it was found that they had started to synthesize rRNA again in normal amounts. Thus, transplantation had induced the somatic nuclei to discontinue rRNA synthesis temporarily but later to recommence synthesis as usual.

Changes in DNA synthesis induced by nuclear transplantation have been investigated in *Xenopus* by Graham, Arms, and Gurdon (1966). The experiments were performed in two parts. First, ^{3}H-thymidine was injected into gastrulae, and the proportion of the endoderm nuclei which incorporated the label within one hour was recorded radioautographically. Second, nuclei from gastrula endoderm cells were injected, together with some ^{3}H-thymidine, into enucleated eggs. After one hour (before the first cleavage) the nuclear-transplant eggs were fixed and sectioned, and the number of nuclei which incorporated the label was again recorded radioautographically. The result of this analysis showed that at least 70 per cent of the transplanted nuclei which could be observed in the sectioned eggs had incorporated ^{3}H-thymidine, whereas only 40 per cent of the same kind of nuclei in the gastrula endoderm had done so within this time. By a similar kind of analysis Graham, Arms, and Gurdon (1966) have shown that over 85 per cent of isolated *Xenopus* brain nuclei are induced to commence DNA synthesis within $1\frac{1}{2}$ hours of injection into unfertilized eggs, even though less than 1 per cent of these nuclei in the intact brain incorporate ^{3}H-thymidine within $1\frac{1}{2}$ hours of its injection into the frog.

The experiments discussed here demonstrate that the transplantation of a living nucleus to egg cytoplasm induces changes in gene activity, as shown by functional and cytological criteria as well as by changes in the synthesis of the two main classes of gene products, RNA and DNA. The rapid, pronounced, and consistent nature of these changes, most of which take place without any adverse effect on normal function, suggests that nuclear transplantation in Amphibia may be a favorable method for identification of one of the mechanisms by which gene activity is controlled.

Gene regulation in relation to the cell cycle

Growing cells pass through cyclic phases of activity, the most obvious manifestations of which are cell division and mitosis. Although cells of many adult animal tissues divide very infrequently, embryonic development is a period of intense mitotic activity. Some synthetic activities are known to take place only during certain phases of the cell cycle (reviewed by Lark 1963). This has been well established for DNA synthesis (Taylor 1960; Stanners and Till 1960), and is true of RNA synthesis to some extent (Sisken 1959; Prescott and Kimball 1961). It is therefore clear that our search for mechanisms by which nucleic acid synthesis might be regulated during embryogenesis should include an examination of the pattern of nucleic acid synthesis in relation to phases of the cell cycle. If sRNA and rRNA were synthesized only during certain phases of the cell cycle, changes in the relative length of these phases during embryogenesis could influence the amount of synthesis which takes place. The question of whether rRNA and sRNA are synthesized continuously throughout interphase or only at certain phases of the cell cycle could be answered directly if it were possible to synchronize the cycles of all the cells of an embryo. However, methods of cell synchronization which do not affect cell metabolism (e.g., Mitchison and Vincent 1965) are not easily applied to embryonic cells, the size of which is unrelated to their cell-cycle phase. At present the most

Table 12.5

Duration in hours of cell-cycle phases of developing *Xenopus laevis* embryos
(from Graham and Morgan 1966)

Developmental stage	Cell-cycle phases				Whole cell cycle
	M	G_1	S	G_2	
Mid-cleavage (6)	0.04	0	< 0.17	< 0.17	0.25
Late gastrula (12)	<0.5	2.0	2.0	3.5	*ca.* 8
Early neurula (14)	<0.5	3.5	4.5	8.0	*ca.* 16

promising approach to this question seems to be to determine the lengths of the cell-cycle phases during embryogenesis and to see whether they are related to changes in RNA and DNA synthesis.

Graham and Morgan (1966) studied the durations of the cell-cycle phases in early *Xenopus* development, by a cytological analysis of eggs and embryos injected with ^{3}H-thymidine. Ten minutes after label injection, eggs were fixed and sectioned and the presence or absence of DNA synthesis determined radioautographically. In any ten-minute labeling period between the first mitosis after fertilization and late cleavage, nuclei in telophase (but not those in metaphase or anaphase) have already started synthesizing DNA. This result shows that nuclei enter the S phase immediately after mitosis and therefore that G_1 is absent during that period of development. The cell cycle is extremely short during cleavage in *Xenopus*, and Graham and Morgan have shown that most of it is occupied by the S and M phases (Table 12.5). Thus, if the G_2 phase is present at all during cleavage, it cannot last more than a few minutes. Graham and Morgan (1966) used the results of various labeling experiments to construct a mathematical model of cell proliferation in *Xenopus* embryos. From this information they determined the duration of the cell-cycle phases during gastrulation and neurulation (Table 12.5). The conclusions from this work relevant to the present discussion are that (1) the G_1 phase is absent and G_2 is very short, if present at all, during cleavage; (2) the G_1 and G_2 phases appear or greatly increase in length at gastrulation; and (3) the relative increase in the cell-cycle phases is approximately the same for G_1, S, and G_2 during gastrulation and neurulation.

In a comparison of the changes in the duration of the cell-cycle phases with changes in the rates of nucleic acid synthesis, it is assumed that the pattern of nucleic acid synthesis observed in whole embryos also applies to endoderm cells. Gurdon and Woodland (unpublished) have in fact found that sRNA synthesis commences in endoderm cells at the end of cleavage, well before rRNA synthesis, just as it does in whole embryos. The durations of the cell-cycle phase and the rates of nucleic acid synthesis can be usefully compared in two respects. First, we may look for an association between the stage of development at which a cell-cycle phase appears and the stage at which a type of nucleic acid synthesis begins. Such an association clearly exists, since sRNA synthesis and rRNA synthesis commence at the end of cleavage, at which stage the G_1 and G_2 phases also appear or increase in length. Secondly, we may look for an association between the relative duration of cell-cycle phases and the relative amount of RNA or DNA synthesis. Clearly a relationship of this kind does not exist. The ratio of sRNA synthesis to rRNA synthesis changes very markedly during gastrulation and neurulation (Fig. 12.8), but the ratio of the duration of G_1 to that of G_2 does not change during the same stages of development (Table 12.5). There is therefore no suggestion from these results that sRNA or rRNA is synthesized during only one phase of the cell cycle. This is consistent with Scharff and Robbins' (1965) results which indicate that rRNA is synthesized throughout the cell cycle of HeLa cells. We may conclude that the absence of G_1 and perhaps G_2 during cleavage could well be important in suppressing sRNA and rRNA synthesis at this stage of development, but that the duration of cell-cycle phases plays no obvious part in regulating the relative amounts of sRNA and rRNA synthesis.

Discussion

The experimental approaches used so far to study the control of gene activity during cell differentiation include the analysis of factors controlling gene activity *in vivo*, the analysis of factors controlling the *in vitro* incorporation of precursors into RNA in cell-free systems, and the introduction into living embryos of purified substances extracted from cells and thought to be of regulatory importance.

Conclusions on the control of RNA and DNA synthesis in vivo

This chapter has been devoted almost exclusively to the embryonic stages of one species, because this avoids the complications of differences between organisms, and because of the paucity of information on the rates of nucleic acid synthesis during embryogenesis in other organisms. Such relevant results as have been obtained in other organisms, discussed by Brown (1965), suggest that comparable patterns of synthesis may take place in sea urchins (Nemer 1963; Wilt 1964; Comb *et al.* 1965) and in fish (Belitzina *et al.* 1963; Spirin, Belitzina, and

Aytkhozhin 1964). A few very general similarities in patterns of RNA and DNA synthesis can be observed between *Xenopus* embryos and bacteria. However, it is clear from Neidhardt's (1964) excellent review on the regulation of RNA synthesis in bacteria that the experiments on bacteria are not sufficiently similar to those carried out on *Xenopus* to justify a detailed comparison at present.

This article has been limited to a discussion of those experiments known to concern gene activity directly during early development. Thus, discussion of the events associated with fertilization in sea urchins has been excluded since the activity of gene products rather than the activity of genes themselves appears to be regulated (Gross 1964). Factors which control protein synthesis or enzyme activity do not necessarily do so at the level of gene transcription (Greengard, Smith, and Acs 1963). Cytological work relevant to the regulation of gene activity has been reviewed by Beermann (1964).

The interpretation of the experiments on *Xenopus* discussed here is complicated by the facts that most biochemical analyses were conducted on whole embryos composed of many different cell types and that heterogeneous populations of molecules were studied. The average rate of synthesis of a class of molecules might obscure quite different rates of synthesis of several component types within the class. Because this is likely to be true particularly of mRNA, it has been largely omitted from discussion in this chapter. These objections can be countered satisfactorily only for DNA and rRNA. DNA is extremely heterogeneous, but, in the absence of genomic changes during cell differentiation (see section on changes in genome composition), the step-by-step doubling of DNA indicates that all the DNA in a cell is replicated once in each cell cycle. The two main sizes of rRNA (18S and 28S) have been shown by Brown and Littna (1964*b*) to be synthesized at coordinate rates throughout early *Xenopus* development, suggesting that the range of molecular types comprising rRNA may all be under the same regulatory mechanism. The uncertainties introduced by the study of heterogeneous populations of cells are alleviated to some extent if one recalls that the rate of rRNA synthesis in the yolky endoderm cells of a hatched *Xenopus* tadpole is similar to that in the fully differentiated nonendoderm cells of the tadpole (Gurdon and Brown 1965). With the methods described previously for studying new synthesis of nucleic acids, it may now be possible to study synthetic patterns in parts of embryos composed mainly of one cell type.

Concerning *actual* mechanisms of gene regulation during cell differentiation little can at present be said, though we may hope that the elucidation of the mechanisms will be facilitated by knowledge of genetic and cytoplasmic conditions that alter gene regulation in a predictable way. However, two general conclusions regarding the normal processes by which nucleic acid synthesis is regulated can be drawn from the results discussed here. The first depends upon the distinction between those patterns of synthesis in which a gene is transcribed an exact number of times in each cell cycle and other patterns of synthesis which are entirely unrelated to the number of cell cycles. Since DNA is replicated once in each cell cycle, any class of molecules which is synthesized the same number of times each cell cycle must be synthesized at the same rate as DNA. We have seen that sRNA and rRNA are not synthesized at the same rate as DNA during early *Xenopus* development, and their synthesis therefore cannot be regulated in relation to the cell cycle as DNA synthesis apparently is.

A second, more positive conclusion depends upon a distinction between the rate of synthesis and the rate of accumulation of a molecule. Earlier in this chapter the evidence was presented that in early *Xenopus* development the rate of synthesis and the rate of accumulation of sRNA are not the same and that the rate of synthesis is adjusted in such a way that the rate of accumulation is kept constant in relation to that of DNA. This situation appears to exemplify a general property of this kind of regulatory process: The rate of synthesis is the factor upon which the process acts, whereas the rate of accumulation is one of the factors to which the process may respond.

The control of incorporation into RNA in cell-free systems

Isolated nuclei, especially of mammalian thymus cells, have been known for many years to be capable of incorporating nucleotides into acid-insoluble components (Allfrey and Mirsky 1957). Recently much excitement has been caused by the finding that histones, the basic proteins characteristically associated with chromosomes of higher organisms, can reversibly influence the amount of incorporation supported by cell-free systems when the histones are dissociated from DNA or reassociated with it (Bonner, Huang, and Gilden 1963; Allfrey and Mirsky 1964). Two main difficulties have affected this work (Bonner and Ts'o 1964). First, the histones extracted from any tissue seem always to be very heterogeneous, and it is uncertain whether a pure histone fraction has yet been isolated. Secondly, the ambitious aim of restoring a complex between extracted histones and DNA in a specific way has not yet been achieved. It is not certain, therefore, whether the main function of histones in relation to DNA is structural or regulatory. However, preparations of pure histone may eventually be obtained which can be usefully introduced into living cells, as has been attempted by Brachet (1964).

Biological activity of molecules extracted from cells

It is of great importance to test the biological activity of molecules thought to have some regulatory function. Hormones are particularly suitable for this kind of analysis owing to their stability during purification and their capacity to penetrate cells. Many different vertebrate, invertebrate, and plant hormones appear to exert their effects by enhancing gene activity: for example, estrogen (Hamilton 1964), cortisone (Kenney and Kull 1963), thyroxin (Tata 1963), ecdysone (Clever 1961), gibberellic acid (Varner and Ram Chandra 1964); but it is not known whether they act directly on genes. There is no evidence so far, however, that hormones are involved in early embryogenesis when cell differentiation is most actively taking place.

The biological activity of large molecules can be tested when they are injected into embryos. An example of this kind of work is that of Markert and Ursprung (1963) and Ursprung and Smith (1965) who have injected purified fractions of liver cell nuclei into fertilized frog eggs. They find that certain fractions, such as albumin and histone, cause arrest of the embryos at the blastula stage after the injection of very small amounts. These injected substances often provoke extensive chromosome damage, and their effects are more drastic than would be expected of substances normally concerned in the regulation of chromosome activity. However, this kind of experiment may be expected to yield important results as methods improve for extracting pure and undegraded macromolecules.

Summary

The South African water frog, *X. laevis*, is especially suitable for the embryological and biochemical analysis of gene activity during cell differentiation, as well as for certain kinds of genetic analysis.

An efficient labeling procedure, followed by the simultaneous fractionation of RNA and DNA from as few as ten embryos, has permitted an estimate of the relative amounts of RNA and DNA synthesized at different developmental stages. The results of these short-term labeling experiments agree with those obtained from long-term labeling experiments in the following respects: sRNA is first synthesized at the late blastula stage, but rapid synthesis of rRNA does not commence until the neurula stage. The amounts of sRNA and DNA synthesized per time per content of DNA decrease progressively after the beginning of gastrulation, but this is not true for rRNA.

The long-term labeling experiments of Brown indicate that the accumulation of sRNA bears a constant relationship to DNA content between the gastrula and tail-bud stages. The short-term labeling experiments described here indicate that sRNA is not synthesized at the same rate as DNA during these stages of development. It is suggested that the rate of sRNA synthesis is regulated in such a way that it accumulates in the cell at the same rate as DNA.

The changing rates of DNA and rRNA synthesis observed in whole embryos also obtain in individual cells and cannot be attributed wholly to changes in the composition of the genome. They are therefore considered to reflect changes in gene activity.

Pronounced changes in gene activity take place after nuclei are transplanted from somatic cells to enucleated egg cytoplasm. This has been demonstrated by morphological and cytological criteria as well as by changes in RNA and DNA synthesis.

The activity of rRNA genes is regulated in such a way that the total amount of rRNA synthesized in a nucleus remains the same even though the number of rRNA genes per genome may change.

The absence of rRNA and sRNA synthesis during cleavage coincides with the virtual absence of the G_1 and G_2 phases of the cell cycle. The synthesis of these classes of RNA commences at the same developmental stage as the G_1 and G_2 phases of the cell cycle appear or greatly increase.

Acknowledgments

I am very sincerely grateful to D. D. Brown for detailed discussion of most of the work included in this chapter, and for the extensive advice and help he has given in connection with the previously unpublished work described here. I am indebted to C. F. Graham for permitting me to describe some of his work before its publication. Stephen Subtelny most kindly supplied a translation of the article by Nikitina (1964). I wish to thank Miss Janet Rooney and Miss Elizabeth Littna for technical assistance. Part of the work described here was done at the Carnegie Institution of Washington (Department of Embryology) in Baltimore, during the tenure of a fellowship for which I am very grateful, and part in Oxford with support from the Medical Research Council.

Literature Cited

ALLFREY, V. G., AND A. E. MIRSKY, 1957. Some aspects of ribonucleic acid synthesis in isolated cell nuclei. Proc. Nat. Acad. Sci. U.S. 43: 821–826.

ALLFREY, V. G., AND A. E. MIRSKY, 1964. The role of histones in nuclear function. *The Nucleohistones,* pp. 267–288. Edited by J. Bonner and P. Ts'o. Holden-Day Inc., San Francisco.

BACHVAROVA, R., E. H. DAVIDSON, V. G. ALLFREY, AND A. E. MIRSKY, 1966. Activation of RNA synthesis associated with gastrulation. Proc. Nat. Acad. Sci. U.S. 55: 358–365.

BARR, H. J., AND H. ESPER, 1963. Nucleolar size in cells of *Xenopus laevis* in relation to nucleolar competition. Exp. Cell Res. 31: 211–214.

BEERMANN, W. 1964. Control of differentiation at the chromosomal level. J. Exp. Zool. 157: 49–62.

BELITZINA, I. V., L. P. GAVRILOVA, M. A. AYTKHOZHIN, A. A. NEYFAKH, AND A. S. SPIRIN, 1963. Informational RNA in the early stages of development of *Misgurnus fossilis.* Dokl. Akad. Nauk S.S.S.R. 153: 463–468.

BONNER, J., R. C. HUANG, AND R. V. GILDEN, 1963. Chromosomally directed protein synthesis. Proc. Nat. Acad. Sci. U.S. 50: 893–900.

BONNER, J., AND P. Ts'O, 1964. *The Nucleohistones.* Holden-Day, Inc., San Francisco.

BOVERI, T., 1899. *Die Entwicklung von* Ascaris megalocephala *mit besonderer Rücksicht auf die Kernverhältnisse.* Gustav Fischer, Jena.

BRACHET, J., 1964. Effects of histones on early embryonic development. Nature 204: 1218–1219.

BRAUN, A. C., 1959. A demonstration of the recovery of the crown-gall tumor cell with the use of complex tumors of single-cell origin. Proc. Nat. Acad. Sci. U.S. 45: 932–938.

BRIGGS, R., AND T. J. KING, 1957. Changes in the nuclei of differentiating endoderm cells as revealed by nuclear transplantation. J. Morphol. 100: 269–312.

BRIGGS, R., J. SIGNORET, AND R. R. HUMPHREY, 1964. Transplantation of nuclei of various cell types from neurulae of the Mexican axolotl (*Ambystoma mexicanum*). Develop. Biol. 10: 233–246.

BROWN, D. D., 1964. RNA synthesis during amphibian development. J. Exp. Zool. 157: 101–113.

———, 1965. RNA synthesis during early development. *Developmental and Metabolic Control Mechanisms and Neoplasia.* Williams & Wilkins, Baltimore.

BROWN, D. D., AND J. B. GURDON, 1964. Absence of ribosomal RNA synthesis in the anucleolate mutant of *Xenopus laevis.* Proc. Nat. Acad. Sci. U.S. 51: 139–147.

BROWN, D. D., AND E. LITTNA, 1964a. RNA synthesis during the development of *Xenopus laevis,* the South African clawed toad. J. Mol. Biol. 8: 669–687.

BROWN, D. D., AND E. LITTNA, 1964b. Variations in the synthesis of stable RNAs during oogenesis and development of *Xenopus laevis.* J. Mol. Biol. 8: 688–695.

CLEVER, U., 1961. Genaktivitäten in der Riesenchromosomen von *Chironomus tentans* und ihrer Beziehungen zur Entwicklung, I. Chromosoma 12: 607–675.

COHEN, S., 1954. The metabolism of $C^{14}O_2$ during amphibian development. J. Biol. Chem. 211: 337–354.

COMB, D. G., S. KATZ, R. BRANDA, AND C. J. PINZINO, 1965. Characterization of RNA species synthesized during early development of sea urchins. J. Mol. Biol. 14: 195–213.

DAVIDSON, E. H., V. G. ALLFREY, AND A. E. MIRSKY, 1964. On the RNA synthesized during the lampbrush phase of amphibian oocytes. Proc. Nat. Acad. Sci. U.S. 52: 501–508.

DAWID, I. B., 1965. Deoxyribonucleic acid in amphibian eggs. J. Mol. Biol. 12: 581–599.

DIBERARDINO, M. A., AND T. J. KING, 1965. Transplantation of nuclei from the frog renal adenocarcinoma. Develop. Biol. 11: 217–242.

ELSDALE, T. R., M. FISCHBERG, AND S. SMITH, 1958. A mutation that reduces nucleolar number in Xenopus laevis. Exp. Cell Res. 14: 642–643.

GRAHAM, C. F., K. ARMS, AND J. B. GURDON, 1966. The induction of DNA synthesis by egg cytoplasm. Develop. Biol. (in press).

GRAHAM, C. F., AND R. MORGAN, 1966. Changes in the cell cycle during early amphibian development. Develop. Biol. (in press).

GRANT, P., 1960. The influence of folic acid analogs on development and nucleic acid metabolism in Rana pipiens embryos. Develop. Biol. 2: 197–225.

GREENGARD, O., M. A. SMITH, AND G. ACS, 1963. Relation of cortisone and synthesis of ribonucleic acid to induced and developmental enzyme formation. J. Biol. Chem. 238: 1548–1551.

GROSS, P. R., 1964. The immediacy of genomic control during early development. J. Exp. Zool. 157: 21–38.

GURDON, J. B., 1960. The developmental capacity of nuclei taken from differentiating endoderm cells of Xenopus laevis. J. Embryol. Exp. Morphol. 8: 505–526.

———, 1962. The developmental capacity of nuclei taken from intestinal epithelium cells of feeding tadpoles. J. Embryol. Exp. Morphol. 10: 622–640.

———, 1963. Nuclear transplantation in Amphibia and the importance of stable nuclear changes in promoting cellular differentiation. Quart. Rev. Biol. 38: 54–78.

———, 1964. The transplantation of living cell nuclei. Advance. Morphogenesis 4: 1–43.

GURDON, J. B., AND D. D. BROWN, 1965. Cytoplasmic regulation of RNA synthesis and nucleolus formation in developing embryos of Xenopus laevis. J. Mol. Biol. 12: 27–35.

GURDON, J. B., AND V. UEHLINGER, 1966. "Fertile" intestine nuclei. Nature 210: 1240–1241.

HADORN, E., 1955. Lethalfaktoren in ihrer Bedeutung für Erbpathologie und Genphysiologie der Entwicklung. Georg Thieme Verlag, Stuttgart.

HAMILTON, T. H., 1964. Sequences of RNA and protein synthesis during early oestrogen action. Proc. Nat. Acad. Sci. U.S. 51: 83–89.

HERRMANN, H., AND R. L. TOOTLE, 1964. Specific and general aspects of the development of enzymes and metabolic pathways. Physiol. Rev. **44**: 289–371.

KENNEY, F. T., AND F. J. KULL, 1963. Hydrocortisone-stimulated synthesis of nuclear RNA in enzyme induction. Proc. Nat. Acad. Sci. U.S. **50**: 493–500.

KIRK, J. T. O., 1963. The deoxyribonucleic acid of Broad Bean chloroplasts. Biochim. Biophys. Acta **76**: 417–424.

KUTSKY, P., 1950. Phosphate metabolism in the early development of *Rana pipiens*. J. Exp. Zool. **115**: 429–460.

LARK, R. G., 1963. Cellular control of DNA biosynthesis. *Molecular Genetics*, part 1, pp. 153–206. Edited by J. H. Taylor. Academic Press, N.Y.

LIN, MEI, 1955. Chromosomal control of nuclear composition in maize. Chromosoma **7**: 340–370.

LOEFFLER, C. A., AND M. C. JOHNSTON, 1964. Permeability alterations in amphibian embryos caused by salt solution and measured by tritiated thymidine uptake. J. Embryol. Exp. Morphol. **12**: 407–424.

McCARTHY, B. J., AND B. H. HOYER, 1964. Identity of DNA and diversity of messenger RNA molecules in normal mouse tissues. Proc. Nat. Acad. Sci. U.S. **52**: 915–922.

MANDELL, J. D., AND A. D. HERSHEY, 1960. A fractionating column for analysis of nucleic acids. Anal. Biochem. **1**: 66–77.

MARKERT, C. L., AND H. URSPRUNG, 1963. Production of replicable persistent changes in the zygote chromosomes of *Rana pipiens* by injected proteins from adult liver nuclei. Develop. Biol. **7**: 560–577.

MENDEL, G. J., 1866. Versuche über Pflanzenhybriden. Verhandl. Naturforsch. Ver. Brünn **4**: 3–47.

MILLER, O. L., 1964. Extrachromosomal nucleolar DNA in amphibian oocytes. J. Cell Biol. **23**: 60*A*.

MITCHISON, J. M., AND W. S. VINCENT, 1965. Preparation of synchronous cell cultures by sedimentation. Nature **205**: 987–991.

MORGAN, T. H., 1934. *Embryology and Genetics.* Columbia Univ. Press, N.Y.

NEIDHARDT, F. C., 1964. The regulation of RNA synthesis in bacteria. Progr. Nucleic Acid Res. **4**: 145–183.

NEMER, M., 1963. Old and new RNA in the embryogenesis of the purple sea urchin. Proc. Nat. Acad. Sci. U.S. **50**: 230–235.

NIEUWKOOP, P. D., AND J. FABER, 1956. *Normal Table for* Xenopus laevis, *Daudin.* North-Holland Publishing Company, Amsterdam.

NIKITINA, L. A., 1964. Transfers of nuclei from the ectoderm and neural rudiments of developing embryos of *Bufo bufo, Rana arvalis*, and *Rana temporaria* into enucleated eggs of the same species. Dokl. Akad. Nauk S.S.S.R. **156**: 1468–1471.

OTAKA, E., H. MITSUI, AND S. OSAWA, 1962. On the ribonucleic acid synthesized in a cell-free system of *E. coli*. Proc. Nat. Acad. Sci. U.S. **48**: 425–430.

PAVAN, C., 1965. Nucleic acid metabolism in polytene chromosomes and the problem of differentiation. Brookhaven Symp. Biol. **18**: 222–241.

PERRY, R. P., 1962. The cellular sites of ribosomal and 4S RNA. Proc. Nat. Acad. Sci. U.S. **48**: 2179–2186.

PICHERAL, B., 1962. Capacités des noyeaux de cellules endodermiques embryonnaires à organiser un germe viable chez l'Urodèle, *Pleurodeles waltlii* Michah. Compt. Rend. **255**: 2509–2511.

PRESCOTT, D. M., AND R. F. KIMBALL, 1961. Relation between RNA, DNA and protein synthesis in the replicating nucleus of *Euplotes*. Proc. Nat. Acad. Sci. U.S. **47**: 686–693.

RABINOWITZ, M., J. SINCLAIR, L. DESALLE, R. HASELKORN, AND H. SWIFT, 1965. Isolation of deoxyribonucleic acid from mitochondria of chick embryo heart and liver. Proc. Nat. Acad. Sci. U.S. **53**: 1126–1133.

RITOSSA, F. M., AND S. SPIEGELMAN, 1965. Localization of DNA complementary to ribosomal RNA in the nucleolus organizer region of *Drosophila melanogaster*. Proc. Nat. Acad. Sci. U.S. **53**: 737–744.

SCHARFF, M. D., AND E. ROBBINS, 1965. Synthesis of ribosomal RNA in synchronized HeLa cells. Nature **208**: 464–466.

SCHRADER, F., AND C. LEUCHTENBERGER, 1950. A cytochemical analysis of the functional interrelations of the various cell structures in *Arvelius albopunctatus* (De Geer). Exp. Cell Res. **1**: 421–452.

SCHULTZ, J., AND E. C. TRAVAGLINI, 1965. Evidence for homeostatic control of ribosomal content in *Drosophila melanogaster* eggs. Genetics **52**: 473.

SINNOTT, E. W., 1960. *Plant Morphogenesis.* McGraw-Hill, N.Y.

SISKEN, J., 1959. The synthesis of nucleic acids and proteins in the nuclei of *Tradescantia* root tips. Exp. Cell Res. **16**: 602–614.

SMITH, L. D., 1965. Transplantation of the nuclei of primordial germ cells into enucleated eggs of *Rana pipiens*. Proc. Nat. Acad. Sci. U.S. **54**: 101–107.

SNYDER, L. H., AND P. R. DAVID, 1957. *The Principles of Heredity.* D. C. Heath and Co., Boston.

SPIRIN, A. S., I. V. BELITZINA, AND M. A. AYTKHOZHIN, 1964. Informational RNA in early embryogenesis. Zhur. Obshcheĭ Biol. **25**: 321–327.

STANNERS, C. P., AND J. E. TILL, 1960. DNA synthesis in individual L-strain mouse cells. Biochim. Biophys. Acta **37**: 406–419.

SUBTELNY, S., AND C. BRADT, 1963. Cytological observations on the early developmental stages of activated *Rana pipiens* eggs receiving a transplanted blastula nucleus. J. Morphol. **112**: 45–59.

TATA, J. R., 1963. Inhibition of the biological action of thyroid hormones by actinomycin D and puromycin. Nature **197**: 1167–1168.

TAYLOR, J. H., 1960. Nucleic acid synthesis in relation to the cell division cycle. Ann. N.Y. Acad. Sci. **90**: 409–421.

URSPRUNG, H., AND K. D. SMITH, 1965. Differential gene activity at the biochemical level. Brookhaven Symp. Biol. **18**: 1–13.

VARNER, J. E., AND G. RAM CHANDRA, 1964. Hormonal control of enzyme synthesis in barley endosperm. Proc. Nat. Acad. Sci. U.S. **52**: 100–106.

WALLACE, H., AND M. L. BIRNSTIEL, 1966. Ribosomal cistrons and the nucleolus organiser. Biochim. Biophys. Acta **114**: 296–310.

WHITE, M. J. D., 1954. *Animal Cytology and Evolution,* 2nd ed. Cambridge University Press, England.

WILT, F. H., 1964. Ribonucleic acid synthesis during sea urchin embryogenesis. Develop. Biol. **9:** 299–313.

YOSHIKAWA, M., T. FUKUDA, AND T. KAWADE, 1964. Separation of rapidly labeled RNA of animal cells into DNA-type and ribosomal RNA-type compounds. Biochem. Biophys. Res. Commun. **1:** 22–26.

IV

Population Genetics

13

The Foundations of Population Genetics

Sewall Wright

Paper No. 1041 from the Department of Genetics, University of Wisconsin. This study was conducted under grant No. GB-1317 from the National Science Foundation.

It was considered appropriate that I should introduce Part IV of this book with a brief account of the early development of population genetics with special regard to my own recollections. These recollections began in 1911 when I heard George Shull give a lecture at Cold Spring Harbor on his inbred lines of maize and on the results of crosses. I recall that I was much impressed, though I cannot claim to have appreciated fully the enormous practical importance of his suggestions.

Population genetics is concerned with describing the genetic compositions of populations, the evolutionary processes that occur in nature, and the ways in which change may be controlled in the improvement of plants and animals and, perhaps, even of man himself. It is especially concerned with processes in cases which are not amenable to detailed genetic analysis.

There are not many basic processes. They include inbreeding and crossbreeding, assortative and disassortative mating, various modes of selection, and increase of variability by exposure to mutagenic agents. Ideas on most of these go farther back than recorded history. There was an approach to scientific study by some of the men who founded the British breeds of livestock in the eighteenth century, notably Robert Bakewell (1726–95).

Population studies entered fully into science with Darwin (1859, 1868). He drew on the experience of livestock breeders and made extensive experiments himself on inbreeding and crossbreeding in plants. His outstanding contributions were, of course, the firm establishment of the theory of organic evolution and the formulation of the hypothesis of natural selection as its primary cause—the hypothesis that slight differences in productivity or mortality among spontaneously occurring

245

variations may build up, step by step, new harmonious patterns of organization that would be inconceivably improbable at a single step.

Darwin, however, did not arrive at valid principles of heredity. An engineer, Fleeming Jenkin (1867), pointed out that under the blending hypothesis of heredity, which Darwin and nearly everyone else at the time accepted as the prevailing rule, all variability tends to be rapidly dissipated, half being lost per generation, unless an equal amount of new variability arises *de novo* in each generation. Darwin was led to concede increasing importance to directed heritable influences of the environment.

The fact of evolution came to be generally accepted, but this was far from the case with the hypothesis of natural selection. Many indeed accepted the hypothesis, especially those interested in such special adaptations as mimicry that do not readily lend themselves to other interpretations. More, however, rejected it at least as a primary cause. A bewildering array of alternative hypotheses had been advocated by the end of the century (see Kellogg 1907). These included direct environmental influences on heredity (as held by Darwin himself in his later writings, along with M. Wagner who in this connection stressed the importance of isolation), heritable effects of use and disuse (as in Cope's kinetogenesis and in other neo-Lamarckian theories), progressive evolution as an essential property of life (Nägeli, also owing its origin to Lamarck), orthogenesis of a more limited scope (Eimer), random differentiation of small colonies (Gulick), and abrupt origin of major changes (the heterogenesis concept of Kölliker and the mutation theory of de Vries).

The association of de Vries' mutation theory with his rediscovery of Mendelian heredity naturally had much influence on the views of the early Mendelians. Speciation by major mutation was soon abandoned as the primary cause of evolutionary transformation but de Vries' observations led to the demonstration of a class of evolutionary phenomena, chromosome aberrations, that is important in the splitting of species.

Among evolutionists in general, such theories as those mentioned continued to flourish at least to the 1930's when the conclusions on the statistical consequences of Mendelian heredity began to be widely recognized. The continued flourishing of these discredited theories is evident in the acceptance by Rensch (1929) and Sumner (1932) of heritable environmental effects as primary causes, in their very important studies of subspecies and local populations (both men later accepted the Mendelian interpretation), in Osborne's (1934) doctrine of aristogenesis, in the theories of Goldschmidt (1940) and Willis (1940) that postulated abrupt origin even of higher categories, and in the wide currency of Lloyd Morgan's (1933) doctrine of emergence.

Actually the answer to Jenkin's apparently devastating criticism of 1867 had been given two years before the criticism was made. The answer was in Mendel's demonstration in 1865 (Mendel 1866) of units of heredity and of the completely symmetrical transmission of alleles, irrespective of dominance. Mendel did not consider populations. It can hardly be doubted, however, that if he had, he would have pointed out at once that gene frequencies would have no tendency to change under random mating and thus that there would be no appreciable loss of variability in a large population. He would undoubtedly have applied the product principle of the theory of probability, which he used throughout his paper, to conclude that the relative frequencies of genotypes are those resulting from random combination within and among loci. Actually, of course, the enunciation of these immediate consequences of Mendelian heredity had to wait until after the rediscovery in 1900, and then for someone sufficiently interested in populations.

This leads to another of the roots of population genetics, the quantitative study of populations, initiated by Galton (1889) and developed by the biometric school under the leadership of Karl Pearson. It is not surprising that the first attempt to formulate the statistical properties of Mendelian populations and to reconcile the views of Galton with those of Mendel was made by a biometrician, Yule (1902). He showed that the unselected, randomly bred descendants of a cross would maintain indefinitely the 1:2:1 ratio of F_2. He went on to show that Galton's law of ancestral heredity, in the generalized form of a multiple regression equation of offspring relative to parents and more remote ancestors, applies to all phenotypes in the descendant population that are not completely determined by genotype, whether because of dominance or because of irregular penetrance. He also clearly formulated the multiple-factor interpretation of quantitative variability (which had indeed been foreshadowed in 1865 by Mendel himself). Castle (1903), in the course of a criticism based on a misunderstanding of Yule's postulates, worked out for the first time the effect of selection in a Mendelian population (selective exclusion of the recessives in each generation). He also showed (as Sturtevant has recently called to my attention) that if selection ceases, the composition of the randomly bred descendants remains constant thereafter, with genotypic frequencies according to the now familiar binomial-square rule. Unfortunately, he did not stress this as a basic principle of population genetics, and it did not attract attention. It is known now as the Hardy-Weinberg law because of independent restatements by Hardy and by Weinberg in 1908.

Weinberg (1909) also showed that genes at different loci tend to approach random combination, though only gradually. I may note here that one of my earliest contributions to population genetics (Wright 1917) was in the application of these principles of random combination within and among loci to distinguish different genetic hypotheses (for coat colors of Shorthorn cattle). I also used the former (Hardy-Weinberg law) in assessing genetic theories of human eye color (Wright 1918). The rate at which two loci approach equilibrium was first demonstrated by Robbins (1918), but it was not until the 1940's that the rather complicated mode by which any number of loci approach equilibrium was formulated by Geiringer (1944).

Pearson (1904) derived the parent-offspring and fraternal correlations expected under Mendelian heredity among the randomly bred descendants of a cross. He thought that there was a serious discrepancy between expected and observed correlations, but Yule (1906) showed that this merely reflected Pearson's assumption that dominance is always complete. Weinberg (1909, 1910) developed systematically the correlations to be expected between relatives of various sorts, allowing for multiple alleles, degrees of dominance, the more familiar interaction effects, and environmental complications. His formulae removed all difficulty in accounting for observed correlations between relatives. With these results, and with Yule's demonstration of the consistency of Mendelian heredity with a generalized law of ancestral heredity and with experimental support for Yule's multiple-factor interpretation of quantitative variability (Nilsson-Ehle 1909; East 1910), the reconciliation between the biometric and Mendelian viewpoints was essentially complete by 1910.

Unfortunately, such bitter antagonism had developed between the British Mendelians, under Bateson's leadership, and the biometricians, led by Pearson, that recognition of population genetics as a valid field for theoretical and experimental research was greatly delayed in England. I recall mentioning to Bateson in 1921 that a certain segregation ratio in my data deviated from expectation by nearly five times its probable error. I might almost as well have stepped on a land mine. Bateson expressed his opinion of biometry in no uncertain terms. British geneticists tend to date population genetics from a paper by Fisher in 1918, in which he repeated and extended (principally to assortative mating) Weinberg's analysis of the correlations between relatives. This was followed by other important theoretical papers in population genetics (to be considered later) and in statistical methodology, especially Fisher's (1925) analysis of variance, which have been very useful in experimental work, but actual experimental population genetics did not get under way in England until Mather's (1941) studies of multifactorial (or "polygenic") heredity in the 1940's.

There was no such delay elsewhere. Davenport (1899) had made the methods of biometry known to Americans by his very useful little book on statistical methods, and the writings of J. Arthur Harris and Raymond Pearl contributed to the integration of Mendelism and biometrics. Johannsen (1903, 1909) performed a similar service for continental Europe and contributed greatly to the subject with his pure line theory. When I went to the Bussey Institution of Harvard in 1912 as a graduate student, it was an active center of experimental research in population genetics. Castle and associates (1906) had made studies of inbreeding, crossbreeding, and selection with *Drosophila,* and he had been engaged for some time in a selection experiment on the hair-color patterns of hooded rats, a project on which I assisted from 1912 to 1915. He carried the means of his plus and minus lines far beyond the limits of variability of the original stock, contrary to the expectations of many geneticists at the time (Castle and Phillips 1914). East and his associates were adding to the understanding of inbreeding and crossing in maize (East 1908; Jones 1917, 1918) and were giving massive support to the multiple-factor hypothesis (East and Hayes 1911; Emerson and East 1913; East 1916). Both Castle and East were wholly Darwinian in their views on evolution in spite of differences in their interpretations of quantitative variability. These differences were ultimately resolved by Castle (1919) in favor of the multifactorial interpretation, by a crucial experiment.

I should not leave the impression that all early work on population genetics in this country was centered at the Bussey Institution. One of the most noteworthy selection experiments was that for opposite extremes in protein content and in oil content in lines of maize, started by Hopkins at the Illinois Experiment Station in 1896 and still going on with continuing progress in all lines (Leng 1962). There were other early selection experiments, notably those with *Drosophila* by MacDowell (1917), by Payne (1920), and by Sturtevant (1918), other inbreeding and crossbreeding experiments (among them, those of Shull [1908], mentioned earlier), and other studies of multifactorial heredity. Establishment of basic principles of population genetics was followed by a rapid expansion at state agricultural experiment stations of applied research, which it is not practicable to review here. The hybrid corn project was only one of these.

My own research program as a graduate student at the Bussey Institution was in the field of physiological genetics, rather than population genetics. My studies of the interaction systems affecting color and various morphological characters of the guinea pig continued from 1914 to 1960, but during the ten years (1915–25) when I was in the U.S. Department of Agriculture, my primary interest shifted to population genetics. Thereafter, I devoted about equal attention to these two fields. They were not as unrelated as might seem.

In 1915, I took charge of an extensive experiment on the effect of inbreeding on guinea pigs, started in 1906 by G. M. Rommel, Chief of the Animal Husbandry Division. Analyses of these data, and those from crosses, gave results (Wright 1922b,c; Wright and Eaton 1929) in harmony with the theories of Shull and East. They led to the development of a general mathematical theory of inbreeding (Wright 1921, 1922a) and to studies of how inbreeding had actually functioned in the development of Shorthorn cattle (Wright 1924; McPhee and Wright 1925), a type of research that was greatly extended by Lush (1946) and associates. My experimental studies of interaction systems led to a strong conviction that for the most effective long-run application to livestock improvement, selection must somehow operate among interaction systems as wholes, something that is obviously impossible under mass selection. My central theoretical problem became that of how to combine inbreeding, crossbreeding, and selection in the most effective way. Tentative conclusions were reached on the application to livestock breeding in 1922 (Wright 1922c) and were applied to the problem of evolution in nature in a paper that was written before I left Washington in 1925 but that was not published until 1931 except for an abstract (Wright 1929a).

I will devote the rest of this chapter to a comparison of the more important Mendelian theories of evolution developed or foreshadowed before 1940. I will not consider the possible role of cytoplasmic heredity of which little was known then, or even now. I will merely mention here the theory of evolution by means of more or less completely isolating chromosome aberrations such as autopolyploidy, hybridization followed by amphidiploidy, and reciprocal translocation. These have to do more with the splitting of species than with their transformation, to which I will limit myself.

Table 13.1 deals with the relatively simple evolutionary processes that occur in essentially panmictic species. The entries under the headings indicate the phases (++ guiding, + essential role, 0 absent, blank irrelevant).

Table 13.1

Possible evolutionary processes in a closed panmictic population (rows). Essential phases (columns) are indicated by $+$, that which ultimately guides the course of evolution is indicated by $++$. Phases that are assumed to be insignificant are indicated by 0. Phases that may be either present or absent are left blank.

Process	Population (panmictic)	Environ- ment change	Variability			Selection among individuals
			Mutation	Storage	Random drift	
A	Large		$++$		0	0
B	Large	0	$+$		0	$++$
C	Large	$+$	$+$	$+$	0	$++$
D	Very small colony		0	$+\rightarrow 0$	$++\rightarrow 0$	0
E	Small		$+$	$+$	$+$	$++$

Mutation Pressure

Process *A*, evolution guided by mutation pressure, is an abstraction that can hardly occur in nature because of the virtual inevitability of greater selection pressures at all loci. The theoretical rate was given by Haldane (1924).

I have been credited recently (Brace 1963) with having advocated this in an early paper (Wright 1929*b*) in connection with the degeneration of useless organs, but actually I was rejecting this interpretation (see Wright 1964) as recognized by Brace himself later (1964) .

Selection under Constant Conditions

Process *B*, evolution guided by selection of favorable mutants, was the most obvious way of bringing Darwin's hypothesis up to date, and it seems still to be the most popular theory. The course of change was, as noted, first worked out by Castle (1903) in a special case. The general cases of favorable dominants or recessives were presented by H. T. J. Norton (in Punnett 1915). A much more comprehensive mathematical theory of the effects of selection under diverse conditions was derived by Haldane (1924, 1927, review 1932).

A discussion by Chetverikov (1926) based on Norton's table stimulated extensive study of hidden variability from rare recessives by Russian geneticists and more recently on a grand scale by Dobzhansky and associates here and in South America.

While process *B* is a form of neo-Darwinism that is not subject to

Jenkin's (1867) criticism (as noted by Chetverikov), it is such an ineffective process in a population that has become adapted to conditions that have remained essentially the same for a long time (the distinction between B and C) that I attributed relatively little importance to it in my papers in 1931 and later. It depends on the occurrence of *novel favorable* mutations, since it can make no use of favorable combinations of the many unfavorable mutations that are kept in balance at low frequencies in the species. I merely assumed this as a rather obvious consequence of the reduction division, but it was given mathematical demonstration by Fisher (1930) in his "fundamental theorem of natural selection." An increasingly favorable interaction system tends, of course, to be built up by process B, since novel mutations are favorable only if they fit into the system already established, but there can be no selection among interaction systems. The point is that in this process the rate of evolution is limited, except for minor secondary readjustments, by the exceedingly rare occurrence of the required kind of mutation.

Selection under Changed Conditions

The same limit does not apply in process C, which differs from B only in that it applies to a species that has become exposed to new conditions to which it is not well adapted. The mathematical results of Norton, Haldane, and Fisher remain pertinent. No distinction is usually made between processes B and C, but the limitation to evolutionary change is so much less drastic under C that it seems desirable to make the distinction. Instead of waiting for a novel favorable mutation, the species, exposed to unfavorable conditions, may draw on its current store of variability in the process of readaptation.

This store depends on various forms of balance: the heterotic balance that occurs when heterozygotes are at an advantage over both homozygotes (Fisher 1922), the balancing of adverse selection by recurrent mutation (Haldane 1927), and the balance that occurs in heterogeneous environments in which selection works against whatever allele happens to become too abundant (not treated mathematically until much later: Wright and Dobzhansky 1946).

In process C the store of variability, while constituting a deleterious load (as termed by Muller 1950), nevertheless includes genes which, though hitherto deleterious, can be drawn on at once if they are more favorable under the changed conditions. These are much more abundant than the novel favorable mutation required in B. Most observed cases of gradual evolution have probably been of this sort: resistance of insects to pesticides, resistance of bacteria to antibiotics, industrial melanism in moths, and the exaggerated development of special characters under artificial selection toward an unnatural extreme.

Process C has, however, an obvious disadvantage—that it is somewhat like a treadmill. Its success depends on deterioration of the environment. If gene effects were additive, which implies a single peak in the system of selective values of available genotypes, restoration of a previous condition would merely restore the previous genotype. In 1931 I attributed little more long-time significance to this process than to B. On further consideration, I concluded (Wright 1932) that because of the virtually inevitable multiplicity of selective peaks at all times, representing different favorable interaction systems, changes under C would be essentially irreversible, and that this process must be considered an important one in evolution. Mayr (1959) was, however, wholly incorrect in classifying me as primarily an advocate of what he called the "classical" or "beanbag" theory of evolution, which I assume refers to processes B and C, and in ignoring the "shifting balance" theory which I actually advocated almost exclusively in 1929 and 1931, and primarily in 1932 and later (see Wright 1960).

I may add that most proposals for eugenic improvement of the human species have come under category C, direct selection toward a specified goal. It is indeed probable that a totalitarian regime persisting for as long a time as Hitler anticipated for the Third Reich could transform the human species to its uses, somewhat as has been done in the specialized breeds of livestock. My own view is that any comparably controlled evolution of mankind would be a disaster. It will be enough if mankind can refrain from destroying the diversification that is the basis for the process by which man has evolved in the past.

Fixation by Close Inbreeding

Process D is merely inbreeding so close that selection is largely ineffective, with fixation of some random combination of genes the consequence. The effects of self-fertilization were presented thoroughly by Mendel (1866). Those of brother-sister mating were arrived at independently by Jennings (1914) and Fish (1914), both stimulated by an erroneous conclusion by Pearl (1913; also corrected by Pearl himself in 1914). I extended these results by means of path analysis to all systems of mating: autosomal diploids (Wright 1921, 1922a), sex-linked loci (Wright 1933), polysomics (Wright 1938). The resulting inbreeding coefficient, F, expresses the relative decrease in heterozygosis and permits modification of the Hardy-Weinberg formula for populations not breeding at random (Wright 1922c).

Only the closer forms of inbreeding, however, lead to the random fixation of process D. I have attributed no evolutionary significance to this process in 1929, 1931 or later, except as it may lead to degeneration and extinction of extremely small, completely isolated colonies. On the other hand, it is a process of great importance in agriculture as a step, for example, in the production of hybrid corn or hybrid chickens.

Two-Phase Shifting Balance
(Random Drift plus Selection)

Process E pertains to populations that are small, but large enough that inbreeding brings about not fixation but only a random drifting of the gene frequencies at many loci around the equilibrium values determined by opposed pressures. The kaleidoscopically changing patterns of gene frequencies in the neighborhood of the currently controlling selective peak may occasionally carry the system across a threshold leading to a higher selective peak, up which it will be carried irreversibly by mass selection. Thereafter, random drifting occurs around this higher peak until another threshold is crossed leading to a still higher peak and so on indefinitely.

The condition for a maximum number of selective peaks at all times is that selection for each quantitatively varying character should be directed toward an optimum value that is well within the range of variability. The condition that these peaks be for the most part at different heights, permitting progressive evolution, is universal pleiotropy at the level of the characters with which the organism encounters its environment. These conditions for process E are in marked contrast with the most favorable condition for process C, which is selection directed toward an extreme value of a particular character.

Process E is the simplest case of what I have called the shifting balance theory in which the evolutionary steps are not gene replacements but shifts in control by successively better interaction systems, composed of genes that cannot be classified consistently as good or bad in themselves. The number of possible combinations from a limited number of mutations being virtually infinite (10^{1000} possible homozygous genotypes from 10 alleles at each of 1000 loci), no definite limit can be set to the number of successively more favorable interaction systems per mutation.

Unfortunately, process E is excessively slow even when conditions for the most favorable sort of balance are met. I attributed some significance to it in 1931 but practically none in 1932 or later. Many critics have seized on the concept of random drift that was proposed and have asserted that I have advocated this as a significant *alternative*

Table 13.2

Evolutionary processes in species in which there is division into partially isolated subpopulations, panmictic in *F*, *H*, and *I*, uniparentally reproducing clones in *G*. Process *H* differs from *F* in the occurrence of introgressive hybridization with another species. Process *I* differs from *F* in the occurrence of polymorphic systems (resulting from switch genes or chromosomal inversions) that are maintained within demes by heterozygous advantage or otherwise and that may evolve largely independently of each other.

Process	Population (subdivided)	Source	Variability			Selection	
			Storage	Random drift		Among individuals	Among demes
F	Total: large	Mutation	+	0			++
	Demes: small	Immigration	+	+		+	
G	Total: large {Mutation / Crossing	+	0			++
	Clones: large	(Mutation)	(+)	0		(+)	
H	Total: large {Mutation / Introgression	+	0			++
	Demes: small	Immigration	0	+		+	
I	Total: large {Mutation / Polymorphism	+	0			++
	Demes: small	Immigration	+	+		+	
	Polymorphic systems	+	+		+	

to natural selection (e.g., Fisher and Ford, 1947, 1950; see Wright 1948, 1951). Actually, I have never attributed any evolutionary significance to random drift except as a trigger that may release selection toward a higher selective peak through accidental crossing of a threshold. Process *E* was practically wholly rejected when its extreme ineffectiveness in this respect was recognized.

We turn now to Table 13.2, which deals with evolutionary processes that are more complicated than those of Table 13.1 because of their occurrence in populations with more complicated mating patterns than panmixia. It is supposed that the total population is divided into numerous subpopulations so that selection occurs on at least two levels: within each ultimate subpopulation according to individual advantage; and among subpopulations, because of differences in rates of population growth and dispersion, according to the adaptiveness of their total genotypic systems.

Three-Phase Shifting Balance
(Random Drift, Intrademe and Interdeme Selection)

In process F the ultimate subpopulations are supposed to be essentially panmictic and sufficiently isolated to permit continually fluctuating genetic differentiation in their gene frequencies at many loci, but not so isolated as to prevent spreading of the more successful interaction systems.

The store of genetic variability of the species is large because of the favoring of different alleles in different places. The local stores are also large, because of the balancing of local selection pressures by immigration from neighboring demes.

The process within each locality is much like that described under process E but should be hundreds or thousands of times as rapid because immigration pressure here takes the place of the weak pressure of recurring mutation and can balance relatively strong selection. In the three-phase shifting balance theory, the occurrence of this process simultaneously in thousands of localities increases the probability that a threshold will be crossed somewhere by perhaps a million fold as compared with process E. In addition, the random drifting of gene frequencies within demes, on which this trial and error process depends, need not be wholly from accidents of sampling as a result of small numbers, but may also arise from local fluctuations in severity and direction of selection (Wright 1931, 1935b), in amount and kind of immigration (Wright 1948), and other causes. The conditions for the existence of multiple selective peaks are as described under E.

Process F is the one that I emphasized, in 1929 and later, as most effective in the long run. It has been recognized since 1932 that a combination of the population structure of F with changes in conditions (as in C), at a tempo sufficiently slow to permit adjustment, is the most favorable situation for rapid, extensive evolution. It is to be noted that, contrary to Mayr's (1959) assertion that I had attributed absolute selective values to each gene, the theory necessarily depended on interactions of the most extreme sort: those resulting from multiple selective peaks. The mathematical treatment of such interaction systems did not, however, begin until 1935 (Wright 1935a,b).

The effects of processes A to F in the presence of multiple selective peaks were illustrated in the 1932 paper by diagrams (Fig. 13.1) in which the surface of selective values in the system of gene frequencies was indicated by contours (Wright 1932).

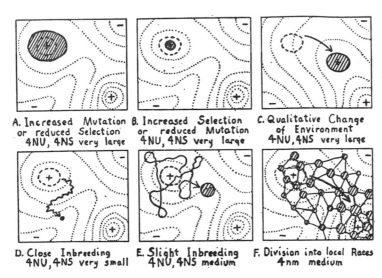

A. Increased Mutation
or reduced Selection
4NU, 4NS very large

B. Increased Selection
or reduced Mutation
4NU, 4NS very large

C. Qualitative Change
of Environment
4NU, 4NS very large

D. Close Inbreeding
4NU, 4NS very small

E. Slight Inbreeding
4NU, 4NS medium

F. Division into local Races
4nm medium

Fig. 13.1—Diagrams of a portion of a multidimensional field of gene frequencies with mean selective values indicated by contours. A low selective peak is shown at the upper left of each diagram, a higher one at the lower right. The species (panmictic in *A* to *E*) is supposed to have occupied the lower peak for historical reasons (region bounded by broken line). The region that the species comes to occupy (*A, B, D*) or one of the regions through which the species (*C, E*) or a subspecies (*F*) passes, under the process stated below, is indicated by a solidly bounded shaded area. In *C* and possibly *E*, the species will later reach the higher peak, and in *F* all subdivisions will come more or less under control of the higher peak by excess emigration from those that reach it first. The processes (*A* to *F*) are the same as in this chapter. *N* refers to total effective population size, *n* (in *F*) to that of a local population. *U* and *S* are coefficients measuring mutation rate and selection, and *m* (in *F*) is the amount of replacement of a local population by immigration representative of the species as a whole. The contours in *C* are those after a change in conditions. Only processes *C* and *F* were considered to be important, with *F* far more important (Wright 1932).

Uniparental Reproduction with Occasional Crossing

Process *G* is the association of prevailing uniparental reproduction with sufficiently frequent crossing and formation of recombinant clones to maintain genetic diversity in the species as a whole. Since selection is necessarily based on the total genotypes instead of merely on the net effects of the separate genes, this system may be considered an extreme variant of process F, with which it was compared briefly in my 1931 paper. It is undoubtedly a very effective process for arriving at the best available genotype for any particular set of local conditions. It is, however, a less modulated process than F for evolutionary advance of the species as a whole.

Gene Duplication

The processes discussed in my 1931 and 1932 papers are, of course, not exhaustive. Duplication of genes or blocks of genes (Bridges 1935; Metz 1947; Wright 1958) might be added as a category of great significance in increasing the amount of genetic material and in complicating gene structure. Such mutations are, however, transmitted in the main like gene mutations, and the *dynamics* of establishment would be essentially similar to the processes discussed. Two more recently developed theories will be added.

Introgression

Hybridization has long been recognized as a process by which new species may arise (see Lotsy 1916). It may also, however, be an alternative to mutation in the transformation of a single species. The systematic development of the thesis that "introgression" (process H), the sorting out of useful blocks of genetic material in the course of repeated backcrossing to the locally predominant species after a cross, is an important evolutionary theory due to Edgar Anderson (Anderson and Hubricht 1938; Anderson 1949). Such previously tested genetic materials have more likelihood of being useful in another context than do random mutations. Introgression should thus be a very useful supplement to mutation in processes B and C. It is treated here, however, as an elaboration of process F, because it is probably most significant in a subdivided species.

Polymorphism

I will end this list with a process (process I) that had been foreshadowed before 1940 by cases of conspicuous polymorphism but that did not come to be recognized as of major evolutionary importance until later. In process I each local population may simultaneously occupy multiple selective peaks by means of multiple alleles, maintained by heterozygous advantage or by selection against overabundance in a heterogenous environment.

At one extreme, alleles at a single locus may each build up an interaction system involving genes scattered throughout the genome and act as a switch for these systems. At the other extreme, the alternative interaction systems may be contained wholly within allelic blocks of genes.

The former has the advantage that the interaction systems may easily be built up by process *F*, but it requires maintenance of the switch mechanism. The latter requires no switch mechanism but depends either on suppression of crossing over after formation of the interaction system or on formation within an already established region of very low crossing over by the relatively ineffective processes *B* and *C*. Probably most polymorphisms are a mixture. Sturtevant and Dobzhansky (1936; Dobzhansky 1955) and Carson (1959) and their co-workers have demonstrated such systems on a grand scale in numerous species of *Drosophila*, characterized by multiple inversions that behave as if they are allelic because of the general absence of crossing over in *Drosophila* males and the relegation of crossover strands within inversions (other than certain kinds of doubles) to the polar bodies (Sturtevant and Beadle 1936). Such systems seem also to be characteristic of those Lepidoptera that have polymorphic mimics (Sheppard 1961) although the mode of suppression of crossing over is not as clear as in the *Drosophila* species. In most cases of strong polymorphism, process *F* probably effects a build-up of alternative interaction systems in at least the rest of the genome.

In conclusion, I hardly need say that there have been many important advances in theoretical population genetics and enormous increases in the amounts of experimental data and of studies of natural populations since 1940. I may add that these developments have by no means exhausted the subject. Because of the multiplicity of varying factors and associated parameters, even in experimental populations, there is still an unfortunately great amount of elasticity in relating theory to observation.

Literature Cited

ANDERSON, E., 1949. *Introgressive Hybridization.* John Wiley & Sons, New York.

ANDERSON, E., AND L. HUBRICHT, 1938. Hybridization in *Tradescantia*, III. The evidence for introgressive hybridization. Amer. J. Bot. 25: 396–402.

BRACE, C. L., 1963. Structural reduction in evolution. Amer. Natur. 97: 39–49.

———, 1964. The probable mutation effect. Amer. Natur. 98: 453–455.

BRIDGES, C. B., 1935. Salivary chromosome maps with a key to the banding of chromosomes of *Drosophila melanogaster*. J. Hered. 26: 60–64.

CARSON, H. L., 1959. Genetic conditions which promote or retard the formation of species. Cold Spring Harbor Symp. Quant. Biol. 24: 87–105.

CASTLE, W. E., 1903. The laws of Galton and Mendel and some laws governing race improvement by selection. Proc. Amer. Acad. Arts Sci. **39**: 233–242.

———, 1919. Piebald rats and selection, a correction. Amer. Natur. **53**: 370–376.

CASTLE, W. E., F. W. CARPENTER, A. CLARK, S. O. MAST, AND W. M. BARROWS, 1906. The effects of inbreeding, crossbreeding and selection upon the fertility and variability of *Drosophila*. Proc. Amer. Acad. Arts Sci. **41**: 731–786.

CASTLE, W. E., AND JOHN C. PHILLIPS, 1914. Piebald rats and selection. Carnegie Inst. Washington, Publ. No. 195.

CHETVERIKOV, S. S., 1926. On certain aspects of the evolutionary process from the standpoint of modern genetics. Proc. Amer. Phil. Soc. (1961) **105**: 167–195, translated from the Russian by Malina Barker, edited by I. Michael Lerner, from the original in Zh. Eksp. noi Biol. **A2**: 3–54.

DARWIN, CHARLES, 1859. *The Origin of Species by Means of Natural Selection*. D. Appleton & Co., New York.

———, 1868. *The Variation of Animals and Plants under Domestication,* vols. I and II. D. Appleton & Co., New York (2nd ed., revised, 1883).

DAVENPORT, C. B., 1899. *Statistical Methods with Special Reference to Biological Variation*. John Wiley & Sons, New York (2nd ed., revised, 1904).

DOBZHANSKY, TH., 1955. A review of some fundamental concepts and problems of population genetics. Cold Spring Harbor Symp. Quant. Biol. **20**: 1–15.

EAST, E. M., 1908. Inbreeding in corn. Conn. Agr. Exp. Sta. Rept. (1907, 1908): 419–428.

———, 1910. A Mendelian interpretation of variation that is apparently continuous. Amer. Natur. **44**: 65–82.

———, 1916. Studies in size inheritance in *Nicotiana*. Genetics **1**: 164–176.

EAST, E. M., AND H. K. HAYES, 1911. Inheritance in maize. Conn. Agr. Exp. Sta. Bull. No. 167.

EMERSON, R. A., AND E. M. EAST, 1913. The inheritance of quantitative characters in maize. Neb. Agr. Exp. Sta. Res. Bull. No. 2.

FISH, H. D., 1914. On the progressive increase of homozygosis in brother-sister matings. Amer. Natur. **48**: 759–761.

FISHER, R. A., 1918. The correlation between relatives on the supposition of Mendelian inheritance. Trans. Roy. Soc. Edinburgh **52**: 399–433.

———, 1922. On the dominance ratio. Proc. Roy. Soc. Edinburgh **42**: 321–341.

———, 1925. *Statistical Methods for Research Workers*. Oliver & Boyd, Edinburgh.

———, 1930. *The Genetical Theory of Natural Selection*. Clarendon Press, Oxford.

FISHER, R. A., AND E. B. FORD, 1947. The spread of a gene in natural conditions in a colony of the moth: *Panaxia dominula*. Heredity **1**: 143–174.

FISHER, R. A., AND E. B. FORD, 1950. The "Sewall Wright" effect. Heredity **4**: 117–119.

GALTON, F., 1889. *Natural Inheritance*. Macmillan, London.

GEIRINGER, HILDA, 1944. On the probability theory of linkage in Mendelian heredity. Ann. Math. Statist. **15**: 25–57.

GOLDSCHMIDT, R., 1940. *The Material Basis of Evolution*. Yale Univ. Press, New Haven.

HALDANE, J. B. S., 1924. A mathematical theory of natural and artificial selection, I. Trans. Cambridge. Phil. Soc. **23**: 19–41.

——, 1927. Selection and mutation, V. Proc. Cambridge Phil. Soc. **23**: 838–844.

——, 1932. *The Causes of Evolution*. Harper & Bros., London.

HARDY, G. H., 1908. Mendelian proportions in a mixed population. Science **28**: 49–50.

[JENKIN, FLEEMING] 1867. Review of *Origin of Species*. North British Review **46**: 277–318.

JENNINGS, H. S., 1914. Formulae for the results of inbreeding. Amer. Natur. **48**: 693–696.

JOHANNSEN, W., 1903. *Über Erblichkeit in Populationen und in reinen Linien*. G. Fischer, Jena.

——, 1909. *Elemente der exakten Erblichkeitslehre*. G. Fisher, Jena.

JONES, D. F., 1917. Dominance of linked factors as a means of accounting for heterosis. Proc. Nat. Acad. Sci. U.S. **3**: 310–312.

——, 1918. The effects of inbreeding and crossbreeding upon development. Conn. Agr. Exp. Sta. Bull. No. 207.

KELLOGG, V. L., 1907. *Darwinism Today*. Henry Holt & Co., New York.

LENG, E. R., 1962. Results of long term selection for chemical composition in maize and their significance in evaluating breeding systems. Z. Pflanzenzücht. **47**: 67–91.

LOTSY, J. P., 1916. *Evolution by Means of Hybridization*. M. Nijhoff, The Hague.

LUSH, J. L., 1946. Chance as a cause of changes in gene frequency within pure breeds of livestock. Amer. Natur. **80**: 318–342.

MACDOWELL, E. C., 1917. Bristle inheritance in *Drosophila*, II. Selection. J. Exp. Zool. **23**: 109–146.

McPHEE, H. C., AND S. WRIGHT, 1925. Mendelian analysis of the pure breeds of livestock, III. The Shorthorns. J. Hered. **10**: 205–215.

MATHER, K., 1941. Variation and selection for polygenic characters. J. Genet. **41**: 159–193.

MAYR, E., 1959. Where are we? Cold Spring Harbor Symp. Quant. Biol. **24**: 1–14.

MENDEL, GREGOR JOHANN, 1866. Versuche über Pflanzenhybriden. Verhandl. Naturforsch. Ver. Brünn 4: 3–47. Translation in *Mendel's Principles of Heredity* by W. Bateson, 1909. Cambridge University Press.

METZ, C. W., 1947. Duplication of chromosome parts as a factor in evolution. Amer. Natur. **81**: 81–103.

MORGAN, C. L., 1933. *The Emergence of Novelty*. Williams & Norgate, London.

MULLER, H. J., 1950. Our load of mutations. Amer. J. Human Genet. 2: 111–176.

NILSSON-EHLE H., 1909. Kreuzungsuntersuchungen an Hafer und Weizen. Lunds Univ. Årsskr. (N. F.) Afd. 2, vol. 5.

OSBORNE, H. F., 1934. Aristogenesis, the creative principle in the origin of species. Amer. Natur. 68: 193–235.

PAYNE, F., 1920. Selection for high and low bristle number in the mutant strain 'reduced.' Genetics 5: 501–542.

PEARL, R., 1913. A contribution toward an analysis of the problem of inbreeding. Amer. Natur. 47: 577–614.

——, 1914. On the results of inbreeding a Mendelian population: A correction and extension of previous conclusions. Amer. Natur. 48: 57–62.

PEARSON, K., 1904. On a generalized theory of alternative inheritance with special reference to Mendel's laws. Phil. Trans. Roy. Soc., A203: 53–86.

PUNNETT, R. C., 1915. *Mimicry in Butterflies*. Cambridge Univ. Press, Cambridge.

RENSCH, B., 1929. *Das Princip geographischen Rassenkreise und der Problem der Artbildung*. Gebr. Bornträger, Berlin.

ROBBINS, R. B., 1918. Some applications of mathematics to breeding problems, III. Genetics 3: 375–389.

SHEPPARD, P. M., 1961. Some contributions to population genetics resulting from the study of the Lepidoptera. Advance. Genet. 10: 165–216.

SHULL, G. H., 1908. The composition of a field of maize. Amer. Breeders Assoc. 4: 296–301.

STURTEVANT, A. H., 1918. Analysis of the effects of inbreeding. Carnegie Inst. Washington, Publ. No. 264.

STURTEVANT, A. H., AND G. W. BEADLE, 1936. The relation of inversions in the X chromosome of *Drosophila melanogaster* to crossing over and nondisjunction. Genetics 21: 554–604.

STURTEVANT, A. H., AND TH. DOBZHANSKY, 1936. Inversions in the third chromosome of *Drosophila pseudoobscura,* and their use in the study of the history of the species. Proc. Nat. Acad. Sci. U.S. 22: 448–450.

SUMNER, F. B., 1932. Genetic distributional and evolutionary studies of the subspecies of deer mice (*Peromyscus*). Bibliogr. Genet., vol. 9.

WEINBERG, W., 1908. Über den Nachweis der Vererbung beim Menschen. Jahreshefte Ver. vaterländisch. Naturkunde Württemberg 64: 368–382.

——, 1909. Über Vererbungsgesetze beim Menschen. Z. Induktive Abstammungs- u. Vererbungs. 1: 277–330.

——, 1910. Weitere Beiträge zur Theorie der Vererbung. Arch. Rassen u. Ges. Biol. 7: 35–49.

WILLIS, J. C., 1940. *The Course of Evolution by Differentiation or Divergent Mutation rather than by Selection*. Cambridge Univ. Press, Cambridge.

WRIGHT, S., 1917. Color inheritance in mammals, VI. Cattle. J. Hered. 8: 521–527.

——, 1918. Color inheritance in mammals, XI. Man. J. Hered. 9: 227–240.

———, 1921. Systems of mating. Genetics **6**: 111–178.

———, 1922*a*. Coefficients of inbreeding and relationship. Amer. Natur. **56**: 330–336.

———, 1922*b*. The effects of inbreeding and crossbreeding on guinea pigs. I. Decline in vigor. II. Differentiation among inbred families. U.S. Dept. Agr., Bull. No. 1090.

———, 1922*c*. The effects of inbreeding and crossbreeding on guinea pigs. III. Crosses between highly inbred families. U.S. Dept. Agr., Bull. No. 1121.

———, 1924. Mendelian analysis of the pure breeds of livestocks. II. The Duchess family of Shorthorns as bred by Thomas Bates. J. Hered. **14**: 405–422.

———, 1929*a*. Evolution in a Mendelian population. Anat. Rec. **44**: 287.

———, 1929*b*. Fisher's theory of dominance. Amer. Natur. **63**: 274–275.

———, 1931. Evolution in Mendelian populations. Genetics **16**: 97–159.

———, 1932. The roles of mutation, inbreeding, crossbreeding, and selection in evolution. Proc. 6th Int. Congr. Genet. **1**: 356–366.

———, 1933. Inbreeding and homozygosis. Proc. Nat. Acad. Sci. U.S. **19**: 411–420.

———, 1935*a*. The analysis of variance and the correlations between relatives with respect to deviations from an optimum. J. Genet. **30**: 243–256.

———, 1935*b*. Evolution in populations in approximate equilibrium. J. Genet. **30**: 257–266.

———, 1938. The distribution of gene frequencies in populations of polyploids. Proc. Nat. Acad. Sci. U.S. **24**: 372–377.

———, 1948. On the roles of directed and random changes in gene frequencies in the genetics of populations. Evolution **2**: 279–284.

———, 1951. Fisher and Ford on the "Sewall Wright Effect." Amer. Sci. **39**: 452–458.

———, 1958. Genetics, the gene, and the hierarchy of biological sciences. Proc. X Int. Congr. Genet. **1**: 475–489.

———, 1960. Genetics and twentieth century Darwinism: A review and discussion. Amer. J. Human Genet. **12**: 365–372.

———, 1964. Pleiotropy in the evolution of structural reduction and of dominance. Amer. Natur. **98**: 65–69.

WRIGHT, S., AND TH. DOBZHANSKY, 1946. Genetics of natural populations. XII. Experimental reproduction of some of the changes caused by natural selection in certain populations of *Drosophila pseudoobscura*. Genetics **31**: 125–156.

WRIGHT, S., AND O. N. EATON, 1929. The persistence of differences among inbred families of guinea pigs. U.S. Dept. Agr., Tech. Bull. No. 103.

YULE, G. U., 1902. Mendel's laws and their probable relation to intraracial heredity. New Phytol. **1**: 193–207, 222–238.

———, 1906. On the theory of inheritance of quantitative compound characters and the basis of Mendel's law: A preliminary note. 3rd Int. Conf. Genet. Rept.: 140–142.

14

The Nature of
Quantitative Genetic Variation

Alan Robertson

Current theories of quantitative genetics, particularly those concerned with the effect of selection, have as their central concept the statistical analysis of the phenotypic variation in a particular measurement. This variation is broken down first into the total hereditary component and the environmental component, and then the former is analyzed into the additive genetic portion and the contributions from dominance and epistasis. The theory has been reasonably satisfactory in the prediction of the response of populations to selection, but a much more detailed description of the quantitative genetic variation is necessary before we can fully understand some of the phenomena that we observe. My main object in this chapter is to discuss in what terms this more detailed description needs to be given, to indicate briefly what evidence we already have on various points, and in what direction future experimentation might go.

I would at the beginning emphasize two points which I believe to be fundamental in these discussions. The first is that we are always dealing with the variation that we observe in a particular measurement made in a certain way on a particular population. It is only too easy to forget this limitation, to pretend to ourselves that we are dealing with a general property of the individual rather than a very specific observation of that property. The second point follows directly from this. We are then analyzing the genetic variation controlled by segregations at particular loci. But this delineation of the loci with which we are concerned is a very arbitrary one; we have imposed it ourselves. In terms of the reproductive fitness of the individual organism, it may be completely meaningless.

Finally, I should apologize early in this chapter that I shall draw a great deal of the evidence from my own work on sternopleural bristles in a large, randomly breeding population of *Drosophila melanogaster*. This characteristic has been the source of material for a great many experiments, but we are still far from understanding completely its genetic variation.

I think that a description of the genetic variation should be in the following terms.

Gene Action

Here I have in mind not so much a specification of variance components as a description in terms of the effects of segregation at the separate loci affecting the character. We should then ask to what extent we find apparent additive action or dominance at the individual loci and what pattern of interaction, if any, we find between different loci. Let me recall the paradoxical situation that, when some of the early theories of gene action were developing in the hands of Sewall Wright (theories which could be presented more simply if gene action was assumed to be additive), it was felt by many geneticists that this approach was not likely to be very fruitful because any geneticist knew that a dominant-recessive relationship was the rule. But as information has accumulated over the years, it has become fairly clear that, for a great many characteristics which are not of fundamental importance for the reproductive ability of the individual, genes must be behaving additively, in the sense that at many of the loci the mean value of the heterozygote must be fairly close to the average of the values for the two homozygotes. Mendel himself was, of course, quite aware that the dominant-recessive relationship was by no means universal, a fact which tended to be overlooked in the early years of classical genetics. Pursuing simplicity further, I think we should not be surprised to find that interactions between loci, for many characteristics, may not be particularly important. We are probably dealing with comparatively small deviations from the balance of the individual organisms, and the deviations will therefore behave in a fairly straightforward and additive manner. But I would rather not go too deeply at this point, because problems of dominance and interactions between loci (both aspects of the buffering of the organism) obviously have considerable evolutionary implications, and I will return to them later when I deal with the correlations between individual measurements and reproductive fitness and the important problem of how natural selection shapes the genetic control of individual measurements.

But I would emphasize that the kind of gene action that may be important to us in any context will very probably depend on the particular phenomena at which we happen to be looking. If, on the one hand, we are trying to improve the egg production of *Drosophila* in randomly breeding strains and, on the other, investigating the effect of close inbreeding on egg production, we may find that in the two situations we are dealing with different sets of loci at which the gene action is quite different. Comparatively rare recessives may be very important in causing inbreeding depression, but their removal from a randomly breeding population may improve it very little and we might have to look to other loci to account for the response to selection.

The Magnitude of Gene Effects

In order to speak usefully about the magnitude of the effects on a particular measurement of gene substitutions at different loci, we must assume interactions between loci to be unimportant. Any specification of the spectrum of effects at these different loci may be regarded alternatively as a statement of the number of loci contributing to its variation, but because I hold the view that the distribution of gene effects will probably be of an exponential kind (so that the smaller the range of effect specified, the greater the number of loci concerned), a statement of the total number of loci contributing to the variation is to me not useful. I assume that the number of loci must be very large and really only limited by our accuracy of measurement of the individual effect. The kind of statement that I would then consider useful would be, as an imaginary example, that, of the difference between extreme selected strains from my population, the most important locus contributed 20 per cent and that perhaps 80 per cent of the difference might result from only 10 loci.

I would like to mention rather anecdotally that in the last three or four years the fog of quantitative variation, which I had assumed to be the result of segregation at a large number of loci, has gradually begun to clear as I have recognized individual segregations almost as personal friends. I would like to give two examples of this in *D. melanogaster*. Quite by chance I discovered that the dominant gene "hairless" (*H*), when introduced into my high bristle line for measurement of the effect of this gene on bristle score in a high background, had the surprising pleiotropic effect of very much shortening the fourth wing vein. On the basis of this observation, I worked out elaborate plans to use the effect as an indicator of one particular aspect of the bristle-forming process, but further genetic analysis showed that it was almost entirely caused by segregation at one locus on the third chromosome. The second example involves the pleiotropic effects of different chromosomes. It is quite simple to substitute the separate chromosomes from my high sternopleural bristle line into the low line. All the chromosomes (even the small fourth) prove to contribute to the differences between the extreme selected lines. Furthermore, the pleiotropic effects of the different chromosomes, measured by their effects on bristle counts on other parts of the fly and on body size, are quite different.

This would suggest that there are a comparatively small number of genes affecting sternopleural bristles on each chromosome, each with its separate pleiotropic effects on the other measurements, so that the chromosomes as units show different pleiotropic patterns.

There has been some progress in recent years in the analysis of quantitative variation in terms of individual loci. In plants Wehrhahn and Allard (1965), using a technique of back-crossing followed by self-fertilization, have recently performed an analysis of the difference in heading time between two varieties of wheat. They have shown that almost all the difference between the two varieties can be accounted for by only four loci. Thoday's group (see, for instance, Thoday, Gibson, and Spickett 1964) have been working with sternopleural bristles in *Drosophila* and, using disassortative mating as a technique for the isolation of segregations with a large effect, have succeeded in locating several loci affecting the character. In Edinburgh we have been doing similar work characterizing the differences between our high and low selected lines. We have, however, encountered a difficult problem in technique. The procedures generally used depend on multiple recessive marker stocks, and a major problem arises from uncertainty about the genetic constitution of those strains at loci affecting bristles. If one can assume that there are no genes in the marker stock which, substituted in the low line, for instance, would reduce the bristle score, then the analysis is simple and straightforward. A similar assumption must, of course, be made for the high line. But since the marker stocks have a completely different origin from the selected line, this may not be a very realistic assumption. Further, it is one which is very difficult to check experimentally. The use of several different marker stocks does not help to solve this problem; it merely introduces new unknowns. The present state of our results is that substitution at as many as ten loci could account for three-quarters of the difference between the two lines. In such analyses, pleiotropic effects of such loci on other characteristics (we have, for instance, found three loci affecting both bristles and body pigmentation) are of great help in that they allow segregations to be followed independently of their effect on bristles.

It seems from our own results that we may have segregation at different loci in our population from those which Thoday is finding in his, but I do not see why we should be particularly surprised by this.

The Distribution of Gene Frequencies

The gradual accumulation of information as to the magnitude of effect and the genetic location of the separate loci affecting any character should permit direct estimates of the gene frequencies in any population. At the moment there is very little evidence on this point. We have been able to estimate indirectly the gene frequencies, in the initial population, of the alleles which we fix in our selection lines (Robertson 1960). The estimate depends on the measurement of the effect of an initial restriction of population size on the limits of advance under selection. If selection under given circumstances fixes genes which are rare in the initial population, then a restriction of the population to a single pair of individuals (followed by subsequent expansion to allow some re-equilibration of linkage before selection) should very greatly reduce the total advance under selection since many of these genes would not be represented in the sample of four gametes from which such a subpopulation was started. Our standard population procedure involves the measurement of 25 flies of each sex and the selection of the extreme ten in each generation. From our initial value of 17.5 sternopleural bristles we can, with this selection procedure, reach a final upward limit in the order of 30 and a downward limit in the order of 11. If we make subpopulations each derived from a single pair, the possible advance under selection is then reduced by about 30 per cent (Fig. 14.1). This finding would suggest that the alleles fixed in the selection procedure are not at very low frequencies in the initial population. But it should be emphasized that the selection limit under any specific selection condition must always be regarded as an artifact of those conditions. We know from experience that, if we try very hard to accumulate all the useful genetic material (by crossing different selected lines, for instance, followed by further selection), we can reach levels of over 50 in the upward direction and about 7 in the downward direction. The original limits were, therefore, artifacts of the method of selection. We have various pieces of evidence to suggest that in these very extreme lines we are now succeeding in fixing genes which, in the initial population, had fairly large effects but were at too low a frequency to have a high chance of fixation. Much more evidence is needed along those lines.

Linkage Relationships

Specification of the linkage relationship among the loci affecting a character, of course, requires *a priori* knowledge of the loci themselves. Except for one case, studied by Gibson and Thoday (1962), in which linkage disequilibrium appears to be maintained by factors other than natural selection for the bristle character itself, we have very little direct information on linkage relationships. To balance this lack of experimental evidence, we have as yet no adequate general theory of the effect of linkage on the advance possible under selection. A fundamen-

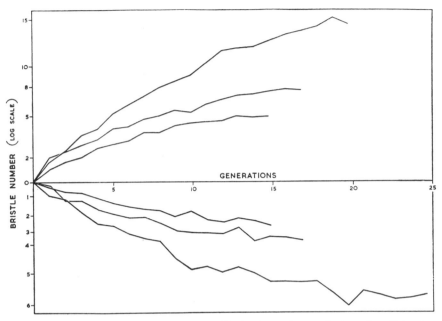

Fig. 14.1.—Response to selection after limitation of population size. Selection 10/25 in each sex. Outer lines from base population; middle lines from sub-populations with one parental pair; inner lines from subpopulations with one parental pair in three consecutive generations.

tal parameter in this respect is the size of the population during selection, and only very recently has a selection theory in finite populations been developed, even for independently segregating genes. If we add the further complication of linkage, an algebraic theory appears to be difficult to develop, and various workers have used Monte Carlo methods on this problem with, as yet, very little in the way of generalizable results. Hill and I have recently been working on this topic in Edinburgh in the very simplest of all situations—that in which selection is assumed to act at the gametic level at only two loci. Our computer runs have covered a wide range of gene effects and frequencies. It can be shown by a simple algebraic analysis of the process that computer runs need be done only at one population size. The preliminary results are interesting in that they suggest several curvilinear relationships in the reduction of the chance of fixation at one locus by segregation at another closely linked to it. Under these circumstances it is not surprising that more complicated models have not given general results. Our results have suggested a comparatively simple way of visualizing the problem in terms of the effective population size. Assuming initial linkage equilibrium between two loci which are very close to one another, consider an allele at a low frequency in the population whose effect is nevertheless so large that under our conditions of selection its chance of eventual fixation is close to unity. At fixation the gametes are genetic replicates of a quite small number of gametes in the early generations of selection. At a locus with a small effect, closely linked to the first one, the frequency of a desirable allele can be increased only within those gametes containing the preferred allele at the first locus. As a result the effective population size in which selection acts on the locus with the smaller effect is very much reduced. Almost all our results can be predicted logically from this approach to the problem, and we have succeeded in developing an algebraic theory to cover the special case in which the expected change in gene frequency at the locus with a small effect is not great. We have still to extend these analyses to more than two loci.

We have done some preliminary experimental work on the effect of the suppression of crossing over in the two major chromosomes on the advance under selection. In our population the second and third chromosomes usually account for about 80 per cent of the response to individual selection for sternopleural bristles. Although I mentioned earlier that the fourth chromosome contributed to the difference between the extreme high and low lines, we have in fact only one line which is genetically different from the parent populations as far as bristle genes on the fourth chromosome are concerned. Two replicate sets of lines were produced containing inversions marked with dominants which would suppress crossing over on the second and third chromosomes. In one set of lines the males were double heterozygotes, and in the other set the inversions were carried in females. In one set, therefore, crossing over is suppressed on the second and third chromosomes, and in the other it is allowed; the genetic constitution of the two sets of lines is otherwise the same. Selection was carried out in the downward selection—for the convenience of the experimenter—until the lines approached fixation. Those in which crossing over had been suppressed had an average response of about 70 per cent of that in the lines in which crossing over was allowed (Fig. 14.2). There was much variation between replicate lines, and not until the 13th generation did the two sets become distinct from one another. Therefore, in selection experiments of the size and intensity we use, 70 per cent of the selection response can be obtained by manipulating whole chromosomes from the base population. Taken together with our computer studies on the

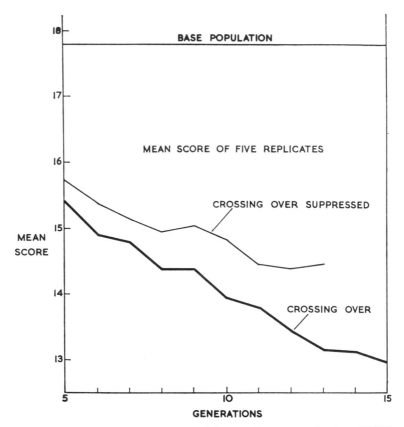

Fig. 14.2.—The average response of five replicates to selection (10/25) with and without suppression of crossing over on the second and third chromosomes of *Drosophila melanogaster.*

effect of linkage on selection limits, these results would suggest that linkage disequilibrium involving bristle-controlling loci is not of great importance. I will return to this point again later.

The Interrelationship of Measurement with Reproductive Fitness

An understanding of the interrelationship of any measurement with reproductive fitness, especially its causal elements, is of fundamental importance in an understanding of the evolution of quantitative genetic variation. Indeed, the answers to many of the questions which I have raised earlier are interconnected with this one. This is the basic problem of why the genetic variation of any measurement is in its present state. It does, in fact, raise some very difficult questions. The primary difficulty comes from the fact that, when dealing with complex organisms, we cannot argue clearly from cause to effect. In one context we may find ourselves treating a particular set of observations as effects, but in another context we may have to treat them as causes of other phenomena.

I can perhaps illustrate this point best by taking as text a comment made to me during a discussion on the contributions of various scientists to the theory of evolution. My colleague remarked, "I can't help feeling that those people who introduced the notion of the selective advantage of a gene have completely confused the issue. After all, natural selection acts on phenotypes." This would make a very good subject for a student essay. It represents a legitimate point of view. Organisms are complex, and it is a great abstraction, if one omits discussion of what are perhaps the important questions of evolutionary theory, to concentrate attention at the level of the individual genes and genotypes. But, on reflection, I feel that this viewpoint avoids one trap to fall into another. It overlooks some quite important problems. The first comes to light when one analyzes the use of the word "phenotype." It brings to mind a picture of a population of adults, each of which can be measured for the character and which compete with one another to pass genes on to the next generation. But what of the selective processes which take place before the character can ever be measured, in fact, before its rudiments are even formed? I have seen clear cases of establishment of a genetic equilibrium within a selection line involving a gene which in the homozygote was lethal at the larval stage but which in the heterozygote increased bristle score. In fact the only logical way (perhaps a not very useful way) to use the word "phenotype" in this context is as a description of the whole life history of the individual.

But there is a more important objection. A necessary condition for genetic change by natural selection is that genotypes shall have different reproductive fitnesses. Only if we can define these different degrees of fitness genotypically can we predict the change in gene frequencies brought about by natural selection, and merely by examining the relative fitnesses of different phenotypes we cannot do this. We have to know not only the type of gene action controlling the measurement but also the way in which the genotypes affecting the measurement control reproductive fitness. I might illustrate the difficulty by a simple example (Table 14.1) involving two loci with no interaction between them, either for fitness or for the metric character. At both loci heterozygotes are fitter than the homozygotes, both of which are assumed to be equivalent. In their effects on the metric character, the

Table 14.1

Interaction among genotype, phenotype, and fitness

	Fitness W			Character X		
	A_1A_1	A_1A_2	A_2A_2	A_1A_1	A_1A_2	A_2A_2
B_1B_1	100	101	100	0	1	1
B_1B_2	101	102	101	1	2	2
B_2B_2	100	101	100	1	2	2

loci are assumed to be equivalent with the high allele being dominant. The equilibrium under natural selection occurs when both gene frequencies are 0.5.

If the frequency of both the alleles dominant for the character X is 0.67, then the mean values for the fitness and for the metric character are $\overline{W} = 100.89$ and $\overline{X} = 1.78$. Averaging the mean fitness values for genotypes with a given value of X, we have

X	0	1	2
$\overline{W}$	100	100.5	101

so that there is a positive regression of $\overline{W}$ on X in this population, and we might say that the optimum value of X is 2. Nevertheless, under natural selection, the gene frequencies return to 0.5, $\overline{W}$ increases to 101, and $\overline{X}$ declines to 1.50. So in this situation, a not very complicated one, natural selection moves the mean of the population away from the observed optimum. The explanation of this in statistical terms is that the additive genetic covariance between fitness and the character (which determines the change of the character under natural selection) is negative whereas the covariance component resulting from dominance is positive and of greater magnitude, giving an overall positive value. The phenotypic covariance between the character and reproductive fitness would have been even further complicated by the addition of an environmental component. With this simple example in mind, I would take the view that discussions of the effect of natural selection on a metric character, based only on the phenotypic relationship of the character to reproductive fitness, are meaningless. There would seem to be a place here for a constructive discussion of what kind of observations we need to make on the correlation between a metric character and reproductive fitness in order to draw meaningful conclusions.

There is ample experimental evidence that many loci must be segregating in wild populations of outbreeding organisms. What is the nature and strength of the forces maintaining the genetic variation in a particular measurement in any population? Here we have two quite distinct kinds of models available to us, of which I will choose two examples as extremes. Each model makes some statements about the nature of the interactions between genes, both within and between loci, in their effect on reproductive fitness. I will assume for simplicity that gene effects on the metric character are additive.

The first extreme model is usually called the "optimum model." It is assumed that the genes affecting a character control reproductive fitness only through their effect on this character in such a way that intermediates have maximum fitness and that fitness declines as the deviation of the measurement from the optimum value increases. This assumption, in effect, involves splitting up the individual organism into a lot of completely separate compartments, so that the genes in any particular compartment affect reproductive fitness only through the final products in that compartment and that there is no interaction with genes in other compartments. One can then speak of the organization of the system of genes controlling a measurement. Spelled out like this, it seems to me a very implausible model from what we know about the nature of organisms. In a sense it imposes a classification on the genetic system based on whatever characteristic the experimenter happens to be looking at.

The other extreme model assumes that the effects on fitness of the loci controlling the measurement are completely independent of the actual value of the measurement and that segregation is maintained in the population by a heterozygote advantage, the cause of which is not specified in any way. This model states very little—merely that there will be no interactions either for fitness or for the measured character between the loci controlling that character. Of course, it does not specify that there will be no genetic interactions within the whole organism for fitness.

How can we distinguish between these two models? In both we would find that the intermediate would have optimum fitness, but one model takes this as a causal element in the scheme, while the other treats it as an effect. But certainly superior fitness of intermediate genotype would be a necessary consequence for any scheme involving the optimum balance of many biochemical and physiological processes in the development of the organism, irrespective of how natural selection has brought about this balance. It is surely to be expected that individuals which are extreme for any characteristic, trivial or important to the fitness and balance of the organism, are likely to be less fit than the average; this would be the necessary consequence of having an unusual genotype.

What evidence do we have concerning the nature of the forces maintaining genetic variability in populations? Again I will refer to some of my own results on that trivial and peripheral characteristic, sternopleural bristles in *Drosophila*. But perhaps there are many other measurements, equally trivial to their possessor, such as fat content in cow's milk or the size of a hen's eggs, that the breeder may be greatly interested in altering by selection.

We can ask first of all how strong the forces are. Some return to the initial value after the relaxation of selection would be expected under either model, although this would depend on the extent to which major genes had been fixed by whatever selection had occurred. We have done several experiments in which we select the population for a few generations, return it to the environment to which it was adapted, and allow natural selection to go on there. A typical example of this consists of a set of three replicate lines, each selected upward with an intensity 10/25 for six generations. Two samples were taken from each line. One sample was put into a standard population cage in which the effect of natural selection could be observed. From the second sample, selection downward was carried out for several generations. All the lines under the conditions of reversed selection returned past the value measured in the original population before selection had started. But the lines relaxed under intense natural selection lost about one-fifth of their original selection response in the first few months—we cannot be very precise about how long this took. They have now been relaxed for nearly two and a half years, probably about 40 generations, and they appear to have changed very little in the last two years. At the time when selection was relaxed, the average response had been 7 bristles. Now after 40 generations of relaxation under the intense competitive conditions of a population cage, the average value of the three lines is still 5.5 bristles higher than that of the base population before selection. A few months ago, we again selected them back toward the artificially selected value, and in 8 generations they had all returned to it. At present we are carrying out a second experiment in which the initial selection is downward, and the early results are very similar to those of the previous experiment. Although such experiments cannot permit one to distinguish between the two different models, the results would certainly suggest that the forces maintaining this genetic variation (insofar as they can be measured in the laboratory) are not very strong and that the genes at a high proportion of the loci must be almost neutral in their effects on fitness.

Recently I quite by chance started an experiment, which, I have since realized, might allow some distinction between the models. In the intermediate optimum model, the selection pressure at any locus will be dependent on the gene frequencies at the other loci in the system. If we could then follow the natural selection at one locus affecting bristles in different bristle backgrounds, we might be able to verify the hypothesis. This experiment we should be able to do in the near future with some of the individual loci affecting bristles which have pleiotropic effects on other characters. But in fact an experiment involving whole chromosomes has already been started. By intensive downward selection we have produced an extreme line with a mean score of about 7 bristles. From this and the extreme high line a homozygous strain was produced containing the third chromosome from the high line and the X, second, and fourth chromosomes from the low line. This homozygous strain has a mean score of about 16 bristles. By crosses of this to the low strain, a population has been created in which the two third chromosomes are now segregating and recombining in an otherwise low background. If the intermediate optimum model is at all correct, then one would expect that the mean in such a population under natural selection should increase fairly rapidly toward the value in the base population. The population has now reached the F_8 generation, and the mean has not changed at all since the F_1, although the variance has, of course, gone down as the genetic material has reassorted itself. We have the necessary lines to start the converse experiment in which the segregation takes place in a high background, and this we intend to do.

If selection acts toward an intermediate optimum, then the chromosomes with an intermediate value for the character because of a balance of plus and minus genes along them will be favored; thus, on the whole, there will tend to be repulsion linkage between genes affecting the character in the same direction. As we can begin to locate individual loci, it should be possible to make direct observations about the favoring of intermediates fairly soon, but the two experiments on populations under natural selection described above would certainly indicate that selection toward an intermediate optimum may not be of importance in the bristle characteristic. Considering these results together with those of the selection experiments in which crossing over was suppressed, I have myself come to the view that linkage disequilibrium is not likely to be important for this measurement.

There is one general problem facing the supporters of the "heterozygote superiority" model. In almost any quantitative characteristic that we examine in a randomly breeding population, we seem to find evidence of genetic variation. Those geneticists working directly with protein polymorphisms are able to detect segregation at more and more loci. At the London Mendel Centenary Meeting, Harris (1966) reported results of his work on ten enzyme systems in human blood. The systems were chosen, not because any polymorphism was expected, but merely because a system for the detection of the enzyme after electrophoresis could be worked out. He found polymorphism at three of the ten loci. This is a surprisingly high figure when one bears in mind that apparently fewer than 30 per cent of the single amino acid substitutions compatible with the genetic code would cause a change in the electrical charge on the protein molecule. Of course, the possibility remains that some of the polymorphisms reflect differences in more than one amino acid. If we have polymorphisms maintained by heterozygote superiority at very many loci, we face the problem of what Neel has called "running out of load space." If all the segregations are being maintained independently by superior fitness of heterozygotes, the populations would have to bear such a heavy segregation load that they would cease to exist. What is the way out of this problem? Some *Drosophila* species have solved it by making a whole bundle of polymorphisms segregate as one chromosome inversion, but we cannot invoke this in cattle or in hens. I myself incline toward the view that many of the polymorphisms are now almost neutral in their effects and stay merely because there is no reason why they should go away. But I think there remains a great deal of work to be done on what might be loosely called the "organization of genetic variation."

The kind of gene action we may expect to find in an analysis of the genetic variation in any measurement will presumably depend on the relationship of that measurement to reproductive fitness. About ten years ago I put forward some ideas about why we find additive gene action in trivial characters like bristle number in *Drosophila,* although I am not sure that I now completely agree with myself. In spite of all the words that have been expended on the evolution of dominance and its advantage to the organism in general, there may still be quite a lot to say on these topics. One general problem that worries me in such discussions of evolution is what should we consider as the starting point for our invoking the explanation of "natural selection" in biochemical and physiological systems. The properties of the system as we see it now are necessary consequences of its present organization, but which of the present properties are there because they were selected for and which of them are unavoidable pleiotropic effects? In the discussion of the evolution of dominance, for instance, it is often assumed that a new mutation will have an effect on fitness in the heterozygote when it first arises within a population. Now one of my colleagues in Edinburgh,

Dr. Kacser, working on the dynamics of chemical flow systems, has suggested that an insensitivity of the rate of flow through the systems to alterations in the parameters controlling most of the steps is a fundamental property of such systems. In other words, a buffering of the system to minor modifications in many of its parameters is a fundamental property of the system as such and does not have to be thought of as a product of natural selection. Something rather along these lines was suggested a while ago by Haldane and Wright, though I should stress that this insensitivity does not depend on the enzymatic control of the steps in the system. Here I am perhaps taking up a point I made earlier in discussing the organization of the genetic system—the difficulty, in this whole field, of distinguishing the right framework in which to apply one's deductive logic. I am also, I think, arguing against what might be called "evolutionary Pangloissism"—the notion that all mechanisms that we find in organisms, whether at the molecular or organismic level, are there because of natural selection for the particular property that we happen to be looking at. In discussing the evolution of feedback systems within organisms, I have been much struck by the necessity to impute motives. Some very simple systems show feedback of a kind. Le Chatelier's principle is well known to students of elementary physical chemistry: that any chemical equilibrium which is perturbed by alteration of external conditions tends to react in such a way as to reduce the direct effect of the perturbation.

I would like to say a few final words on what I see to be the mutual relationship between quantitative genetics and molecular genetics. It cannot be said that studies of quantitative genetics have contributed much to other branches of genetics, although obviously they are very relevant to the general problem of how organisms are shaped by evolution. So, though I cannot see that we have much to contribute to molecular genetics at present, we may have a great deal to contribute when it is applied at the organismic and population level. I can visualize our making use of recent advances in various ways. In the first place, I see that the pleiotropic effects of genes at different loci (most directly observed as bands on starch gel plates) will be of great help to us in the analysis of genetic variation in terms of individual loci. There must be segregation at many loci affecting the different metric characters that have been studied. Workers on polymorphisms, using electrophoretic and immunogenetic methods, can also point to segregation at a great many loci. The time must come when these two disciplines will interpenetrate one another. It is perhaps not surprising that most of the studies of the effects of biochemical polymorphisms on quantitative characters have up to the present been rather disappointing. Each sample of segregations represents only a small proportion of the loci segregating in any population, and the overlap is therefore very small. Perhaps, in animal breeding, if we look for enzyme polymorphisms in functionally very active tissue like liver or mammary gland, we might have more chance of success in this.

As we begin to identify more of the loci controlling variation in individual measurements, then we will perhaps gain more insight into the causal nature of the developmental processes which lie behind the measurements, although in this we are always handicapped by being limited to those parts of the system at which we can detect segregation. So a strict reliance on the population genetics method might give us only a very patchy understanding of what is happening. In my more despondent moments I sometimes feel that we will not be able to understand thoroughly the evolution of the genetic system that affects quantitative variation in any particular measurement until we can understand properly the evolution of the biochemical and spatial organization which lies behind it. The problem of the immediate future is essentially the understanding of the organization of the whole system. The description of this organization will need to be at three different levels—genetic, biochemical, and biophysical. It may well prove that the development of our understanding of these will go hand in hand.

Literature Cited

GIBSON, J. B., AND J. M. THODAY, 1962. The effects of disruptive selection. VI. A second chromosome polymorphism. Heredity 17: 1–19.

HARRIS, H., 1966. Enzyme polymorphisms in man. Proc. Roy. Soc. B 164: 298–310.

ROBERTSON, A., 1960. A theory of limits in artificial selection. Proc. Roy. Soc. B 156: 234–249.

THODAY, J. M., J. B. GIBSON, AND S. G. SPICKETT, 1964. Regular responses to selection. 2. Recombination and accelerated response. Genet. Res. 5: 1–19.

WEHRHAHN, C., AND R. W. ALLARD, 1965. The detection and measurement of the effects of individual genes involved in the inheritance of a quantitative character in wheat. Genetics 51: 109–119.

15

Inbreeding and Gene Fixation in Natural Populations

Hampton L. Carson

With a simplicity so characteristic of him, the late J. B. S. Haldane (1957) wrote, "The principal unit process in evolution is the substitution of one gene for another at the same locus." Indeed, evolutionary genetics must center attention on the dual process of gene fixation and loss; any factor which contributes to this process cannot help being important in evolution. Two major mechanisms are effective in producing gene fixation in sexually reproducing organisms. The first of these is selection. Darwin's discovery stands as a major achievement of nineteenth century biology; the identification of the gene as the essential target of selection, although delayed well beyond Darwin's death, was an inevitable consequence of the union of genetic and evolutionary theory.

The second mechanism which is instrumental in bringing about fixation is inbreeding. Its effect on gene fixation was, of course, first discovered by Mendel. Haldane (1936) has pointed this out and has paraphrased Mendel's discovery mathematically, ascribing to him the first description of the rate of decline of the heterozygous condition in a self-fertilized diploid.

Inbreeding is a system of mating in which offspring are produced by somewhat closely related parents rather than a random sample of possible mates (panmixis). In his early and definitive series of papers on mating systems, Wright (1921a–e) constructed the basic theory of the nonpanmictic systems. That such systems are extremely widespread in both natural and artificial populations and that they can have important evolutionary consequences have been emphasized by Wright (e.g., 1932, 1946, 1964) in a series of later papers.

When a population is not indefinitely large, the theoretical random-mating population breaks up into a series of subpopulations or lines showing some degree of inbreeding. Accordingly, expressions of the degree of inbreeding have little meaning unless they can be related to the condition existing in a given base population (Falconer 1960). Because

281

common ancestry is a law of life, any real population always shows some departure from the random state. Increasing the mating of relatives in a population increases the degree of the dispersion of gene frequencies among a series of relatively inbred lines. This dispersive process with its resultant cumulative effects of accidents of sampling is as basic a consequence of sexual reproduction as Mendelian inheritance itself.

The dispersive process can be described either as an effect of population size in producing accidents of sampling (i.e., random drift: Wright 1931) or as an effect of inbreeding. In his earlier papers, Wright treated the dispersive process from the point of view of inbreeding. Later, he was attracted by the mathematical advantages of theoretical investigations of the effects of population size. The brilliance of these calculations has led some reviewers and synthesizers of evolutionary thought to lose sight of the fact that the essential feature is the dispersion of gene frequencies, resulting mostly from the increased inbreeding imposed by reduction of population size.

Throughout Wright's treatment, and implied if not expressed in subsequent fundamental work on inbreeding (e.g., Fisher 1949; Robertson 1952; Crow and Morton 1955), is the proposition that the dispersive process alone is seldom absolutely pivotal in changes of gene frequency or in gene fixation. Dispersive events form the foundation upon which mutation and selection may operate to effect evolutionary events of much greater significance than any one factor could produce individually.

This chapter will emphasize the importance of the dispersive process in evolutionary change, especially as it occurs in small populations necessarily in a state of relative inbreeding. Outbreeding, the generation of recombinational variability, heterosis, and balanced polymorphism have been stressed from the time of Darwin's book on crossbreeding (1876) to the most recent evolutionary concepts in the present decade (e.g., Grant 1963; Mayr 1963). Theoretical and experimental investigations of these topics represent a great achievement of modern population genetics. Outbreeding, however, accompanied by heterosis and polymorphism, leads to clustering and to equilibrium at intermediate gene frequencies. Conversely, inbreeding leads to dispersion and permits gene fixation, interdeme selection, and species formation. Inbreeding is therefore of paramount importance in evolutionary kinetics.

Much of the early work on inbreeding concerned the apparently harmful effects of this process in nature, in plant and animal breeding, and in human populations (e.g., East and Jones 1919). Even now, despite the comprehensive genetic explanation of inbreeding depression and the demonstration of the apparent absence of harmful effects in "normally" inbreeding plants and animals, a tendency remains for the importance of inbreeding in the evolutionary process to be underrated. Perhaps this is partly influenced by human attitudes toward both strong inbreeding and outbreeding (see, for example, Haller 1963). On a more technical level a strong preoccupation with heterotic effects may have interfered to some degree with an appreciation of inbreeding as a natural evolutionary force.

Mating Systems Involving Inbreeding

Self-fertilization

Among sexually reproducing plants and animals, the most extreme form of inbreeding is self-fertilization. As Wright (1921*b*) has pointed out, the effective population size in such a case is equal to unity in each subpopulation. Predictions about the consequences of continued self-fertilization have received considerable attention, perhaps primarily because this mating system is relatively easy to handle mathematically. The manageability of such calculations is matched at the other extreme by those for random mating in an infinitely large population. It has already been pointed out that the randomly bred population is rarely found in nature. The same extreme rarity seems also to be attached to continued obligatory self-fertilization.

Baker (1953), who has stressed that an understanding of reproductive patterns is essential for the understanding of variation and the evolutionary potential of different species of plants, refers to self-fertilizing organisms as "habitual inbreeders." He has pointed out that there is no known case where a sexual species is never outcrossed. Under certain geographical circumstances, however, self-fertilization strongly prevails; thus Hair (1956) has found that all the New Zealand species of *Agropyron* are self-fertilizing although rare outcrosses cannot be excluded as a possibility.

Brewbaker (1954) listed the following familiar crop plants as largely self-fertilizing: wheat, rice, barley, peanuts, soybeans, tobacco, tomato, peppers, beans, citrus fruits, cotton, and sorghum. In none, however, has reproduction become subsexual in that outcrosses are impossible. In the grass *Poa*, however, Müntzing (1933, 1940) has shown that sexuality has broken down; in some instances a stable system of apomixis has become substituted. Fryxell (1957) has provided an extremely useful list of the mode of reproduction of higher plants although in his list, as in many such formulations, one is impressed by the lack of important information for many species. Plants which are habitually self-fertilizing rarely show either inbreeding depression or heterosis. In this regard, they differ from those plants which are largely cross-fertilized, namely, maize, rye, sugar beets, cucumbers, carrots, celery, cabbage, grapes, almonds, raspberries, and strawberries.

These facts raise an interesting question for the evolutionist: Why has natural selection so obviously favored cross-fertilization in some instances and self-fertilization in others?

Stebbins (1950), Dobzhansky (1951), Mayr (1963), and many others have stressed that selection for heterozygotes with heterotic properties has played an important role in the evolution of the well-known extraordinary devices which assure outcrossing in many instances. It is less clear, however, why selection for heterosis should not have universal relevance.

Baker (1955) has argued that self-compatibility permits many plants, as well as some Crustacea and possibly other animals, to establish themselves after "long-distance" dispersal. This consideration suggests that the positive selective value of self-fertilization is, in at least some cases, related to ecological factors and dispersal rather than to some positive advantage of the mating system *per se*. Stebbins (1957) has pointed out that self-fertilization is frequent in plant populations adapted to certain types of temporary or newly available habitats. Colonizers of such situations appear to possess a considerable selective advantage if they can quickly build up large populations of well-adapted individuals which can then be maintained genetically constant over a number of generations. Self-fertilization fulfills these conditions; the system is flexible in that genetic variability can be produced on subsequent outcrossing.

Although devices which help to sustain heterozygosity are numerous in nature, they are by no means universal, and true homozygosity is surely achieved in many organisms under self-fertilization. In order to achieve true homozygosity, however, the plant must divest itself of its genetic load, and this is a real biological barrier. Kimura (1959) has calculated that one lethal equivalent per gamete is, on the average, an effective barrier to the adoption of self-fertilization by an outcrossing species. Possibly ecological factors might be strong enough, given interdeme selection, to help a plant or animal over this barrier.

Sib mating

In many species of plants and animals, specifically those which are self-incompatible or dioecious, mating of sibs represents the closest possible system of inbreeding. A system of parent-offspring matings is, however, equivalent to that of brother-sister matings in its major effects.

Regular systems of sib matings have been widely used by plant and animal breeders in line-breeding procedures. These systems have the great advantage of being easy to handle both theoretically and experimentally. In natural populations, however, a regular system of sib mating over many generations probably never occurs. Moreover, unlike the elaborate self-incompatibility mechanisms widely found in self-fertilization systems, intrinsic, genetically determined schemes which prevent sib matings are rare. A well-known exception is found in certain species of the fungus gnat *Sciara* (Metz 1938). Females are of two types: male-producing and female-producing. They occur in a one-to-one ratio. Since all the progeny of any one female are unisexual, the closest inbreeding which can occur is mating of cousins.

Despite the apparent paucity of specific genetically determined incompatibilities, many ecological factors appear to reduce the probability of sib matings. Schemes which prevent self-fertilization rarely, if ever, also prevent sib matings. Thus, a large and important avenue for inbreeding is left open in the natural populations of most organisms.

Lesser degrees of inbreeding

From the point of view of natural populations, it is clear that in dioecious organisms no regular system of sib mating is likely to prevail. If inbreeding exists, it probably involves a mixture of many types of matings, such as sibs, parent-offspring, double first cousins, second cousins, and so forth. As will be described in a later section, the consequences of most of these systems—or, more exactly, these irregular patterns—of inbreeding are quite similar, the differences being largely a matter of the rate at which the genetic changes in population composition are effected.

The pattern of matings at these mixed levels of inbreeding is undoubtedly of great importance for an understanding of the structure of a population and its genetic fate. Despite this, no data have been obtained, no doubt because of methodological difficulties although it should be possible to obtain some data for laboratory populations.

Mixtures of methods

For the animal or plant breeder, manipulation of inbreeding and outbreeding in the transfer of genes from one line to another is a standard technique of extraordinary usefulness, especially where self-fertilization can be employed following an outcross. There is probably no other mating system which can fix diversity faster than this. Accordingly assessments of the combinations of inbreeding and outbreeding which must be the rule in most natural populations are highly desirable.

For those plants which are facultative self-fertilizers and which have genetic variants that may be used for markers, estimations of the relative amounts of inbreeding and outbreeding within the species are possible. Jain and Allard (1960) recognized three types of mating systems in such forms, namely, (1) exclusive or predominant outcrossing, (2) predominant self-fertilization, or (3) mixed self-fertilization and outcrossing.

Of considerable interest for this commemorative volume is the work of Harland (1948) on the garden pea *Pisum sativum*. This species, as it is grown around the world and was grown in Mendel's garden, tends to be strongly self-pollinated. Harland, however, has reported that Ethiopian populations of this species, which appear to represent ancestral endemic ones, give considerable evidence of natural outcrossing. Similar data have been published by Rick (1950) for the tomato plant. Wild plants collected in regions where the species is apparently native may show as much as 50 per cent cross-pollination, despite the fact that the cultivated varieties grown around the world are characteristically self-fertilizing.

Haskell (1953, 1954) has shown that natural populations of the groundsel (*Senecio*) and the tetraploid blackberry (*Rubus*) depart systematically from the self-fertilization characteristic of their cultivated forms; the amount of outcrossing in the latter species appears to be 17 per cent.

Another well-known plant, *Vicia faba,* is generally considered to be a self-fertilizing species, but Rowlands (1958) has shown that, under some circumstances, this is not so. The flower of this species is entomophilous. When grown in certain areas or seasons, however, *Vicia faba* may be forced to be largely self-fertilized because there are not enough insect vectors present to maintain crossbreeding. Presumably the amount of outcrossing would be greatest in those areas where the species is endemic. Holden and Bond (1960) have shown that beans of this species grown in winter are heavily outcrossed when compared to those grown at other seasons.

Allard and Workman (1963) have found that outcrossing in the lima bean varies from season to season but remains generally low; that is, it rarely exceeds 5 per cent for any population or season. Harding and Tucker (1964) have found similar variation in *Phaseolus lunatus* and have concluded that the natural populations of this organism must have a very complex mating system.

Workman and Allard (1962) prepared a matrix model for mixed self-fertilization and random outcrossing and noted that this type of system is especially conducive to the powerful evolutionary force of deme formation followed by interdeme selection.

Crosby (1949, 1959) has studied the interesting polymorphic condition which exists in the flowers of the primrose. In most areas of England, flower dimorphism ("pins" *vs.* "thrums") assures a very high degree of outcrossing. In two areas, however, the heterostylic condition is replaced by homostyly, with the result that these particular populations are strongly inbred.

The Consequences of Inbreeding

Inbreeding has three rather closely related effects. The first is its strong tendency to induce the differentiation of a previously large, randomly bred population into a series of subpopulations or inbred lines. Indeed, a population which is not breeding at random must, in fact, be inbreeding, and some dispersion of gene frequencies must occur accordingly. Secondly, as various subpopulations are differentiated, the amount of genetic variability within each small subpopulation becomes reduced. In the third place, there is an increased frequency of homozygotes at the expense of heterozygotes. The latter is really only a slightly more precise statement of the second effect.

Differentiation of subpopulations

Wright (1921*d*) has provided basic calculations to show how dispersion of gene frequencies will occur if a large population becomes subdivided into breeding units with small effective population sizes. In the absence of any differential reproduction on the part of any genotypic class—that is, in the absence of selection—the whole population, the aggregate of the various lines, will retain all original genetic variability. This means that, in the absence of interdeme selection, random mating would eventually restore the composition of the original population.

Falconer (1960) has pointed out that there are two ways of regarding the phenomenon of dispersion and deducing its consequences. The dispersive process may be regarded as a matter of sampling in populations of small size or it may be regarded from the point of view of inbreeding. If the former viewpoint is adopted, one may look upon the population size as being instrumental in forcing a particular mating system involving inbreeding on the subpopulation concerned. From the latter point of view, the dispersive process can be described in terms of genotypic changes resulting from matings between related individuals.

Among the most satisfactory demonstrations of the dispersive process in laboratory materials is that of Buri (1956) on *Drosophila melanogas-*

ter. He traced the fate of 105 lines of this species, each consisting of 16 individuals in each generation. The base population had two alleles at the brown locus with initial frequencies of 0.5. Similar studies have been made by Kerr and Wright (1954*a,b;* Wright and Kerr 1954).

The divergence of genetic compositions between purposely inbred lines of common origin is a well-known phenomenon in animal and plant breeding. In most cases, selection and inbreeding are practiced together, although sometimes only natural selection is allowed. Thus Wright (1934) reported on digit variability in twenty-three inbred lines of guinea pigs. A recent study of *D. melanogaster* by Lints (1961) further documents this phenomenon; seven sib-mated lines derived from a single wild female diverged in size, viability, and development time.

The approach to homozygosis

Much is known about the theory of inbreeding, the basic calculations having been made principally by Wright (1921*a–e*, 1922) and Haldane (1936, 1937). The monograph of Fisher (1949) is the standard work in the field. Inbreeding has generally been studied through investigation of theoretical genetic changes within an idealized population in which mutation, selection, and migration are excluded and in which the generations are discrete.

Relationship is a law of life in bisexual populations. Each individual has two parents, four grandparents, eight great-grandparents, and so forth; thus, traced back n generations, he will have 2^n ancestors. In relatively few ascendent generations, the number of individuals required to provide separate ancestors for each present individual has become a very large number, larger than any real population can harbor. Therefore mating of two individuals having a more or less recent common ancestor is a highly probable event in most populations. Any condition promoting such consanguineous matings leads to correlation between the male and female gametes that unite to form the offspring. Following Li (1961), the results of a consanguineous mating may be represented for a single locus with alleles A and a, having gene frequencies of p and q, as follows:

	♀ $p(A)$	♀ $q(a)$
♂ $p(A)$	$p^2 + \varepsilon$	$pq - \varepsilon$
♂ $q(a)$	$pq - \varepsilon$	$q^2 + \varepsilon$

in which ε represents a positive fraction. Let F be the correlation coefficient between the uniting gametes. Calculation shows that $F = \varepsilon/pq$ or $\varepsilon = Fpq$. Wright (1921*b*) has defined F as the inbreeding coefficient of the population.

One of the most striking and important effects of inbreeding, as shown by the above, is the increase of the proportion of homozygotes at the expense of heterozygotes. Application of the above equations to situations of various gene frequencies will easily demonstrate the well-known corollary that inbreeding does not change the gene frequency but merely introduces association between the uniting gametes.

Continued inbreeding of any sort will result in a continued decrease of heterozygosity and a corresponding increase in homozygosity, generation by generation. Crow (1954) and Falconer (1960) have pointed out that there are two kinds of homozygotes produced in populations. If the two genes are replicates of one gene present in a common ancestor, the homozygote is called "identical" or "identical by descent." In the other type of homozygote, whose phenotype is usually not recognizably different from that of the identical homozygote, the two genes present are not replicates of one original gene and might be derived from two different mutational events. Such a homozygote, called "independent," could conceivably arise even in an interracial or interspecific cross. The inbreeding coefficient is thus a property of an individual; specifically it is the probability that two genes at any locus are identical by descent, and it expresses the degree of relationship between the parents of an individual.

Because of the very great importance of "pure" or inbred lines in practical plant and animal breeding and in genetic and other biological research, a very great deal of attention has been given to inbreeding as it may occur under a variety of subsidiary conditions. Thus Haldane (1930, 1936; see also Fisher 1949) showed that the ultimate rate of decrease of heterozygosis for autotetraploids under self-fertilization will be 0.83, whereas the corresponding value for diploids is 0.5. His calculations also showed that in diploid maize, after 20 generations of self-fertilization, all but one plant in 2500 would be expected to be fully homozygous. Nevertheless, the average length of chromosome which remains heterozygous in the exceptional plants is 2.5 units. Wright (1933) calculated the effects of inbreeding on sex-linked genes, and Haldane (1937) extended earlier calculations on the theoretical results of continued brother-sister mating.

Robertson (1952) has analyzed the interaction of population size and inbreeding for completely isolated strains of a given size that were tending toward fixation without mutation or selection. Under these circumstances, the inbreeding coefficients changed successively and the gene frequencies in these lines followed a succession of distributions depending on the coefficients.

Moran (1958) has shown that homozygosity is approached nearly twice as fast in a population in which generations overlap. Watterson (1959a,b) has considered the effects of various types of assortative mating and has shown that the approach to homozygosity is very rapid with complete positive assortative mating; however, the effect of assortative mating varies according to whether the population is monoecious or dioecious and to what degree the sex ratio deviates from unity.

In natural populations the effects of both inbreeding and assortative mating on the genetic load are important (Crow and Kimura 1965). Both processes decrease heterozygosity and thus increase the segregation load in the population. Formation of inbred lines, followed by elimination of certain lines carrying a high frequency of subvitals, might be expected to have a cleansing effect on the larger population. The importance of interdeme selection in the cleansing effect is great.

From the evolutionary point of view, the main consequence of the inbreeding–population-size effect is the approach of the various lines toward homozygosity. Most of the theoretical subconditions which have been considered do not alter this fundamental fact; they affect primarily the rate at which homozygosity is acquired.

The retention of heterozygosity in inbred lines

The principal exception to the generalization in the preceding paragraph is the case wherein either selection or some other agency preserves heterozygosity even in small inbred populations. Because of the widespread interest in heterosis and the importance of retention of genetic variance in populations, these exceptions have received considerable attention.

One of the most persistent folklores of modern population genetics is that the expectations of the classical theory of inbreeding are frequently not realized. Thus many inbred lines appear to carry more genetic variability than would be expected (see review by Lerner 1954). For example, Gowen, Stadler, and Johnson (1946) have shown that a number of long inbred lines of D. melanogaster retain considerable heterozygosity. It was not clear to what degree mutation, selection for heterozygotes, and the occurrence of balanced lethal systems have each contributed to this condition. Durrant and Mather (1954) found that even the long-inbred Oregon strain of D. melanogaster retains variability and concluded that this variability arose from recent mutations rather than from any inefficiency of the original inbreeding. Thompson and Rees (1956) have shown that rye, which normally shows inbreeding depression when forcibly inbred, can in some instances retain heterozygosity, such as that for a chromosomal interchange with apparent heterozygous advantage in one inbred line.

There is considerable evidence that, under mixed mating systems of inbreeding and outbreeding, considerable genetic variability can be maintained. For example, from evidence of heterozygous advantage in a closed population of barley, Jain and Allard (1960) concluded that the decay of variability because of inbreeding should be very low in a system of occasional outcrosses followed by self-fertilization. Their formulation agrees closely with the earlier purely theoretical formulation of Hayman (1953), who stressed that imperfect self-fertilization combined with widespread pollen dispersal is a powerful force for the storage and release of variability in plants.

The theoretical studies of inbreeding have gone beyond the observations of the genetic state of long inbred lines. Bartlett and Haldane (1935), Haldane (1936), Mather and Hayman (1952), and Hayman and Mather (1953) have considered the progress of inbreeding when homozygotes are at a disadvantage. Heterozygosis in an approximately pure line can result either from the cohesive force of linkage or from the process of mutation. Linkage is a powerful force for maintaining considerable variability when the genes involved have selective advantage in the heterozygote. Thus, Hayman and Mather have made calculations which show that, depending on the mating system, homozygote disadvantage may halt the dispersive process imposed by small-population–inbreeding effects. Only a moderate amount of heterozygote advantage is apparently sufficient to prevent complete fixation and bring the population to equilibrium. Although Haldane (1956) was critical of Hayman and Mather's calculations, the rebuttal (Hayman and Mather 1956) answered the objections satisfactorily and the theoretical point appears to be established.

Although he did not consider inbreeding coefficients, Robertson (1962) found that heterozygote advantage in a small population is a very potent factor in maintaining genetic variation within the population if the equilibrium gene frequency is close to 0.5. The effect, however, drops off rapidly at other frequencies. Bodmer and Parsons (1960) have shown that, when a balanced polymorphism already exists in a population, a newly arising third allele need not have heterozygote advantage to become established if there is some inbreeding.

The effects of linkage are not well known. Although Gowen, Stadler, and Johnson (1946) assumed that balanced lethals could accumulate easily in inbred lines, Bennett's (1958) calculations show that the mutation rate would have to be very high for development of such systems to be a serious probability. Bateman and Mather (1951) found that genetic variance in ear internode length in barley declined more rapidly than expected during self-fertilization of the F_2 generation of a cross between two strains. They considered this to result either from linkage of plus or minus polygenes in coupling or from a selection in favor of homozygotes.

Reeve and Gower (Reeve 1955, 1957; Reeve and Gower 1958) considered selection, mutation, and linkage in relation to various types of mating systems involving inbreeding and concluded that, in the maintenance of genetic variability, selection between inbred lines derived from a large base population will be much more effective than selection within lines. If selection is severe against homozygotes at a few points on a chromosome, it will retard the progress toward fixation by inbreeding. Reeve suggests that, as inbreeding progresses, the severity of selection against homozygotes and the number of loci at which it acts will generally increase. The result will be that the average progress toward fixation will lag increasingly far behind that expected from the classical theory. From the point of view of inter-line selection, lethals may speed up the rate of progress toward homozygosity with mild inbreeding, provided that balanced lethal systems are not formed.

Papers by Kimura and Crow (1963) and Robertson (1964) revived interest in the question, originally raised by Wright 1921e), concerning the effect, in small populations, of nonrandom mating designed to produce a maximum avoidance of inbreeding. In such a mating system, the least related individuals are always mated, that is, double first cousins in a population of 4, quadruple second cousins in a population of 8, octuple third cousins in a population of 16, etc. Kimura and Crow showed that the initial decline in heterozygosity is minimal in this system but that there are other systems, such as circular pair mating and circular mating, which retain more heterozygosity. Robertson's calculations further document the fact that maximum avoidance systems are not universally the best for the retention of genetic variance. In fact, the initial decline in heterozygosity may be ahead of that expected from random drift alone.

Although many of the theoretical studies cited above apply directly only to planned or regular systems of artificial inbreeding, they are not without their implications for natural populations. There is little question that certain inbred lines, from the many which could be formed from a large base population, will retain considerable heterozygosity. If natural selection preserves such lines, much homozygosity in small populations may be avoided. Unfortunately, data are scarce on this point, and the actual situation is largely unknown.

Fixation of genes

The discussion of heterozygosity in inbred lines is in a sense a digression from the theme of this chapter. Consideration given to it must not reduce the appreciation of what is by all means the foremost evolutionary effect of inbreeding, namely, the fixation of genes. The dispersive process, aided by selection favoring homozygotes, is a powerful and effective system for the fixation of genetic diversity.

The rigor of the theoretical calculations that have shown this system of fixation is hardly duplicated in natural populations. When fixation occurs, a diagnosis of its paramount causes is ordinarily impossible. It is nonetheless tempting to suggest that the forces of random drift, inbreeding, and selection are coordinated, as they are when manipulated by the animal or plant breeder.

Inbreeding from samples of wild populations is, of course, the standard method for demonstrating recessive mutants which are concealed in normally outbred populations (e.g., Spencer 1947; Dobzhansky 1951). The mutants disclosed may be lethals, semilethals, and subvitals, or indeed supervitals. They may be oligogene visibles or cryptic chromosomal aberrations, or they may be polygenes with very small individual effects.

Inbreeding depression and heterosis

Practically all animals and plants which are normally outcrossed suffer some depression, when inbred, of the mean phenotypic value for characters connected with reproductive capacity or physiological efficiency. The depression is ordinarily quickly and easily reversed upon outcrossing. Lerner (1958) has pointed out that the more a character affects fitness, the more important it becomes in contributing to the depressive effects of inbreeding.

Despite the fact that depression is one of the most dramatic effects of the inbreeding process, fitness does not erode continuously but undergoes equilibration after a few generations. Many highly vigorous and stable inbred lines are known and have been known from the days of Darwin and Mendel. It was the basic work of King (1918, 1921) on inbreeding in rats that established without question the important point that inbreeding, alone and of itself, is not responsible for the widely observed depression.

Loeb, King, and Blumenthal (1943) determined, on the basis of transplantation compatibility, that great genetic similarity exists between individuals within lines, some of which had been inbred by brother-sister matings for about 100 generations. Lyon (1959), following the course of inbreeding depression in three inbred strains of mice, described the genetic load in terms of the number of post-implantation fetal deaths. In a similar study, Bowman and Falconer (1960) recorded litter size in twenty inbred strains, using this character as a measure of the inbreeding depression. Mean litter size declines 0.56 young for each

10 per cent increase in the inbreeding coefficient. Seventeen of the twenty lines were lost by the time the inbreeding coefficient reached 70 per cent. As will be discussed later, however, the three lines which survived in this experiment were strong, and one survived indefinitely, reaching 99 per cent inbreeding without dropping below the mean of the noninbred control. In these three lines, favorable dominants were apparently fixed. Deol *et al.* (1960) provide evidence, however, that considerable genetic variation continues to arise within inbred strains of mice, despite the fact that classical theory would require genetic homogeneity. They document the continual formation of sublines and ascribe it to the rapid fixation of newly arisen mutants.

Hutt (1950) has summarized the major effects of inbreeding in poultry, the strongest manifestation being reduction in hatchability of eggs. The decline in fitness is documented by Düzgünes (1950) for leghorns, and further interpretations have been provided by Schultz (1953).

Although earlier data indicated a contrary conclusion, Lundquist (1947, 1953) found no conclusive evidence for a difference between the effects of inbreeding in diploid and tetraploid rye.

The nature of inbreeding depression in *D. melanogaster* has been studied by Tantawy and Reeve (1956), and Latter and Robertson (1962) have measured the decline in fitness in terms of a competitive index, obtained by placing inbred flies in competition with a particular tester genotype. The index was found to decline 2.7 per cent for every 1 per cent increase in the value of F.

The converse of inbreeding depression, heterosis, has received an enormous amount of attention, and no attempt will be made to deal with the subject in this review. Suffice it to say that inbreeding results in a loss of vigor in nearly all species of animals and plants which are normally cross-fertilized (Kirk 1933) and this vigor is restored by crossbreeding. The self-fertilizing plants which retain at least a small avenue of cross-fertilization undergo depression upon resumption of self-fertilization following such crosses.

Interaction of Inbreeding, Random Drift, and Selection in Natural Populations

In any consideration of inbreeding effects, the reviewer must draw heavily upon the rich literature from animal and plant breeding and laboratory studies. The understanding of evolutionary patterns, however, necessitates extrapolation of inferred principles to the infinitely complex natural situation. Most of the theoretical considerations and the observational data to be considered in this section therefore lack precision. Falconer (1960), for example, has pointed out that small iso-

lated natural populations frequently show differentiation between localities and between successive generations. Since these very phenomena are the expected consequences of random drift, it is tempting to
ascribe them to random drift. Three further conditions must be
fulfilled, however, before such a conclusion can be justifiably drawn.
The effective population size must be small enough, the subpopulations must be well isolated, and the genes concerned must be subject to
very little selection.

The formation of demes

As noted previously, the expectation that inbreeding should lead to
homozygosity is probably not realized very often in natural populations. Nevertheless, the decline of heterozygosity in local populations,
relative to their large outbred counterparts, is doubtless a universal
phenomenon. Wright (1940, 1943, 1946) has given special consideration to this condition. From the evolutionary point of view, the most
mobile situation is one in which a larger population is broken up into
relatively small, semi-isolated subpopulations. At first, Wright (1943)
referred to the subpopulations as *panmictic units* but later adopted the
term *neighborhoods,* which better describes their relatively inbred
character. Another very useful term for such a subpopulation unit is
the *deme,* as proposed by Gilmour and Gregor (1939) for a more or less
isolated local breeding community (gamodeme).

Although their calculations stress random-mating systems, Crow and
Morton (1955) have made a useful re-evaluation of the ways in which
gene frequency drift can be measured in small populations. They have
made a distinction between the *systematic factors* (selection, mutation,
and migration) which tend to carry the gene frequency to an equilibrium point and the *dispersive factors* which cause gene frequencies to
scatter. Such systems under natural conditions undoubtedly show complex interactions as demes are formed.

Under almost all types of mating systems, demes should tend toward
homozygosity, and the more rigorous the inbreeding system, the more
pronounced this tendency will be. In systems where gamete formation
is followed by parthenogenesis and chromosome doubling, an extreme
form of deme formation is observed (Nei 1963).

Interdeme selection

Whenever a population has formed demes, a new and important
kind of selection enters the picture, namely, intergroup or interdeme
selection, through which adaptive differences between groups can become established (Wright 1937, 1945). If the population is large and

freely interbreeding, intragroup selection is paramount. Natural selection tends to maximize the mean fitness and to seek an equilibrium. Since the early monograph of Fisher (1930), intragroup selection has received the most attention. In a challenging paper, Lewontin (1961) called attention to the mathematical difficulties of handling interdeme selection, which to the plant and animal breeder is about equivalent to family selection. He suggests that the effectiveness of interdeme selection is related to the rate of extinction of demes. Phyletic extinction, especially at the level of the local population, may be more closely related to progressive evolutionary change than is ordinarily thought. Although a single choice between two types may appear to be merely eliminative, it can indeed be creative in the evolutionary sense.

Among the natural animal populations which appear to have a structure conducive to interdeme selection are those of various species of land snails (e.g., Gulick 1905; Crampton 1932; Mayr and Rosen 1956; Lamotte 1952). The very low vagility of these animals seems obviously related to their considerable interneighborhood differentiation. Thus, inbreeding, drift, and dispersion of gene frequencies have probably been an important accompaniment of the isolation which is characteristic of their populations. In some situations, as on the oceanic islands of the central Pacific, the differentiation is such that the groups are generally accorded specific rank. Gulick, for example, has recognized 200–300 species and more than 1000 "varieties" of the family Achatinellidae on the island of Oahu, Hawaii, alone. Polymorphic land snails of the genus *Cepea* manifest dispersion by distinct interpopulation gene frequencies; it is obvious in this case that inbreeding is accompanied by selection (Sheppard 1951).

Inherently low vagility is only one of many factors, most of which are ecological, which promote dispersion. Thus, isolation may be by time and season, or it may involve noncyclical climatic changes. Migration or long-distance transportational rates may be changed, and a given area may be subject to repeated volcanic eruptions and lava flows which produce isolation.

From the evolutionary point of view, the main consequence of such isolating mechanisms is deme formation, although in many cases it is hard to uncover the particular events which have contributed to the observed dispersion. For example, Philip (1938) reported that several mouse populations from a Scottish coal mine showed an unexpected lack of heterozygotes. The author ascribed the predominance of homozygosity to the breaking up of the population into comparatively small mating units, but whether the fact that these were mine populations was pertinent to the situation is difficult to say.

The speciation of snails and other organisms of low vagility on oceanic islands is not entirely a reflection of the intrinsic low mobility of the organisms. A recent monograph (Hardy 1965) documented the extraordinary development of the highly mobile flies of the family Drosophilidae on the Hawaiian Islands. Ecological factors, including meteorological, altitudinal, volcanic, and insular conditions, appear to be pivotal in the dispersion into species of the descendants of the original colonizers. The ecological factors leading to inbreeding may also guide natural selection into reciprocal adaptation and the adjustments of mating. O'Donald (1960) has shown that in birds imprinting may lead to consanguineous matings with the consequence that homozygosity develops almost as fast as it does by sib mating. He calculates that 4.7 generations are required for homozygosity to be attained under sib mating and 6.3 under imprinting. It is possible that the assortative mating found in the blue goose and the snow goose may result from an imprinting system.

The various inbreeding mating systems in plants, described earlier, are conducive to differentiation of micropopulations into so-called microspecies. The enormous differentiation in *Erophila,* for example, a habitually self-fertilized species, is apparently caused by very rare outcrossings, which produce many new forms that become stabilized (Winge 1940).

The genus *Bromus* includes several species which are predominantly self-fertilized (Knowles 1943; Harlan 1945). Harlan studied 232 varieties that had descended respectively from 232 wild plants. The swarms of local races found are explained by facultative cleistogamy, but highly heterozygous interracial hybrids are occasionally formed. Apparently, this heterozygosity is reduced rapidly under self-fertilization.

Baker (1953, 1960), who has described many similar examples of plant races, has concluded that race formation is frequently an outcome of the dispersive effects of the mating system combined with selection. High-altitude and marginal races in *Trifolium* (Daday 1954) represent a comparable phenomenon. The thorough and beautiful study of races in *Gossypium hirsutum* by Hutchinson (1951) shows that allotetraploidy does not inhibit race formation. However, because the species appears to have been Tertiary in origin, there was ample opportunity for it to have formed races as a diploid before tetraploidy ensued.

The interesting and diverse reproductive methods manifested by many Protozoa have been reviewed by Sonneborn (1957). Deme formation under bisexual reproduction is very strong in *Paramecium aurelia,* for example, where the 16 varieties are essentially inbred lines.

What appears in some cases to be a random-mating pattern may sometimes be better understood if some inbreeding is assumed. The Australian grasshopper *Moraba scurra,* which is confined to prairie remnants around cemeteries in New South Wales, has a disjunct distribution. If random mating within the population inhabiting one cemetery is assumed, the data on fitness and interaction between inversion polymorphisms yield a curious result (Lewontin and White 1960). However, if the data are recalculated with assumed F values of 0.10 to 0.15, a stable equilibrium is predicted, in accordance with long-range observations (Allard and Wehrhahn 1964).

Clearly deme formation is very widespread in nature. Wherever there are demes, the possibility for interdeme selection exists. Natural selection would appear to have extensive material on which to work at the interdeme level. The question arises, however, whether demes, with their reduced variation, have any evolutionary future if they subsequently expand. Are demes always less vigorous than outbred populations? Does the general condition of homozygosity impair the evolutionary future of an organism? The facts suggest a negative answer to both of these questions.

The evidence seems to indicate that the majority of inbred lines produced by dispersion and intrademe selection do show reduced vigor, for reasons which are well known. By the same token, however, it is well known that inbreeding depression results from the segregation and fixation of deleterious recessives. Although most inbred lines derived from a large outbred population may show this effect, there is no reason why all should. Darwin (1876) in his monograph on cross- and self-fertilization in plants gave many examples of what later came to be known as inbreeding depression. Nevertheless, he emphatically pointed out that this depression is by no means an invariable rule and provided much data on a particularly vigorous inbred line of *Ipomea,* which he called "Hero."

Similar reports of vigorous inbred lines or small demes are scattered throughout the literature. For example, in *Tetrahymena,* Nanney (1957) has shown that the various manifestations of inbreeding depression, such as death at conjugation or failure to complete nuclear reorganization, arise gradually over several generations. Nevertheless, some strains may surmount each of the crises and become as vigorous as the original crossbred strains. Results of this kind are reminiscent of the classical work of Hyde (1924), who studied fertility in 17 inbred lines of *D. melanogaster.* Exceptionally high fertilities were found in several stocks, indicating that depression is not an invariable concomitant of inbreeding, even in normally cross-fertilizing organisms. Sang (1964) studied the nutritional requirements of four inbred lines of the same species and found that they did not differ greatly from hybrids between the lines.

Dobzhansky and Spassky (1953) studied concealed variability in *D. pseudoobscura* and *D. persimilis* by making certain chromosomes homozygous. Although a large number of lethals, semilethals, and subvitals were found, between one and two per cent of the chromosomes tested showed supervital properties.

Bowman and Falconer (1960), in their definitive study of inbreeding depression and heterosis in mice, observed the expected loss of lines and of heterosis for most cases, but one inbred line survived indefinitely and reached 99 per cent inbreeding without dropping below the noninbred control. Three other lines, furthermore, did not show any depression with as much as 81 per cent inbreeding. McCarthy (1965) has shown that the embryonic lethality found in inbred strains of mice is not necessarily caused by mutant recessive lethals.

The great preoccupation of many investigators with the very real and important effects of heterosis has perhaps diverted attention from the existence of exceptional vigorous inbreds. I agree with the suggestion of Bowman and Falconer (1960) that inbred vigor may result from the fixation of favorable dominants. As Hayman and Mather (1953) have pointed out, nothing is gained from slow inbreeding; it merely artificially sustains heterozygosity. Natural selection, therefore, might favor fast and close inbreeding that leads rapidly to homozygous demes. In a natural evolutionary situation where interdeme selection obtains, it seems likely that such vigorous demes would be positively selected.

In many plants where the mating system includes elements of both inbreeding and crossbreeding, such interdeme selection should be important. Selection between closed strains has been studied extensively by Suneson (1949) and Morley (1959). Kirk (1927) reported that certain self-fertilized lines in red clover had a greater fitness than his random sample. Later (Kirk 1933), however, he reinterpreted these data.

It appears to be generally true that the demes or inbred lines formed in natural populations are not so strongly inbred and isolated as to be completely closed to crossbreeding. The mating system may preserve genetic variation even within small localities if there is any crossbreeding at all (Weil and Allard 1964; Workman and Allard 1964; Iman and Allard 1965). Iman and Allard pointed out that natural populations of *Avena fatua* in California, which show 1–12 per cent outcrossing, are able to stand the mild loss of vigor accompanying inbreeding, because the flexibility of outbreeding is combined with the maintenance, through inbreeding, of specific, highly adapted genotypes.

Inbreeding, species formation, and adaptive evolution

Species formation is in a sense the terminal process of dispersion. The process begins as inbreeding in populations, progresses through deme formation to race formation, and finally has as its result the permanent intergroup fixation of genetic diversity. Following Mayr's (1954) statement of the founder principle, Carson (1959, 1965) has strongly emphasized the role of outpost or marginal populations as sites where significant genetic events, such as those described in this chapter, could be expected to occur most readily. He has further suggested that the inbreeding-drift effect may be accompanied by homoselection—that is, the increased natural selection for homozygotes under outpost-population conditions.

Where the intrinsic conditions cause low rates of dispersal, as illustrated most graphically among snail populations (Diver 1940), the great number of small, discrete populations may indeed serve as avenues for intense speciation, especially through interdeme selection. This is a fundamental law of all populations. However, each species, immediately following its formation, is not necessarily best adapted to the local conditions in which it finds itself. The chance elements of dispersion and inbreeding and the exigencies of local geography frequently, in fact usually, have fortuitous results. In each local situation, selection must do the best it can with the material available to it. A species is always sensitive to drastic changes in its fitness, but this does not mean it is always the best product that can be produced in response to a local situation.

Probably for that reason swarms of sympatric species or, as the extreme case, sympatric sibling species may coexist. Events which are conducive to species formation are not necessarily those which provide novel evolutionary advances. Thus, in the Morabinae, a group of wingless Australian grasshoppers, allopatric speciation has produced a complex mosaic of species inhabiting the continent. Rather than a strict product of adaptive response, such differentiation can be better viewed as principally dispersive, aided particularly by low vagility of the insect and its propensity for small populations. Certainly a minimal fitness must be maintained, but it is not necessarily accomplished by local ecotype formation.

Dispersion and proliferation of inbred demes, races, or incipient species may be accomplished as efficiently by periodic declination of numbers and worsening of conditions as by slow peripheral spread, which apparently was the process in the Morabinae. Thus the key dispersive events may be brought about by sudden destruction of a population, leaving remnants—multiple parallel populations—which would then be subject to inbreeding and fixation.

As has been pointed out by Dobzhansky (1951) and others, certain chromosomal conditions, such as pericentric inversions and translocations, should undergo adverse selection in the heterozygous condition. Thus, because each, immediately following its origin, must go through a heterozygous stage, natural selection should reject it. On the other hand, karyotype differences of this sort occur almost universally *between* species, although such differences rarely exist in the heterozygous condition *within* species populations. This implies that some condition, related to the formation of species, permits fixation of these karyotype differences. The effects discussed in this chapter could easily produce such conditions, and, again, they would not be expected to bear any relationship to the adaptive norm.

The process of mutation is continually adding genetic variability to a population. As long as this variation exists in large outbred populations, its potential for changing the species may not be realized; when it is dispersed into small populations, which maintain minimal fitness, unexpected and novel properties may emerge. For example, a number of strains of the normally bisexual species *D. mercatorum,* when studied in the laboratory, show an extremely low rate of thelytokous parthenogenesis. In most cases, less than one egg per thousand develops. This type of reproduction is probably never functional in natural populations of this species as they now exist. Nevertheless, by selection and by sequestering this variation in small laboratory populations, Carson (1962) has been able to produce laboratory stocks which reproduce wholly by parthenogenesis such that between three and four per cent of the unfertilized eggs give normal diploid female progeny. Novel properties in domestic plants and animals have been produced usually by the closely related process of strong inbreeding.

Inbreeding is a powerful force for dispersion because it can operate within a large species population, even in its center. Under some conditions, the effects characteristic of marginal geographical situations may also be observed in geographical centers, without strong geographical isolation. Perhaps the most striking and extreme way in which these effects could be brought about would be through self-fertilization in plants. The result would be the formation of a mosaic of complete or partial isolates and the disruption of gene flow between them. Under these conditions such a series of isolates could, with only minor ecological changes, become sympatric.

One of the theoretical difficulties which always arise when such a formulation as the above is advanced is the decline of genetic variability which accompanies the dispersive effect. With no variability, how can evolution proceed through recombination and selection? Two answers can be proposed. First, when a former isolate or small population proliferates its numbers and again becomes large, new genetic variability can arise not only by virtue of the larger number of individuals but because outbreeding allows it to be easily carried in the recessive state. Secondly, and perhaps more important, interdeme selection, from among a myriad of isolates, each genetically different, is a most powerful force for changing the composition of the group.

Since the days when Mendel first realized the significance of the homozygotes he produced by inbreeding and since Darwin first puzzled over the isolated populations on the Galapagos Islands, the stage has been set for an unraveling of the curious relationship in nature between inbreeding and crossbreeding. Wright (1964), whose thoughtful and active development of this field has extended over a period of nearly fifty years, has concluded that the evolutionary process has three phases. These are a phase of random drift of the sets of gene frequencies within demes, a phase of intrademic selection, and a phase of interdemic selection. The mathematical aspects of the theory are associated principally with the first two phases. In the third phase, a high selective peak acquired in one of the demes spreads through the species because of its surplus population and excess dispersion. The delicate interplay of extinction and differential reproduction, so long exploited at the level of the deme by animal and plant breeders, is indeed the core of the evolutionary process.

Literature Cited

ALLARD, R. W., AND P. L. WORKMAN, 1963. Population studies in predominantly self-pollinated species. IV. Seasonal fluctuations in estimated values of genetic parameters in lima bean populations. Evolution 17: 470–480.

ALLARD, R. W., AND C. WEHRHAHN, 1964. A theory which predicts stable equilibrium for inversion polymorphisms in the grasshopper *Moraba scurra*. Evolution 18: 129–130.

BAKER, H. G., 1953. Race formation and reproductive method in flowering plants. Symp. Soc. Exp. Biol. 7: 114–145.

——, 1955. Self-compatibility and establishment after "long-distance" dispersal. Evolution 9: 347–348.

——, 1960. Reproductive methods in flowering plants. Cold Spring Harbor Symp. Quant. Biol. 24: 177–191.

BARTLETT, M. S., AND J. B. S. HALDANE, 1935. The theory of inbreeding with forced heterozygosis. J. Genet. 31: 327–340.

BATEMAN, A. J., AND K. MATHER, 1951. The progress of inbreeding in barley. Heredity 5: 321–348.

BENNETT, J. H., 1958. Lethal genes in inbred lines. Heredity 10: 263–270.

BODMER, W. F., AND P. A. PARSONS, 1960. The initial progress of new genes with various genetic systems. Heredity 15: 283–299.

BOWMAN, J. C., AND D. S. FALCONER, 1960. Inbreeding depression and heterosis of litter size in mice. Heredity 1: 262–274.

BREWBAKER, J. L., 1964. *Agricultural Genetics.* Prentice-Hall, Inc., Englewood Cliffs, N.J.

BURI, P., 1956. Gene frequency in small populations of mutant *Drosophila.* Evolution 10: 367–402.

CARSON, H. L., 1959. Genetic conditions which promote or retard the formation of species. Cold Spring Harbor Symp. Quant. Biol. 24: 87–105.

———, 1962. Selection for parthenogenesis in *Drosophila mercatorum.* Genetics 47: 946.

———, 1965. Chromosomal morphism in the widespread species of *Drosophila. The Genetics of Colonizing Species,* pp. 503–531. Edited by H. G. Baker and G. L. Stebbins. Academic Press, Inc., New York.

CRAMPTON, H. E., 1932. Studies on the variation, distribution and evolution of the genus *Partula.* III. The species inhabiting Moorea. Carnegie Inst. Washington Publ. No. 410: 1–335.

CROSBY, J. L., 1949. Selection of an unfavorable gene-complex. Evolution 3: 212–230.

———, 1959. Outcrossing on homostyle primroses. Heredity 13: 127–131.

CROW, J. F., 1954. Breeding structure of populations. II. Effective population number. *Statistics and Mathematics in Biology,* pp. 543–556. Iowa State College Press, Ames, Iowa.

CROW, J. F., AND M. KIMURA, 1965. The theory of genetic loads. *Genetics Today,* vol. III, pp. 495–505. Proc. XI Int. Congr. Genet. Edited by S. J. Geerts. Pergamon Press, New York.

CROW, J. F., AND N. E. MORTON, 1955. Measurement of gene frequency drift in small populations. Evolution 9: 202–214.

DADAY, H., 1954. Gene frequencies in wild populations of *Trifolium repens.* II. Distribution by altitude. Heredity 8: 377–384.

DARWIN, C., 1876. *The Effects of Cross and Self Fertilization in the Vegetable Kingdom* (2nd ed., 1898). Appleton & Co., New York.

DEOL, M. S., H., GRÜNEBERG, A. G. SEARLE, AND G. M. TRUSLOVE, 1960. How pure are our inbred strains of mice? Heredity 1: 50–58.

DIVER, C., 1940. The problem of closely related species living in the same area. *The New Systematics,* pp. 303–328. Edited by J. Huxley. The Clarendon Press, Oxford.

DOBZHANSKY, TH., 1951. *Genetics and the Origin of Species.* Columbia Univ. Press, New York.

DOBZHANSKY, TH., AND B. SPASSKY, 1953. Genetics of natural populations. XXI. Concealed variability in two sympatric species of *Drosophila.* Genetics 38: 471–529.

DURRANT, A., AND K. MATHER, 1954. Heritable variation in a long inbred line of *Drosophila.* Genetica 27: 97–119.

DÜZGÜNES, O., 1950. The effect of inbreeding on reproductive fitness of S.C.W. Leghorns. Poultry Sci. **29**: 227-235.

EAST, E. M., AND D. F. JONES, 1919. *Inbreeding and Outbreeding.* J. B. Lippincott Co., Philadelphia.

FALCONER, D. S., 1960. *Introduction to Quantitative Genetics.* The Ronald Press, New York.

FISHER, R. A., 1930. *The Genetical Theory of Natural Selection.* Oxford Univ. Press, Oxford.

———, 1949. *The Theory of Inbreeding.* Oliver & Boyd, Edinburgh.

FRYXELL, P. A., 1957. Mode of reproduction of higher plants. Bot. Rev. **23**: 135–233.

GILMOUR, J. S. L., AND J. W. GREGOR, 1939. Demes: A suggested new terminology. Nature **144**: 333–334.

GOWEN, J. W., J. STADLER, AND L. E. JOHNSON, 1946. On the mechanism of heterosis—the chromosomal or cytoplasmic basis for heterosis in *Drosophila melanogaster.* Amer. Natur. **80**: 506–531.

GRANT, V., 1963. *The Origin of Adaptations.* Columbia Univ. Press, New York.

GULICK, J. T., 1905. Evolution, racial and habitudinal. Carnegie Inst. Washington Publ. No. 25: 1–269.

HAIR, J. B., 1956. Subsexual reproduction in *Agropyron.* Heredity **10**: 129–159.

HALDANE, J. B. S., 1930. The theoretical genetics of autopolyploids. J. Genet. **22**: 359–372.

———, 1936. The amount of heterozygosis to be expected in an approximately pure line. J. Genet. **32**: 375–391.

———, 1937. Some theoretical results of continued brother-sister mating. J. Genet. **34**: 265-274.

———, 1956. The conflict between inbreeding and selection. I. Self-fertilization. J. Genet. **54**: 56–63.

———, 1957. The cost of natural selection. J. Genet. **55**: 511–524.

HALLER, M. H., 1963. *Eugenics: Hereditarian Attitudes in American Thought.* Rutgers Univ. Press, New Brunswick, N.J.

HARDING, J., AND C. L. TUCKER, 1964. Quantitative studies of mating systems. I. Evidence of the non-randomness of outcrossing in *Phaseolus lunatus.* Heredity **19**: 369–381.

HARDY, D. E., 1965. Diptera: Cyclorrhapha, II. *Insects of Hawaii,* vol. 12. Univ. of Hawaii Press, Honolulu.

HARLAN, J. R., 1945. Natural breeding structure in the *Bromus carinatus* complex as determined by population analyses. Amer. J. Bot. **32**: 142–148.

HARLAND, S. C., 1948. Inheritance of immunity to mildew in Peruvian forms of *Pisum sativum.* Heredity **2**: 263–269.

HASKELL, G. 1953. Adaptation and the breeding system in groundsel. Genetica **26**: 468–484.

———, 1954. The genetic detection of natural crossing in blackberry. Genetica **27**: 162–172.

HAYMAN, B. I., 1953. Mixed selfing and random mating when homozygotes are at a disadvantage. Heredity **7**: 185–192.

HAYMAN, B. I., AND K. MATHER, 1953. The progress of inbreeding when homozygotes are at a disadvantage. Heredity **7**: 165–183.

HAYMAN, B. I., AND K. MATHER, 1956. Inbreeding when homozygotes are at a disadvantage: A reply. Heredity **10**: 271–274.

HOLDEN, J. H. W., AND D. A. BOND, 1960. Studies on the breeding system of the field bean, *Vicia faba* (L.). Heredity **15**: 175–192.

HUTCHINSON, J. B., 1951. Intra-specific differentiation in *Gossypium hirsutum*. Heredity **5**: 161–193.

HUTT, F. B., 1950. *Genetics of the Fowl.* McGraw-Hill Co., New York.

HYDE, R. R., 1924. Inbreeding, outbreeding, and selection with *Drosophila melanogaster*. J. Exp. Zool. **40**: 181–215.

IMAN, A. G., AND R. W. ALLARD, 1965. Population studies in predominantly self-pollinated species. VI. Genetic variability between and within natural populations of wild oats from differing habitats in California. Genetics **51**: 49–62.

JAIN, S. K., AND R. W. ALLARD, 1960. Population studies in predominantly self-pollinated species. I. Evidence for heterozygote advantage in a closed population of barley. Proc. Nat. Acad. Sci. U.S. **46**: 1371–1377.

KERR, W. E., AND S. WRIGHT, 1954a. Experimental studies of the distribution of gene frequencies in very small populations of *Drosophila melanogaster*. I. Forked. Evolution **8**: 172–177.

KERR, W. E., AND S. WRIGHT, 1954b. Experimental studies of the distribution of gene frequencies in very small populations of *Drosophila melanogaster*. III. Aristopedia and spineless. Evolution **8**: 293–302.

KIMURA, M., 1959. Conflict between self fertilization and outbreeding in plants. Ann. Rep. Nat. Inst. Genet. Japan **9**: 87–88.

KIMURA, M., AND J. F. CROW, 1963. On the maximum avoidance of inbreeding. Genet. Res. **4**: 399–415.

KING, H. D., 1918. Studies on inbreeding. I. The effects in inbreeding on the growth and variation in the body weight of the albino rat. J. Exp. Zool. **26**: 1–54.

———, 1921. Studies on inbreeding. IV. A further study of the effects of inbreeding on the growth and variability in the body weight of the albino rat. J. Exp. Zool. **29**: 71–111.

KIRK, L. E., 1927. Self-fertilization in relation to forage crop improvement. Sci. Agr. **8**: 1–40.

———, 1933. The progeny test and methods of breeding appropriate to certain species of crop plants. Amer. Natur. **67**: 515–531.

KNOWLES, P. F., 1943. Improving an annual brome grass, *Bromus mollis* L. for range purposes. J. Amer. Soc. Agron. **35**: 584–594.

LAMOTTE, M., 1952. Le rôle des fluctuations fortuites dans la diversité des populations naturelles de *Cepaea nemoralis* (L.). Heredity **6**: 333–343.

LATTER, B. D. H., AND A. ROBERTSON, 1962. The effects of inbreeding and artificial selection on reproductive fitness. Genet. Res. **3**: 110–138.

LERNER, I. M., 1954. *Genetic Homeostasis.* Oliver and Boyd, Edinburgh.

———, 1958. *The Genetic Basis of Selection.* John Wiley & Sons, New York.

LEWONTIN, R. C., 1961. Evolution and the theory of games. J. Theoret. Biol. 1: 382–403.

LEWONTIN, R. C., AND M. J. D. WHITE, 1960. Interaction between inversion polymorphisms of two chromosome pairs in the grasshopper *Moraba scurra.* Evolution 14: 116–129.

LI, C. C., 1961. *Population Genetics.* Reinhold Publ. Co., New York.

LINTS, F. A., 1961. Diversity by inbreeding in *Drosophila.* Genetica 32: 177–199.

LOEB, L., H. D. KING, AND H. T. BLUMENTHAL, 1943. Transplantation and individuality differentials in inbred strains of rats. Biol. Bull. 84: 1–12.

LUNDQUIST, A., 1947. On self-sterility and inbreeding effect in tetraploid rye. Hereditas 33: 570–571.

———, 1953. Inbreeding in autotetraploid rye. Hereditas 39: 19–32.

LYON, M. F., 1959. Some evidence concerning the "mutational load" in inbred strains of mice. Heredity 13: 341–352.

McCARTHY, J. C., 1965. The effect on litter size of crossing inbred strains of mice. Genetics 51: 217–222.

MATHER, K., AND B. I. HAYMAN, 1952. The progress of inbreeding where heterozygotes are at an advantage. Biometrics 8: 176.

MAYR, E., 1954. Change of genetic environment and evolution. *Evolution as a Process,* pp. 157–180. Edited by J. Huxley. Allen and Unwin, London.

———, 1963. *Animal Species and Evolution.* Harvard Univ. Press, Cambridge.

MAYR, E., AND C. B. ROSEN, 1956. Geographic variation and hybridization in populations of Bahama snails (*Cerion*). Amer. Mus. Novitates No. 1806: 1–48.

METZ, C. W., 1938. Chromosome behavior, inheritance and sex determination in *Sciara.* Amer. Natur. 72: 485–520.

MORAN, P. A. P., 1958. A general theory of the distribution of gene frequencies. I. Overlapping generations. Proc. Roy. Soc. B 149: 102–112.

MORLEY, F. H. W., 1959. Natural selection and variation in plants. Cold Spring Harbor Symp. Quant. Biol. 24: 47–56.

MÜNTZING, A., 1933. Apomictic and sexual seed formation in *Poa.* Hereditas 17: 131–154.

———, 1940. Further studies on apomixis and sexuality in *Poa.* Hereditas 26: 115–190.

NANNEY, D. L., 1957. Inbreeding degeneration in *Tetrahymena.* Genetics 42: 137–146.

NEI, M., 1963. The efficiency of the haploid method of plant breeding. Heredity 18: 95–100.

O'DONALD, P., 1960. Inbreeding as a result of imprinting. Heredity 15: 79–85.

PHILIP, U., 1938. Mating systems in wild populations of *Dermestes vulpinus* and *Mus musculus.* J. Genet. 36: 197–211.

REEVE, E. C. R., 1955. Inbreeding with the homozygotes at a disadvantage. Ann. Human Genet. **19**: 332–346.

———, 1957. Inbreeding with selection and linkage. I. Selfing. Ann. Human Genet. **21**: 277–288.

REEVE, E. C. R., AND J. C. GOWER, 1958. Inbreeding with selection and linkage. II. Sib-mating. Ann. Human. Genet. **23**: 36–49.

RICK, C. M., 1950. Pollination relations of *Lycopersicon esculentum* in native and foreign regions. Evolution 4: 110–122.

ROBERTSON, A., 1952. The effect of inbreeding on the variation due to recessive genes. Genetics **37**: 189–207.

———, 1962. Selection for heterozygotes in small populations. Genetics **47**: 1291–1300.

———, 1964. The effect of non-random mating within inbred lines on the rate of inbreeding. Genet. Res. **5**: 164–167.

ROWLANDS, D. G., 1958. The nature of the breeding system in the field bean (*V. faba* L.) and its relationship to breeding for yield. Heredity **12**: 113–126.

SANG, J. H., 1964. Nutritional requirements of inbred lines and crosses of *Drosophila melanogaster*. Genet. Res. **5**: 50–67.

SCHULTZ, F. T., 1953. Concurrent inbreeding and selection in the domestic fowl. Heredity **7**: 1–21.

SHEPPARD, P. M., 1951. Fluctuations in the selective value of certain phenotypes in the polymorphic land snail *Cepaea nemoralis* (L.). Heredity **5**: 125–134.

SONNEBORN, T. M., 1957. Breeding systems, reproductive methods and species problems in Protozoa. *The Species Problem*, pp. 155–324. Amer. Ass. Advance. Sci. Publ. No. 50.

SPENCER, W. P., 1947. Mutations in wild populations of *Drosophila*. Advance. Genet. **1**: 359–402.

STEBBINS, G. L., 1950. *Variation and Evolution in Plants*. Columbia Univ. Press, New York.

———, 1957. Self fertilization and population variability in the higher plants. Amer. Natur. **91**: 337–354.

SUNESON, C. A., 1949. Survival of four barley varieties in a mixture. Agron. J. **41**: 459–461.

TANTAWY, A. O., AND E. C. R. REEVE, 1956. Studies on quantitative inheritance. IX. The effects of inbreeding at different rates in *Drosophila melanogaster*. Z. induktive Abstammungs- u. Vererbungslehre **87**: 648–667.

THOMPSON, J. B., AND H. REES, 1956. Selection for heterozygotes during inbreeding. Nature **177**: 385–386.

WATTERSON, G. A., 1959a. Non-random mating and its effect on the rate of approach to homozygosity. Ann. Human Genet. **23**: 204–220.

———, 1959b. A new genetic population model and its approach to homozygosity. Ann. Human Genet. **23**: 221–232.

WEIL, J., AND R. W. ALLARD, 1964. The mating system and genetic variability in natural populations of *Collinsia heterophylla*. Evolution 18: 515–525.

WINGE, O., 1940. Taxonomic and evolutionary studies in *Erophila* based on cytogenetic investigations. Compt. rend. trav. lab. Carlsberg, Sér. Physiol. 23: 17–39.

WORKMAN, P. L., AND R. W. ALLARD, 1962. Population studies in predominantly self-pollinated species. III. A matrix model for mixed selfing and random outcrossing. Proc. Nat. Acad. Sci. U.S. 48: 1318–1325.

WORKMAN, P. L., AND R. W. ALLARD, 1964. Population studies in predominantly self-pollinated species. V. Analysis of differential and random viabilities in mixtures of competing pure lines. Heredity 19: 181–189.

WRIGHT, S., 1921a. Systems of mating. I. The biometric relations between parent and offspring. Genetics 6: 111–123.

——, 1921b. Systems of mating. II. The effects of inbreeding on the genetic composition of a population. Genetics 6: 124–143.

——, 1921c. Systems of mating. III. Assortative mating based on somatic resemblance. Genetics 6: 144–161.

——, 1921d. Systems of mating. IV. The effects of selection. Genetics 6: 162–168.

——, 1921e. Systems of mating. V. General considerations. Genetics 6: 169–178.

——, 1922. Coefficients of inbreeding and relationship. Amer. Natur. 56: 330–338.

——, 1931. Evolution in Mendelian populations. Genetics 16: 97–159.

——, 1932. The roles of mutation, inbreeding, crossbreeding and selection in evolution. Proc. VI Int. Congr. Genet. 1: 356–366.

——, 1933. Inbreeding and homozygosis. Proc. Nat. Acad. Sci. U.S. 19: 411–420.

——, 1934. An analysis of variability in the number of digits in an inbred strain of guinea pigs. Genetics 19: 506–536.

——, 1937. The distribution of gene frequencies in populations. Amer. Natur. 23: 307–320.

——, 1940. The statistical consequences of Mendelian heredity in relation to speciation. *The New Systematics*, pp. 161–183. Edited by J. Huxley. The Clarendon Press, Oxford.

——, 1943. Isolation by distance. Genetics 28: 114–138.

——, 1945. Tempo and mode in evolution: A critical review. Ecology 26: 415–419.

——, 1946. Isolation by distance under diverse systems of mating. Genetics 31: 39–59.

——, 1964. Stochastic processes in evolution. *Stochastic Models in Medicine and Biology*, pp. 199–244. Edited by J. Gurland. Univ. of Wisconsin Press, Madison.

WRIGHT, S., AND W. E. KERR, 1954. Experimental studies of the distribution of gene frequencies in very small populations of *Drosophila melanogaster*. II. Bar. Evolution 8: 225–240.

16

Human Populations

L. L. Cavalli-Sforza

This work has been supported by grants from the U.S. Atomic Energy Commission and by Euratom-CNR-CNEN Contract No. 012-61-12, BIAI.

Biologists and, more especially, geneticists are indebted to Mendel in two ways. Not only did he open an extremely fruitful field of research whose roots, as we can witness in this book, have expanded widely and deeply into all fields of biology, but in addition, he also set a rigorous precedent for scientific thinking at the very beginning of our science. It is really remarkable how few of the papers that have followed can meet the standards of that touchstone, "Versuche über Pflanzenhybriden."

The theoretical developments that have followed Mendel's work have been primarily in the field of population genetics, largely thanks to the work of Fisher, Haldane, and Wright. The mathematical theory of evolution is of great scientific importance and aesthetic value. Its complexity is certainly unprecedented in biology. However, in applications to real populations, especially human populations, where controlled experiments cannot be performed, we encounter all the difficulties of a nonexperimental science, in which conclusions cannot be supported with the same strength of evidence that can be attained in experimental work. It is no wonder, therefore, that we have been witnessing lively debates in this field.

In spite of the difficulties and the battles, the thesis that man is a useful organism for studies of population genetics (Buzzati-Traverso 1950; Cavalli-Sforza 1958), quite apart from our own special interest in him, is proving largely right. Workers in the field will agree, however, that this type of research proceeds rather slowly. It will be clear why work is slow if one considers that even the test of Mendelian inheritance becomes a problem in a nonexperimental organism like man. The assumption of random mating allows the use of human data for the purposes of genetic study, so long as departures from it are small,

309

even though we cannot arrange controlled matings. But the retrieval of information from the data demands the use of involved numerical methods. Before the age of computers, however, it had been shown that man, like other organisms, has characters which regularly show Mendelian inheritance—that is, which behave as good genetic markers —as well as many traits possessing all degrees of Mendelian irregularity and all types of complications. Simple physiological considerations suggest the rule that any biochemically (or immunologically) defined variation is likely to belong to the category of good markers, while biochemically undefined variation is much more probably in the category of poor markers.

The proof of Mendelism for our own species is essentially a facet of population genetics. Therefore, it is not surprising that the test for Mendelism unavoidably brings to the fore the major factors of evolution. To what extent can these factors be analyzed in man? Experience today suggests that mutation, selection, and population structure can all yield to analysis, though to different extents. In this chapter, we will discuss briefly some problems falling under those three headings and will also consider an approach to the reconstruction of those events of human evolution that are interpretable from genetic data and models.

Mutation

The study of mutation rates in man has made considerable progress. Several mutation rates have been estimated fairly accurately, estimates for dominant markers being by far the most reliable.

The classification into point and nonpoint mutations is reliable only for mutants of genes whose phenotypic counterpart is an adequately defined protein. The only other criterion available, namely, the appearance or nonappearance of cytological alterations, provides a poor basis for the classification of mutants. We have learned from the very strong effect of high maternal age on the incidence of mongolism (Penrose 1934) how a mutation, whose chromosomal nature is clear, can be susceptible to environmental conditions. Moreover, some of the markers, such as chondrodystrophy, which have been favorites in the study of mutation rates show an unexplained strong dependence on paternal age (Penrose 1955), an association which may throw some doubt on their identification as point mutations.

In theory, man should not be too bad an organism for the study of spontaneous mutation rates. Much of what we know today on mutation rates comes from bacteria or phage. The earth with its content of some three billion individuals of our species is like an ordinary bacterial culture grown to saturation, at least from the point of view of the number of individuals. So, when we plate a bacterial culture to screen it for mutants, we are conducting an experiment of roughly the same size as the search for mutants in the whole human species. Naturally, we are far from knowing enough about every living individual to be able to compute mutation rates in the whole human species. This is clearly a pity; many markers obtained from blood proteins are as good point mutations as there can be, and from this point of view, man would be an excellent organism. The extension of mutation studies to a very large section of the population remains a task of importance, which I hope some scientist with a considerable capacity for organization will undertake in the future. It is also worth remembering that there is at least one stage when it is very easy to obtain blood from both parent and offspring, namely, at birth.

One open problem is how representative of all mutations are those that are selected for study. I suspect that if mutation rates could be estimated for more markers, and if account could be taken of the unseen tail of the distribution curve, namely, where all the mutation rates are so low that one would not expect to see even one mutant in the whole population, average mutation rates would turn out to be rather lower than the present estimate, which is 2 or 3×10^{-5} (Crow 1961).

Indirect estimates of mutation rates, such as are obtainable for recessive characters, are, of course, the least satisfactory. They have, however, the advantage that they can supply cumulative estimates of mutation rates. The best known example is that of autosomal lethal equivalents as determined by Morton, Crow, and Muller (1956), whose method has greatly stimulated the collection of data on inbreeding effects. Their analysis has shown that estimates thus obtained are exposed to different sources of bias, which are not always easy to assess (Levene 1963). Numbers of lethal equivalents estimated in this way should be considered with some caution, especially when they are small. Even more caution is necessary when we convert lethal equivalents to mutation rates. It has been necessary in computations to introduce quantities of which we know practically nothing in the human species, such as average fitness for heterozygotes. Recourse, therefore, must be had to rather remote relatives of man, such as *Drosophila,* but one wonders if, in such a case, even the order of magnitude can be safely accepted. Again, here is a field where much still remains to be done to improve the accuracy of data and the reliability of conclusions.

I have tried to introduce an indirect method for estimating mutation rates of sex-linked recessive lethals by estimating their accumulation with age from the correlation between the age of an individual and the probability that his (or her) daughter carries a sex-linked recessive lethal. Human families are not large enough, however, to permit a direct assessment of a sex ratio distorted by a sex-linked lethal, and since further breeding is not possible, the average sex ratio must be used. Thus unavoidably the method is open to unpredictable factors, but the stability shown by the sex ratio under a number of circumstances has offered some reasonable hope that the method would be sufficiently free of noise to provide information on the point at issue.

The first analysis comprised a study of the correlation between the sex ratio of children (stillborn and alive) and the age of their maternal grandfather when their mother was born. A sample of some 180,000 children (about 1/200th of the Italian population) gave very encouraging results, especially with respect to the data on stillbirths. The accumulation of mutants with age was estimated to a reasonable order of magnitude, though perhaps it was too high (Cavalli-Sforza 1961, 1962b). However, a second sample of some 800,000 children from another source—namely, birth certificates for the year 1960, to which the year of birth of the mother's father had been added—gave results which were in disagreement with the first sample and showed essentially no effect. The matter should be clarified by data obtained in the general census of the Italian population, but although this was carried out at the end of 1962, we still have been unable to obtain the tabulations.

We have tried what is essentially the same approach in research on hemophilia, carried out in collaboration with Barrai and De Nicola. We have asked for the years of birth of the parents and grandparents of hemophiliacs. To date, 658 cases have been collected, thanks to the help of organizations and specialists throughout the world. Families in which the mother of the hemophiliac is a carrier, and no evidence excludes her as a new mutant, have been identified, and the age of the mother's parents at her birth have been compared with suitable controls. This research is still going on, and since the National Hemophilia Foundation of America has agreed to help us, data are flowing in at a remarkable rate. At the moment the deviation is in the expected direction but is not significant. In this method, analysis is confined to a single (late-acting) lethal of the X chromosome, rather than to the totality of early-acting lethals, and has the advantage of facilitating the comparison between mutant formation during reproductive and pre-reproductive periods. In fact, accumulation of mutants with parental age considers only the mutant formation during the reproductive period, and estimation, by the standard methods, of mutation rate for a whole generation permits us to calculate also the pre-reproductive mutation rate by subtraction. It is interesting to note that the approach used was independently suggested by Penrose (personal communication) some time ago.

In conclusion, studies of mutation have been variously rewarding in man, and there is room for much improvement in the returns from research efforts. It is to be remembered, however, that the study of mutation is closely linked with that of its balancing factor, selection.

Selection

If in the field of mutation there is room for people with organizing capacity and ambition, it is also true in another field—selection. Here the quantities to be estimated are generally not so small and therefore, occasionally at least, smaller population samples are sufficient. The fact remains, however, that many selective coefficients, especially those that relate to the majority of polymorphisms in which we are interested, are fairly small, so that their accurate estimation usually demands study of a larger number of individuals than has been tested so far. But this is at least one field in which we can hope to exploit for genetic purposes such facilities, unique to the human species, as hospital records and government archives, where much information on each of us is accurately stored, often to no avail (Cavalli-Sforza 1958).

The first big experiment of routinely collecting and coordinating data on human beings for information of genetic interest was started, thanks to the pioneering work of Newcombe (1964), several years ago and is already bearing fruit. It is quite clear to me that this kind of example must be followed and will be followed in several other countries. Clearly, the potential of such enterprises is measured by two quantities: the number of individuals that can be tested and the average reliability of the tests which are carried out on those individuals. When data from the general population are used, very often the average reliability is not high. The reliability of data, of course, varies with the degree of development of the country from which information is extracted; but even for the most highly developed large countries, I suppose dissatisfaction arises from the erratic reliability of individual data, as a result of ethnic, cultural, or economic variation. Because of the high quality of medical care and of demographic data in Iceland, and also in view of the low immigration rate, a study has been started there with the cooperation of a number of research workers, with the objective of covering as many genetic aspects of the whole population as possible.

Whenever governmental archives containing reliable and useful information are available, the information can be transformed into a more easily retrievable form by the use of modern computers. Problems such as those that I will mention now will then become extremely easy to solve.

Some time ago, we tried to conduct a prospective study of individuals who underwent a medical test and anthropometric examination at military conscription in about 1910 in the town of Parma (Conterio and Cavalli-Sforza 1959). The follow-up of demographical facts of these individuals through the local archives proved extremely time-

Table 16.1

Follow-up of Parmese men born in 1890–91 whose stature was measured in 1910–13
(Conterio and Cavalli-Sforza 1960)

Status in 1958 (or earlier)	Stature	
	Mean	Variance
Married	165.3	35.2
Single	165.4	55.5
Significance	not sig.	sig.[a]
Dead	164.5	45.6
Surviving	165.8	39.7
Significance	sig.[b]	not sig.

[a] Difference significant with $P = 1\%$.
[b] Difference significant with $P = 5\%$.

consuming, and eventually we were able to obtain information only on death and marriage, but not on fertility. Inasmuch as the anthropometric test at conscription was a superficial one, we limited our analysis to traits that could be measured with sufficient accuracy at the time of the visit, namely, stature and chest girth. Table 16.1 shows that with respect to stature and chest size two types of selection had set in. As the result of deaths a small amount of directional selection was observed with respect to stature, apparently favoring the taller individuals in this group. This selection was, however, insufficient to explain the general trend, observed throughout the region, toward an increase in stature, a trend which is probably largely a phenotypic phenomenon. There was also another type of selection resulting from marriage, this time a stabilizing selection. The optimal stature for marriage seemed to be nearer the average, at least for Parmese men born in 1890 and 1891, so that the variance of stature for individuals who married was smaller than that for those who remained single, there being no difference between the means.

Practical difficulties were encountered in the use of the existing archives, since they did not permit us to evaluate the fertility of these individuals. We were thus unable to complete a study of fitness which would otherwise have been possible with the Malthusian parameter. This index of fitness, which combines information on mortality and fertility, was suggested by Fisher (1930) in his book, *The Genetical Theory of Natural Selection,* but has not been used until very recently. In a recent paper Bajema (1963) estimated Malthusian parameters to test selection for intelligence. Intelligence was shown some time ago to be correlated with fertility in a way that suggested the possibility of rapid deterioration of the human species in this respect. Bajema's results show that this is probably a transient situation, so that we need not worry about our future intelligence. Of course, in making use of this conclusion for long-range projections, we must remember not only that it is restricted to one given area and time but also that it is limited by our ignorance of the correlation between genotype and phenotype in the character considered.

The study of selection in human populations is very promising but still largely undeveloped. Not only can we hope to measure accurately selective parameters and distinguish the phase of life at which selection acts, but we can also hope to unveil selection mechanisms, that is, observe how much as well as how and why one type has an advantage over another in a given environment. Naturally, these mechanisms are not so simple to understand as one might superficially hope. Thus we are still largely unaware of how sickle cell trait carriers are more resistant to malaria, even though we are reasonably assured that this is one clearcut case of heterozygous advantage.

Genetic Drift

In the above problems we may note that demography is always involved at least indirectly (Cavalli-Sforza 1962a). Demography provides, however, a major key to problems of population genetics when population structure and especially genetic drift are being studied.

It has been noted by authors who have investigated human populations living in primitive conditions, such as Australian aborigines (Kirk 1965) or Eskimos (Laughlin 1950), or populations that have lived in isolation for other reasons (usually religious: e.g., Glass 1954; McKusick *et al.* 1964), that these populations show fluctuations in gene frequencies which are probably caused by drift. Under what conditions is it possible to improve the precision of this statement?

Two criteria can help us decide if variation encountered between populations results from drift. (1) The variation expected because of drift can be computed and compared with the observed variation if the size of the isolates and their interchange of genes are known for a sufficiently long period. (2) If, for the genetic systems considered, drift is the only or the predominant cause of variation, *all* genetic systems should show the same variation. Clearly, the more severe the isolation is, the greater is the likelihood that variation results from gene drift, because then the relative contributions of disturbing factors, such as the variation of selection intensities, will be proportionately less important. Also, if we study a limited and homogeneous area, local variation in selective intensity is less likely to undermine the validity of this criterion.

We set out some time ago to analyze drift in a population which seemed especially suitable for the test (Cavalli-Sforza and Conterio 1960; Cavalli-Sforza 1963b; Cavalli-Sforza, Barrai, and Edwards 1964). To this end, we have estimated gene frequencies in 75 villages of a region in which we could hope to study the demography in unprecedented detail. While demographic data could permit us to estimate the amount of drift expected, the variation of gene frequencies in the area would provide observed variances to compare with the expected ones. An additional control was supplied by the fact that, in the area studied, conditions of isolation varied in an almost continuous way, thus providing a further check of the calculations of the importance of drift.

The area chosen corresponds approximately to the valley of the Parma River, leading to the town of Parma. A sample of some 3000 adults was examined for, among other things, three genetic systems, namely, ABO with four alleles, MN with two alleles, and Rh with 5 antisera. The area is divided into nine administrative units which have quite different geographic conditions, according to their elevations. The urban part was excluded from the investigation, leaving essentially three subregions: the upper part of the valley, which is mountainous; the hills in the middle; and the plain near Parma in the north, which is the richest and the most densely populated subregion. Each subregion included several administrative units, the "communes," and each of these comprised several villages.

The results were rather clearcut. There was significant variation between villages in the less densely populated, upper part of the valley, while there was no significant variation in the lower part. The statistical variation was approximately the same for all the genetic systems investigated, due consideration being given to the gene frequencies and the number of alleles tested. The variation between villages in the upper part of the valley for the different gene systems is shown in Table 16.2.

The correlation of the variation with population density is shown in Figure 16.1, where variation is represented on the ordinate as the variance between villages of a "commune," averaged for all the genetic systems tested and computed in such a way as to eliminate the variation

Table 16.2

Heterogeneity for blood group gene frequencies between villages in upper
Parma River Valley and estimated σ^2/pq values

Blood group alleles	χ^2	df	Significant	σ^2/pq
MN	102.76	36	yes	0.048
A_1	98.74	33	yes	0.052
A_2	40.23	33	no	—
B	76.08	33	yes	0.034
O	110.25	33	yes	0.061
r^a	81.77	33	yes	0.038
R_1	75.46	33	yes	0.033
R_2	54.54	33	yes	0.017
Other Rh	80.01	33	yes	0.037
			mean:	0.0356 ± 0.006

^{a} Rh frequencies computed with inefficient method.

from random sampling. The figure shows that the variation between the lower density villages is significantly different from zero, while in the more densely populated parts, the variation is practically zero.

We may add that population density in this area is a fairly precise inverse measure of isolation. In fact, migration is relatively constant over the whole area, and, if anything, is greater in the denser part. Under the model of isolation by distance, suggested by Wright (1943, 1946), density therefore remains the only factor which determines local differentiation. Figure 16.1 shows that our internal control has been quite useful: There is a fairly clear gradient of local differentiation, presumably caused by drift, which in any case follows the gradient of isolation in the area.

The second criterion mentioned previously, namely, the equality of variation for the different alleles investigated, also holds, at least approximately (Table 16.2). An exact analysis of this point is difficult, but we are working on a suitable statistical test to check it more accurately.

We will now examine the first criterion—whether the amount of local differentiation observed in the area does agree with the expected quantity. This requires an analysis of the demography of the area, which has proved a task of some complexity. We set out ambitiously to examine the demography of the last 300 years insofar as the available archives would permit, with special attention to the area with presumed high drift. This research is still in progress, and the data now available on migration are based on the following: a sample of the

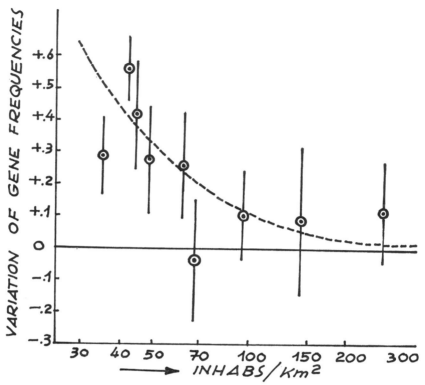

Fig. 16.1.—Variation of gene frequencies between villages plotted against population density. Each point represents one "commune" of the Parma River Valley. A value approximately proportional to σ^2/pq, explained in more detail elsewhere (Cavalli-Sforza 1965), is given in the ordinate while in the abscissa is the density of the "commune."

population now living in the whole area of the Parma Valley (and neighboring area); a complete elaboration covering all three centuries for just one small parish; marriage data for the three centuries for the whole area.

We may summarize our conclusions on the analysis of the demographic data that are relevant to the study of drift in the following way. Migration can be conveniently studied through the quantity suggested by Wright in his work on isolation by distance, namely, the distance between birthplaces of parents and offspring. However, when analyzed, the distances do not obey a normal distribution but rather a very asymmetrical type of distribution (Cavalli-Sforza 1963a). Whatever the origin of this skewness, there are several convenient ways of representing the distributions. For our present purposes a not unreasonable method is to use a sum of normal distributions, over one or two dimensions at will, with different migration coefficients or "standard deviations" of distances (Cavalli-Sforza, Barrai, and Edwards 1964). Good results, in practice, are obtained from the sum of three such distributions, of which one has a very slow migration ($\sigma = 0.6$ km) and contains the majority of migrants (75 per cent for mother-offspring and 85 per cent for father-offspring). Smaller components show more extensive migration, from 10 to 100 times greater, approximately. In the area examined, most migration takes place at marriage; when people of two different villages marry, one (usually the bride) moves to the mate's village.

It seemed unsatisfactory to use the island model—the first model of isolation suggested by Wright—because in the Parma Valley migration is strongly dependent upon the distance between the villages. One can show that isolation, measured as the reciprocal of cross migration, increases markedly with the square of the distance (Cavalli-Sforza 1958). Wright's model of isolation by distance is also imperfect in our case and cannot be easily adapted to it for at least two reasons. First, the distribution of villages is neither one dimensional nor two dimensional, but in the area which shows most local differentiation it is just intermediate between one and two dimensions (Cavalli-Sforza 1958; Cavalli-Sforza, Barrai, and Edwards 1964). Secondly, in addition to geographic isolation, there is a certain amount of social isolation, as indicated by a correlation coefficient between husband and wife, for socio-economic conditions, of just below 0.5. It is also not easy to fit to our migration data the "stepping-stone" model suggested by Kimura and Weiss (1964), and, therefore, I am unable to assess the usefulness of this model in our case.

The isolation by distance model in one and in two dimensions, when the variation resulting from social conditions is ignored and the largest normal component (namely, the slowest) is taken as a measure of migration, supplies estimates of variation which are not far from the variations actually observed. In fact, this model gives an expected variation which is smaller than the variation found and thus leaves room for other isolation factors, such as those resulting from assortative mating for social conditions.

However, since, after using classical theoretical models, we were still dissatisfied, it was decided also to use an independent approach, namely, the simulation of this population on a computer. We have set up an artificial population of some 5000 individuals subdivided into 22 villages that correspond to a fraction of those of the upper Parma Valley, this being the highest number that we were able to use with an IBM

7040 computer with a storage capacity of $32k$. The simulated population was subjected to a law of cross migration between villages, duplicating as closely as possible the observed pattern, and was given distributions of mortality, fertility, and age at marriage similar to those observed, as well as a distribution of socio-economic conditions and a rule of correlation at marriage for age and socio-economic conditions, again corresponding as closely as possible to the real ones. Programmed gene frequencies for our three blood group systems corresponded, at the beginning, to those observed in the real population and were considered to be subject to Mendelian rules of transmission (without selection, in the experiments carried out so far). Transmission rules had to be arbitrarily assigned for socio-economic conditions, of which nothing is known for this area.

The whole process was carried out using, by means of random numbers, probability tables for each of the aspects that we have enumerated—death, reproduction, migration, choice of mate according to socio-economic conditions, age, and geographic origin, and transmission of hereditary characters to offspring. In each of these respects, our population can be considered as undergoing a finite Markov process. The initial programmed population was fed with age and village size distributions close to the equilibrium values in order to reduce the time to reach equilibrium. Time is discontinuous in the model, and in order to speed up the process, we had to choose an arbitrary interval of time. Our cycle corresponds to one decade. The generation time is therefore about three cycles in our populations, but even so, the populations reproduce fairly slowly compared with the rate we would like. The main trouble that was experienced in earlier versions of this simulation experiment (Barrai and Barbieri 1964) involved the rules to keep the population under satisfactory birth control. The rule we adopted in the latest version was to have fertility determined by the number of blank spaces left in the computer by deaths occurring in preceding cycles. This gives a fairly stable, unfluctuating population. Occasionally, because of the vagaries of the sampling process connected with the migration matrix, a village died out, but this was a rare event.

Conclusions obtained to date with the artificial population can be summarized as follows. Drift at first caused variation to accumulate rather rapidly, after which local differentiation tended to level off quickly (see Fig. 16.2). The time necessary to reach equilibrium is not large compared with the time during which we know that density and migration in the area have not changed markedly, namely, in the last three centuries and perhaps the last millennium. Therefore drift could have reached equilibrium in this area. We have tested three

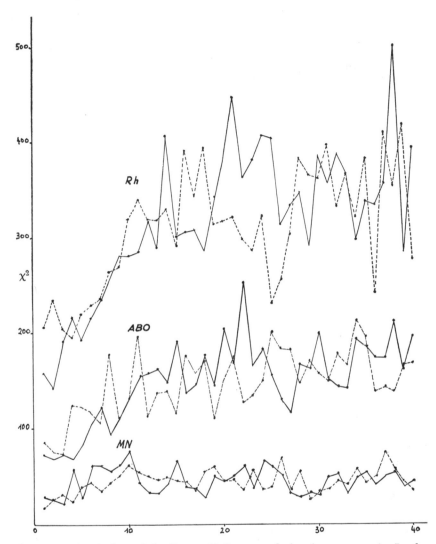

Fig. 16.2.—Simulation of the Parma Valley population in a computer. In the abscissa is the number of cycles (each generation corresponds to about three cycles); in the ordinate, χ^2 values between 22 villages for the gene frequencies of three blood group systems (two alleles for MN, four for ABO, seven for Rh). The broken and solid lines represent duplicate experiments.

levels of correlation for socio-economic conditions at marriage ($r = 0$, $r = 0.45$, $r = 0.8$), but their effect, if present, was small. The variation expected, according to the simulated populations as well as the isolation by distance model, corresponds very closely to that observed (see

Table 16.3

Variation between villages after 40 cycles in the simulated population, given as
σ^2/pq values averaged for all alleles

Socio-economic correlation (r)	Exp. no.	ABO	MN	Rh	Means
0.00	I	0.038	0.048	0.025	0.033 ± 0.004
	II	0.031	0.022	0.034	
0.45	I	0.043	0.024	0.045	0.031 ± 0.005
	II	0.035	0.014	0.024	
0.80	I	0.028	0.053	0.027	0.033 ± 0.005
	II	0.045	0.018	0.027	
Means		0.037 ± 0.003	0.030 ± 0.007	0.030 ± 0.003	0.032 ± 0.003

Tables 16.2 and 16.3). Therefore, we think we can conclude that a large part of the variation in this area results from drift. Variations in selective conditions which could increase the observed variance cannot be large; nor can the effects of stabilizing selection (if any) have been large unless local variation of selective conditions and stabilizing selection happen to balance each other out exactly for three different genes—a rather improbable coincidence.

It was also encouraging that very similar results were obtained by another independent method. We analyzed the frequencies of consanguineous marriages in this area and corrected them for effects resulting from choice of mates according to age, as well as for differential migration of the two sexes, two factors that we have noted strongly affect the frequencies of consanguineous marriages. After such corrections, we determined isolate sizes in the manner suggested by Dahlberg and found them to be fairly similar to the neighborhood sizes of Wright's theory as well as to the sizes of the villages themselves (Cavalli-Sforza, Barrai, and Edwards 1964).

Polymorphisms and drift in human populations

The area in which we have found evidence for drift has a population density which is about five times lower than the average for Italy as a whole. But it is still higher than the average population density for, say, the United States or the world today. If drift occurs in the area studied, it must be primarily because our population has a very low geographic mobility: The average distance between birthplace of parent and that of offspring is on the order of five kilometers, or, expressed in another way, 80 per cent of the children are born in the same village as their parents, where villages are defined as averaging fewer than 300 inhabitants.

For a long time during the history of man, population densities must have been exceedingly low. Density estimates for populations that lived by hunting and food-gathering are on the order of 0.01 per square kilometer (Braidwood and Reed 1957). Of course, there may have been higher mobility than in the population studied by us, simply because of the exigencies of a hunting life.

Because of our lack of knowledge of genetic mobility of primitive populations, it is very difficult to guess what the amount of drift could have been throughout, say, the Pleistocene period. However, the estimation of genetic mobility in conditions such as those that prevailed then is well worth the trouble. There are still a few populations living today under conditions not too different from those of the Pleistocene, and the opportunity to obtain appropriate estimates should not be missed. But even without such quantities, we may still be able to make some educated guesses.

We can, in fact, consider, in terms of genetic mobility, the quantity of variation now observable in polymorphic systems. With gene frequencies not too far from 0.5, the polymorphic systems permit good estimates of genetic variation, although, of course, we do not usually know what forces maintain the gene frequencies at an intermediate level. We do not even know for the majority of them whether they are transient or stable. We may estimate the variances of alleles of such polymorphic systems for the whole world, ignoring, for the time being, the fact that these estimates are very approximate because the samples available today are hardly representative. We then see that standardized variance values, σ^2/pq, vary a great deal from one gene to another. Thus, one observes σ^2/pq values of 0.05 or lower for such systems as Kell, ABO, etc., and values almost reaching 0.5 for Gm^a, Fy, Rh^o, which are the most variable alleles (Cavalli-Sforza 1965; Cavalli-Sforza, Barrai, and Edwards 1964).

The mere fact that these variances vary so much indicates that drift alone cannot be responsible for all of them. No accurate analysis of this problem has yet been carried out, because of statistical difficulties, but we hope to be able soon to substantiate this tentative statement. The fact remains, however, that drift may certainly explain a fair amount of the observed local differentiation and that somewhere between the extreme observed σ^2/pq values a smaller range or distribution of values should represent the amount of differentiation expected to result from drift alone. Alleles whose variances are above this yet unknown range should be those for which selective conditions have varied from place to place or from time to time. If they had continued varying in an unpredictable way, they would have been subject to what has been called "selective drift," which, as Kimura (1954) has shown, is formally closely similar to "random drift." More discussion of this point will be found in the articles by Cavalli-Sforza (1965) and Cavalli-Sforza, Barrai, and Edwards (1964).

Below this range are variances belonging to alleles for which stabilizing selection has reduced fluctuations caused by drift. While remembering that we do not know the magnitude of the drift range, let us imagine for the moment that the average of the observed variances is the drift value, just to see if that value would demand an inordinate amount of variation because of drift.

The world σ^2/pq, averaged for some twenty alleles, is 0.15 (Cavalli-Sforza, Barrai, and Edwards 1964). If we allowed drift to go on within populations without migration to check it, it would require a relatively short time for a population isolate of, say, 100 members to reach this σ^2/pq value, namely, only 25 generations or 500 years. With a larger isolate of, say, 1000 members, 5000 years would be necessary, and 50,000 years for an isolate size of 10,000, which is perhaps larger than one would assume for a population living under primitive conditions. If migration breaks the isolation and we use equilibrium values, then the mean σ^2/pq value would correspond to $Nm = 1.5$. This means for an isolate size, N, of 10,000, a migration rate, m, slightly above one per 10,000. Such a migration rate is not unreasonably low for groups living very far from one another, as is true of the ethnic groups that have been considered here in the computation of the variances; with smaller isolate sizes, larger migration frequencies would of course still be compatible with the observed variation.

We thus see that there has been ample time for the variance postulated above with reasonable isolate sizes to have been reached. Even if migration has checked drift, the observed differentiation among ethnic groups seems roughly compatible with that expected. I think these estimates, however approximate, are enough to show that drift must have played a substantial part in determining the variation observed in human populations for polymorphic systems. It remains likely, though, that the variation observed from system to system very probably demands for its explanation the existence of different selective conditions, at least for the more variable polymorphic systems. Stabilizing selection also may be important for the less variable polymorphic systems. In this respect, it is interesting to note that the least variable polymorphic systems (e.g., ABO) exist also in other primates (Moor-Jankowski and Wiener 1965), although such investigations are, at the moment, not sufficiently advanced to permit satisfactory comparison with the human polymorphisms.

Analysis of human evolution

One reason why we are interested in the finding that drift may have had an important part in the evolution of human polymorphisms is that it provides a useful model for phylogenetic analysis, namely, for reconstructing evolutionary history on the basis of present and past gene frequencies when available (Cavalli-Sforza and Edwards 1965; Edwards and Cavalli-Sforza 1964).

Drift, whether random or "selective" as in the model developed by Kimura, will cause gene frequencies to oscillate randomly from time to time and from one population to another. This "random walk" of gene frequencies will be superimposed upon the branching of populations because of the colonization of new areas and new habitats.

Such a model of a random walk in time, accompanied by repeated branching of the populations, is perhaps frequently applicable to real biological situations, but until recently it has proved very resistant to numerical analysis. We have, therefore, used other methods which are numerically simpler; the underlying models for the analyses are similar but not identical and are somewhat less specific. For this reason they can more easily accommodate other biological situations, which may occur with unknown frequency and which do not fit the uncomplicated random walk and branching picture: for example, the occurrence of large selective "accidents" in one or more populations, the appearance of lines with high evolutionary rates, or the fusion between lines that had split earlier.

One model we have used is that of the "minimum evolutionary path." To reconstruct the dichotomies which have occurred in the history of the population, we compute the "net" that unites the populations in the multidimensional space formed by all the genes investigated. The chosen net is that which uses the minimum amount of string to connect all the points.

Another independent model which we have called "additive" assumes that all populations formed by successive dichotomies from a unique initial population have accumulated between one dichotomy and the next a certain amount of evolution, and that the amounts of evolution accumulated in each time interval are added to those previously accumulated. It is then possible to estimate the amounts of evolution accumulated in each time interval by the solution of suitable systems of equations in which these amounts are the unknowns. The observed differences between populations, expressed in appropriate scales, are the known values.

Using three bodies of data, we have applied these methods to human examples. The first group of data was from a systematic sampling of five blood group systems, a total of 20 alleles, in supposedly aboriginal populations of five continents (three per continent). The number of possible evolutionary trees, even excluding the apex of each tree, is so great that only a very minute fraction of the possible trees could be studied, but we have approximate methods to select the most likely ones. The analysis carried out so far has indicated as very likely a tree showing three quite clearcut groups: the Africans, the Caucasoids (including Asiatic Indians), and the more heterogeneous Asiatics (including Pacific and Amerindian populations). If constant evolutionary rates are assumed, the first split should have occurred between Asiatics and the rest. We have not given standard errors for this tree, but all short segments are likely not to differ significantly from zero. Therefore, the shape of the tree could easily be altered at those segments as a response to the addition of new genes or to changes in the samples used.

Anthropometric characters, rather than gene frequencies, of 15 populations not dissimilar to those used for the five blood group systems constituted the second group of data (Cavalli-Sforza and Edwards 1964). Results were not very different from those above except for one marked change, namely, that Australians and Africans were not as distinct as they had been when blood group gene frequencies were considered.

In the third example (Cavalli-Sforza 1965) we were interested in increasing the number of genes used by adding other markers such as serum proteins, phenylthiocarbamide tasting, and, in general, all markers for which sufficient information exists. Average gene frequencies were computed from all data reported in the literature on populations belonging to the particular ethnic groups considered, the number of which was reduced to seven. Ethnic groups and alleles studied are given in Table 16.4. The data and analysis on these seven populations (Fig. 16.3) are slightly different from those shown in another paper (Cavalli-Sforza 1965) written some months ago, because it has since been decided to change the quantity chosen to represent the genetic distances on the basis of gene frequencies.

Table 16.4

Distances (sums of chords in angular transformation) computed from the following alleles: A, B, O; MS, Ms, NS, Ns; P, p; CDE, CDe, Cde, cDE, cdE, cDe, cde; K, k; Lu^a, Lu^b; Le^a, Le^b; Fy^a, Fy^b; Di^a, Di^b; Hp^{1s}, Hp^{1F}, Hp^2; T, t; Gm^a, Gm^{ax}, Gm^b, Gm^{ab}; Gc^1, Gc^2, Gc^{ab}. Populations: *A*, Europeans; *B*, Extra European Caucasoids; *C*, Mongolians; *D*, American Indians; *E*, Eskimos; *F*, Africans; *G*, Australians and Melanesians. Revised from Cavalli-Sforza (1965).

	B	C	D	E	F	G
A	0.385	1.124	1.105	1.030	1.238	1.183
B		0.908	0.978	0.852	1.225	1.001
C			0.761	0.997	1.188	0.833
D				0.874	1.248	0.939
E					1.607	0.754
F						1.538

The analysis of these seven populations was carried out fairly completely. All possible trees (a total of 945) were analyzed with both the method of minimum evolution and that of additive trees. With both methods one most probable tree was found, as shown in Figure 16.3.

Doubling the genetic information on genetic markers and using an essentially independent set of data for the gene frequencies has left the picture practically unchanged from that for the 15 populations and five blood group systems. This increases our confidence in the use of gene frequencies to trace the history of human evolution and in phylogenetic analysis by these methods.

We have not yet attempted to feed into the models the hypothesis that some dichotomies may be followed by fusions, although in theory that possibility can be envisaged. In the early history of man, however, numerically important fusions between populations that had diverged to a fair extent must have been relatively rare—not as frequent, certainly, as the increase in means of transportation permits today. The shortness of some segments in the middle of the tree indicates, however, that either slower rates of evolution or early fusions did take place.

The picture of the studies on human populations I have presented here cannot aspire to be a representative sample, since the choice of subjects has obviously been greatly biased by my own personal interests. But I hope it can help to spread the idea that, in addition to other merits, demography makes human data useful for aims beyond immediate man-limited interests. The use of such data for genetic purposes may well become easier and more efficient in the future.

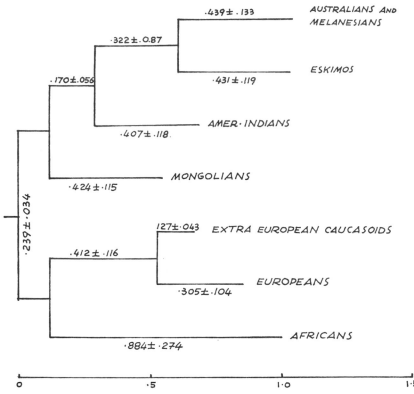

Fig. 16.3.—The evolutionary tree determined most likely by the minimum evolutionary path method from the figures of Table 16.4. The position of the first split is given by an assumption of approximately constant evolutionary rates.

I hope this picture also helps to show how the schemes of Mendelian inheritance are as useful in man as in any other organism, and that, in addition, it is fruitful to test in man the theory of evolution in Mendelian populations.

Summary

The genetic analysis of human populations has provided abundant evidence that the human species, like all comparable organisms, obeys the Mendelian rules of inheritance. In addition, it has permitted us to observe and measure the effects of the classical evolutionary factors, mutation, selection, and population structure. The abundance and detail of the medical and demographic information available on human individuals make our species especially suitable for classical genetic studies. Some work on mutation and selection with demographic material has been reviewed briefly, while studies on population structure, aimed especially at measuring genetic drift, have been discussed in somewhat more detail. In principle the extent to which drift can operate in determining local variation between populations sufficiently isolated from each other can be predicted with accuracy if population structure is adequately known. The analysis of one human population in northern Italy where demographic knowledge was adequate has shown that, when isolation is sufficient, local variation is found in the expected amount for all genetic systems investigated. Because available models of local differentiation are only imperfectly representative of real situations, an artificial population was established in a computer, simulating in all important respects the real population.

Consideration on a world basis of the standard polymorphisms, such as those for blood groups and serum proteins, about whose response to selective forces little is known, reveals on purely numerical grounds that drift may have played a substantial part in determining differences between ethnic groups. On the other hand, there are very remarkable differences in the variation of world gene frequencies from one genetic system to another and even from one allele to another. This suggests that the variation in the least variable systems is buffered by balanced selection or that the variation of the more variable systems is enhanced over that caused by drift by local or historical differences in selection, or that both these effects are true.

Edwards and I have made an effort to use available data on gene frequencies in human ethnic groups with a view to reconstructing the history of evolutionary divergence in the human species. We have done this by fitting suitable phylogenetic models to the data and selecting out of the many possible ones the mode of branching that gave the best fit. Models employed so far consider only the possibility of branching, not of subsequent fusion. This and other complications will have to be taken into account at another time because of the difficulties encountered in numerical analysis. Two almost independent bodies of data, one with 15 ethnic groups and five blood group systems (a total of 20 alleles) and one with seven groups but 13 systems (including the five above), gave parallel results. These analyses suggest that the earliest split in human evolution may have occurred between Asiatics (a heterogeneous group including populations of the Pacific area as well as American Indians) on one hand and Caucasoids and Africans on the other, and that these two latter groups separated somewhat later. A more rigorous assessment of the validity of these conclusions as well as their refinement will demand further work but we are at or near the point where the accumulated data can, if suitably employed, supply evidence on phylogenetic problems of our species.

Literature Cited

BAJEMA, C. J., 1963. Estimation of the direction and intensity of natural selection in relation to human intelligence by means of the intrinsic rate of natural increase. Eugen. Quart. **10**: 175–187.

BARRAI, I., AND D. BARBIERI, 1964. Drift in una popolazione simulata. Atti Ass. Genet. Ital. **9**: 233–245.

BRAIDWOOD, R. J., AND C. A. REED, 1957. The achievement and early consequences of food-production: A consideration of the archeological and natural-historical evidence. Cold Spring Harbor Symp. Quant. Biol. **22**: 19–31.

BUZZATI-TRAVERSO, A. A., 1950. Genetic structure of natural populations and interbreeding units in the human species. Cold Spring Harbor Symp. Quant. Biol. **15**: 13–23.

CAVALLI-SFORZA, L. L., 1958. Some data on the genetic structure of human populations. Proc. X Int. Congr. Genet. **1**: 389–407.

———, 1961. Un metodo per la stima della frequenza di mutazione nell'uomo: Risultati preliminari. Atti Ass. Genet. Ital. **6**: 151–162.

———, 1962a. Demographic attacks on genetic problems: Some possibilities and results. *The Use of Vital and Health Statistics for Genetic and Radiation Studies,* pp. 221–233. Proc. Seminar U.N. and W.H.O., Geneva (1960). United Nations, N.Y.

———, 1962b. Indagine speciale su alcune caratteristiche genetiche della popolazione Italiana. Istituto Centrale di Statistica, Roma, Note e Relazioni No. 17.

———, 1963a. The distribution of migration distances: Models and applications to genetics. *Human Displacements,* pp. 139–158. Edited by J. Sutton. Entretiens de Monaco en Sciènces Humaines, 1st session (1962). Hutchette, Paris.

———, 1963b. Genetic drift for blood groups. *The Genetics of Migrant and Isolate Populations,* pp. 34–39. Edited by E. Goldschmidt. Williams and Wilkins Co., Baltimore.

———, 1965. Population structure and human evolution. Proc. Roy. Soc. B **164**: 362–379.

CAVALLI-SFORZA, L. L., I. BARRAI, AND A. W. F. EDWARDS, 1964. Analysis of human evolution under random genetic drift. Cold Spring Harbor Symp. Quant. Biol. **29**: 9–20.

CAVALLI-SFORZA, L. L., AND F. CONTERIO, 1960. Analisi della fluttuazione di frequenze geniche nella popolazione della Val Parma. Atti Ass. Genet. Ital. **5**: 333–344.

CAVALLI-SFORZA, L. L., AND A. W. F. EDWARDS, 1965. Analysis of human evolution. *Genetics Today,* vol. 3, pp. 923–933. Edited by S. J. Geerts. Proc. XI Int. Congr. Genet., The Hague, The Netherlands.

CONTERIO, F., AND L. L. CAVALLI-SFORZA, 1959. Selezione per caratteri quanti-
tativi nell'uomo. Atti Ass. Genet. Ital. 5: 1–10.

CROW, J. F., 1961. Mutation in man. *Progress in Medical Genetics,* vol. 1,
pp. 1–26. Grune and Stratton, New York & London.

EDWARDS, A. W. F., AND L. L. CAVALLI-SFORZA, 1964. Reconstruction of evolutionary trees. *Phenetic and Phylogenetic Classification,* pp. 67–76. Systematics Ass. Publ. No. 6

FISHER, R. A., 1930. *Genetical Theory of Natural Selection.* Clarendon Press,
Oxford.

GLASS, B., 1954. Genetic changes in human populations, especially those due
to gene flow and genetic drift. Advance. Genet. 6: 95–139.

KIMURA, M., 1954. Process leading to quasi-fixation of genes in natural populations due to random fluctuation of selection intensities. Genetics 39: 280–
295.

KIMURA, M., AND G. H. WEISS, 1964. The stepping stone model of population
structure and the decrease of genetic correlation with distance. Genetics
49: 561–576.

KIRK, R. L., 1965. The distribution of genetic markers in Australian aborigines. Australian Inst. Aboriginal Stud., Canberra, Occasional Papers in
Aboriginal Stud. No. 4: 1–67.

LAUGHLIN, W. S., 1950. Genetic analysis of racial traits, II. Blood groups,
morphology and population size of the Eskimos. Cold Spring Harbor Symp.
Quant. Biol. 15: 165–173.

LEVENE, H., 1963. Inbred genetic loads and the determination of population
structure. Proc. Nat. Acad. Sci. U.S. 50: 587–592.

McKUSICK, V. A., J. A. HOSTETLER, J. A. EGELAND, AND R. ELDRIDGE, 1964.
The distribution of certain genes in the old order Amish. Cold Spring
Harbor Symp. Quant. Biol. 29: 99–114.

MOOR-JANKOWSKI, J., AND A. S. WIENER, 1965. Primate blood groups and
evolution. Science 148: 255–256.

MORTON, N. E., J. F. CROW, AND H. J. MULLER, 1956. An estimate of the
mutational damage in man from data on consanguineous marriages. Proc.
Nat. Acad. Sci. U.S. 42: 855–863.

NEWCOMBE, H. B., 1964. Pedigrees for population studies, a progress report.
Cold Spring Harbor Symp. Quant. Biol. 29: 21–30.

PENROSE, L. S., 1934. The relative aetiological importance of birth order and
maternal age in mongolism. Proc. Roy. Soc. B 115: 431–450.

———, 1955. Parental age and mutation. Lancet 2: 312–313.

WRIGHT, S., 1943. Isolation by distance. Genetics 28: 114–138.

———, 1946. Isolation by distance under diverse systems of mating. Genetics
31: 39–59.

V

Latitude of Genetics

17

Mendelism, 1965

George W. Beadle

After reading the several excellent papers presented in honor of Mendel at the 1965 general meeting of the American Philosophical Society (Vol. 109, No. 4, of the *Proceedings*), I spent many days wondering what I might reasonably contribute for this commemorative volume. While so doing, I received a copy of a new book which so effectively and appropriately summarizes a hundred years of genetics that I was much tempted to abstract it for this meeting. I refer to *Molecular Biology of the Gene* by James D. Watson (1965). I shall not plagiarize to quite that extent, but I do recommend the book with genuine enthusiasm.

Many writers, including Dunn (1965) and Dobzhansky (1965), have pondered the question of why Mendel's paper was unappreciated—and almost undiscovered—for thirty-five years. The *Proceedings of the Natural History Society of Brünn,* in which Mendel's paper was published in 1866, was widely distributed in Europe and the United States; there were some 120 persons and institutions on the subscriber-exchange list. In addition, so it is said, Mendel had forty reprints to distribute—which he presumably did. Carl von Nägeli's lack of appreciation is understandable, despite the extensive correspondence he carried on with Mendel, for he worked with species of *Hieracium* (hawkweed) which, unknown to Nägeli, were partially apomictic and thus produced seeds of purely maternal origin. This same unfortunate choice of material presumably cost Mendel his faith, for, with Nägeli's advice, he too investigated what he thought was hybridization in that genus.

Probably to his other contemporaries Mendel's theory was so simple that it must have seemed wholly incredible. Today, a century later, we are somewhat more receptive to simple ideas in biology, but even now there is a persistent intuitive distrust of simplicity in a system as obviously complex as a living organism. This is evidenced by many other examples, among them Wöhler's synthesis of urea in 1828, Miescher's isolation and characterization of nucleic acid in 1871 (Glass 1965), Sumner's crystallization of the enzyme urease in 1926 and his demonstration of its protein nature, and Stanley's "crystallization" of tobacco mosaic virus in 1935. I shall mention other examples in relevant contexts.

There is no firm evidence that Darwin knew of Mendel's work. It is argued that, if he had, he would almost surely have seized upon it as the answer to the seemingly fatal objection of Fleeming Jenkin that newly arisen mutations would be quickly swamped out in a few generations through blending inheritance. Mendel seems clearly to have appreciated that he had the answer, judged from comments in his own paper. Sir Gavin de Beer (1965) confirms that Mendel did indeed know about Darwin and *The Origin of Species,* pointing out that Mendel had a copy of the German edition in which he made careful marginal notes and also that Alexander Makovsky had read a paper before the Natural History society of Brünn on January 11, 1865, in which he enthusiastically supported Darwin's theory. This was just one month before Mendel first presented his results to the same society. Furthermore, a personal friend of Mendel, Gustav von Niessel, is reported to have said that Mendel was not antagonistic to Darwin's theory, but that he thought there was something missing and hoped his own work would supply the needed facts (de Beer 1965).

Why, then, did Mendel not refer to Darwin? It is doubtful if anyone will ever know with certainty, but de Beer suggests that, because a few years earlier the Austrian emperor had negotiated a concordat with the Vatican imposing strict censorship on newspapers, expression of public opinion, and university teaching, the mention of Darwin would almost surely have cost Mendel his position as an Augustinian canon.

We shall probably never know the answer to the reciprocal question: Did Darwin really not know of Mendel's work? Dobzhansky (1965) and others argue that, if he had known, he would of course have understood and appreciated it. That is a reasonable assumption, but one cannot be sure. After all, Focke, the author of the great 1881 monograph on plant hybridization, read Mendel's paper, referred to it, and, like others, completely missed the point. The *Proceedings of the Natural History Society of Brünn* was available to Darwin, well known to have been a systematic reader. Also, in view of the fact that Mendel was not reticent, as evidenced by his extensive correspondence with von Nägeli, and was obviously interested in evolution, it seems strange that he would not have put Darwin high on his reprint mailing list.

I believe the most thorough analysis of Mendel's classic paper, together with a reconstruction of his methods, is that of R. A. Fisher (1936). Among Fisher's many significant conclusions is that Mendel must have had the essentials of his final interpretation clearly in mind well before completing the experimental work—this conclusion being based mainly on the fact that the observed genetic ratios are incredibly close to the ratios the theory predicted. Fisher calculates that in the overall results one would expect a fit as good as Mendel reports only one time in 30,000 repetitions. There are four possible explanations: (1) that Mendel was incredibly lucky; (2) that he consciously biased the results in favor of the theory; (3) that he unconsciously biased the results; (4) that the Fisher analysis is incomplete.

One must agree that we can reasonably dismiss the first on the grounds of simple incredibility. Fisher grants that the third possibility is reasonable but insufficient to account for the observed goodness of fit. And of course he does not seriously consider the fourth point. By exclusion he clearly implies conscious bias—in the vernacular, "fudging the data."

I am not willing to accept this conclusion. In the first place, there can be little doubt that Mendel both knew and grew his peas, for subsequent workers have verified all of his observations in detail. If he did not fabricate the whole story, which he clearly could not have done, there was no reason for him to have tampered with any of it. I suggest that a combination of the third and fourth possibilities provides a satisfactory explanation.

First, consider the possibility that Fisher's statistical analysis is not entirely correct. It assumes random samples taken from egg and sperm populations of infinite size in which the true ratios are one to one. As every botanist knows, this assumption is considered valid for eggs but is clearly *not* valid for the sperm-carrying pollen grains. Pollen populations in a given anther or flower are definitely finite and produced in *exactly* a one-to-one ratio for a given gene pair, because each mother cell gives rise to four daughters, the two kinds always distributed in a two-to-two ratio. Furthermore, since pea flowers are self-fertilized before they fully open, the pollen grains that fertilize the flower that produces a given pea pod are very few in number and likely to come from an even smaller number of two-to-two quartets. Thus if one pea seed in a pod carries one allele of a pair from the pollen, the next one is more likely than not to carry the alternate allele.

Some years ago Professor Sturtevant and I explored this possibility to see if it was sufficient to account for the apparent bias. It works in the right direction but is not sufficient, even if alternate forms of pollen grains are assumed to have functioned always in an exact one-to-one ratio.

Let us, then, explore the phenomenon of unconscious bias. Fisher considers one kind only, misclassification of some individuals—for example, a shriveled round pea scored as "wrinkled." As every experimenter in genetics knows, some classifications are difficult and may easily be unconsciously biased in favor of a preconceived hypothesis.

I am personally very sensitive to this source of error, for I once discovered a loose genetic linkage in maize between floury endosperm and a second endosperm character known to be on chromosome 9, a linkage that I subsequently concluded was the result of my "wanting" to find it. The floury character is often difficult to score, and I believe I unconsciously put the doubtful ones in the piles that would suggest linkage. Fortunately, I recognized the possibility of this kind of error in time to withdraw a manuscript I had submitted for publication.

There is a second kind of bias that Fisher does not take into account in his final conclusion. As he points out, Mendel clearly had his hypothesis in mind before completing all his work and therefore expected certain numerical ratios. It is also clear, as Fisher deduces, that Mendel did not classify all the pea plants and seeds he grew. Presumably he classified enough to convince himself that the result was as expected. It is perfectly natural under these circumstances to keep running totals as counts are made. If, then, one stops when the ratio "looks good," statistically the result will be biased in favor of the hypothesis. A seemingly "bad" fit may be perfectly plausible statistically, but one may not think so and add more data to see if it improves, thereby raising interesting questions, some mathematical and some psychological.

A modification of this type of bias is encountered when the data from several populations segregating for the same traits are not all reported. In these circumstances there is almost sure to be unconscious bias introduced in the selection of representative examples, unless special care is taken to avoid it. This, too, is an entirely plausible source of bias in Mendel's results.

Sewall Wright once pointed out to me that many reported data in genetics are "too good" to be random samples. Most of us are subject to the same prejudices as are here assumed to have influenced Mendel.

I therefore conclude that Mendel was very human, but not dishonest.

Dunn (1965) argues that Mendel must have had his hypothesis in mind before beginning his experiments with peas, and speculates at length as to how he could have arrived at it. I suggest that this is an unnecessary concern. Mendel clearly had in mind clearcut qualitative traits which he proposed to investigate, for the record shows that he selected on just this basis the 34 horticultural varieties on which he made preliminary observations and which he subsequently reduced to 22 for the experiments. The first hybrid plants he grew included those from round and wrinkled parents. The pea seeds on the first generation plants would be in the ratio of three round to one wrinkled. It seems evident that he observed this, probably early in the fall. If so, he had the entire winter to speculate before planning the next summer's experiments. I suggest that he then worked out the theory from the observed result. As Sturtevant noted in Chapter 2 of this volume, Mendel's knowledge of mathematics, chemistry, and physics no doubt influenced his approach to the problem.

I shall say little about the classical period of genetics that flourished, especially in Britain and the United States, after the "rediscovery" of Mendel's paper. Incidentally, the rediscovery is itself a fascinating chapter that was completed only recently by Sturtevant (1965) in his book on the history of genetics.

For many years there were doubts about the validity of Mendelian genetics in the minds of many. Prior to his conversion by a white-eyed *Drosophila*, Thomas Hunt Morgan himself had reservations. In a paper delivered before the American Breeders' Association in 1908 (Morgan 1909), he said:

The superior jugglery [of Mendelism] sometimes necessary to account for the results may blind us, if taken too naively, to the common-place that the results are often so excellently "explained" because the explanation was invented to explain them. We work backwards from the facts to the factors, and then, presto! explain the facts by the very factors that we invented to account for them.

R. A. Emerson, one of the ardent early supporters of Mendelism, followed Morgan on that program with a paper in which he greatly amused the audience by explaining that the inheritance of a coat-color character in the garden bean could not be accounted for by one gene pair but could with two. He was right.

Three years later, in response to Morgan's report on linkage and recombination of two sex-linked genes in *Drosophila*, Emerson (1911) protested that the explanation in terms of crossing over could not be right because, ". . . *it certainly will not account for the purity of extracted recessives and dominants as exhibited by their behavior in F_3 and later generations. To overlook this is to neglect the fundamental part of Mendelism.*" Emerson was more prophetic than he knew, for we now recognize that intragenic recombination does indeed occur and that alleles do not always emerge from a hybrid as they went in.

William Bateson, that militant and effective protagonist of Mendelism, had his difficulties too in accepting the rapid advances in the new science he had worked so hard to establish. He never wholeheartedly accepted the chromosome theory of inheritance except for a brief period after he had personally examined C. B. Bridges' cytological evidence showing that rare aberrations in the behavior of fourth chromosome and sex-linked genes in *Drosophila* are exactly paralleled by the predicted aberrations in chromosome transmission. Thereafter he is said to have reverted to his state of skepticism, even as he was responsible for introducing cytological studies into the research program of the John Innes Horticultural Institution.

Like Mendelism, biochemical genetics began with a remarkable investigator whose work remained unappreciated for a third of a century. I refer to A. E. Garrod, later Sir Archibald, English physician and biochemist who, shortly after the turn of the century, proposed that the disease alkaptonuria in man is a Mendelian recessive trait. He knew it was characterized by urinary excretion of large amounts of alkaptone or 2,5-dihydroxyphenylacetic acid and soon formulated the hypothesis that it involves a gene defect, with associated absence of an enzyme responsible for the cleavage of the ring of alkaptone, and that alkaptone accumulates and is excreted instead of being degraded as in normal persons. This interpretation was published in *Lancet* in 1902, was later further investigated, and was reported in several stages, first to the Royal Society, then in a 1909 edition of *Inborn Errors of Metabolism,* and finally in a revised edition in 1923 (Garrod 1923).

Garrod used alkaptonurics to elucidate the metabolic pathway by which alkaptone is produced from the amino acids phenylalanine and tyrosine, thus demonstrating for the first time the use of a genetic trait as a powerful tool in biochemistry.

Bateson, with whom Garrod had consulted on the genetic aspects of alkaptonuria, referred to the disease in his 1909 and later editions of *Mendel's Principles of Heredity,* but thereafter alkaptonuria all but disappeared from the standard textbooks of genetics. Geneticists evidently regarded alkaptonuria as just another Mendelian trait and failed completely to see the biochemical implications. Biochemists made the complementary error; that is, they regarded it as interesting biochemistry but did not recognize its genetic significance.

Among biochemists, Sir Frederick Gowland Hopkins seems to have come closest to appreciating the significance and usefulness of Garrod's inborn errors of metabolism. Writing in the 1913 *Report of the British Association,* he said:

Extraordinarily profitable have been the observations made upon individuals suffering from those errors of metabolism which Dr. Garrod calls "metabolic sports, the chemical analogues of structural malformations." In these individuals Nature has taken the first essential step in an experiment by omitting from their chemical structure a special catalyst which at one point in the procession of metabolic chemical events is essential to its continuance. At this point there is arrest, and intermediate products come to light.

It was Sewall Wright (1941) and J. B. S. Haldane (1942) who first brought Garrod's work to my attention. Until then I had thought that the studies of Wright (1927; see also 1942) on guinea pigs, Caspari and Kühn (see Kühn, Caspari, and Plagge 1935) on the meal moth, Scott-Moncrieff (1936) on flower pigments, Ephrussi and me (Beadle and Ephrussi 1936) on *Drosophila* eye colors, and Tatum and me (Beadle and Tatum 1941) on specific biosynthetic reactions in the bread mold *Neurospora* were the experimental bases for the one-gene–one-enzyme hypothesis that led us to devise the *Neurospora* approach.

The one-gene–one-enzyme hypothesis, later to be more properly called the one-gene–one-polypeptide hypothesis, is another example of a concept that was strongly resisted, again, I believe, because it seemed too simple to be true. I recall well the year 1953 when, at the Cold Spring Harbor Symposium on Synthesis and Structure of Macromolecules, there appeared to be no more than three of us who remained firm in our faith.

The year 1938 has special importance in genetics, for it was then that Emory Ellis, then a postdoctoral fellow at the California Institute of Technology, introduced Max Delbrück to bacterial viruses as potential genetic material. I need not elaborate on the role these remarkable creatures have played in the development of modern molecular genetics. They were soon shown to have genes, linearly arranged much like those of higher organisms.

In 1944, another landmark year, Avery, MacLeod, and McCarty (1944) reported that a transforming substance of pneumococcus could be reduced to deoxyribonucleic acid (DNA) as pure as they were able to obtain it. One interpretation, now known to be correct, which was not offered in the original paper but which Avery recognized fully, as evidenced by an unpublished letter to his brother, was that transformation was the replacement of a mutant form of a gene for polysaccharide by its counterpart from the donor cell. That is, Avery was aware that transformation might be the result of transfer of an actual gene from donor to recipient and that the gene was therefore DNA. Sewall Wright suggested this same interpretation, but it was not widely accepted. How could it be so simple? In a review of biochemical genetics written in 1945, I referred to the work of Avery, MacLeod, and McCarty in the following cautious words: "There is, however, recent evidence from work on the nucleic acid of pneumococci suggesting that this component may possibly play a part in determining the specificities of individual genes" (Beadle 1945). I can no longer be proud of that double qualification.

By 1952, the matter was settled, at least in bacterial viruses, for in that year Hershey and Chase demonstrated, by labeling with radioactive phosphorus or sulfur, that the DNA component of these parasites is alone transmitted from one generation to the next. Since these viruses have genes, clearly those genes are DNA. From this finding we could assume that the nuclear genetic information of all organisms is either DNA or ribonucleic acid (RNA).

The Hershey-Chase evidence prompted James D. Watson to join forces with Francis H. C. Crick at the Medical Research Council Unit at Cambridge University in an attempt to work out the detailed molecular structure of DNA. In the manner so clearly described by Watson (1965) in the book previously mentioned, they did this in 1953 in a matter of months. I regard the working out of the double helical structure of DNA as the most significant single advance in biology of this century, comparable to Mendel's and Darwin's nineteenth-century contributions. I say that because the characterization of this structure has catalyzed a truly amazing increase in our knowledge of chemical genetics. It at once suggested how DNA might carry information, how it could be replicated with precision, and how it could undergo mutational change, and it later stimulated a series of investigations that have told us how DNA information is used in the synthesis of specific proteins.

Again there were skeptics. I recall that one distinguished nucleic acid biochemist said he believed the Watson-Crick DNA structure to be correct but to have nothing to do with replication. Or, as another example, a fellow biologist asked me in all seriousness, several years after the Watson-Crick structure had been adduced, why I put so much emphasis on molecular genetics. Maybe, he suggested, the gene was a fad and would go out of fashion!

Today we know that a gene is a segment of DNA (or RNA in some viruses), perhaps 1000 to 2000 nucleotides in length, that serves to determine the amino acid sequence in a specific protein chain. We know that the gene replicates in the manner suggested by Watson and Crick, namely, by separation of the two single DNA strands of opposite polarity, each serving as a template against which complementary nucleotides become ordered to reconstruct a double helix like the original.

Specificity is conferred through hydrogen bonding within the pyrimidine-purine nucleotide base pairs, thymine-adenine and cytosine-guanine. The evidence for this mode of replication comes from the work of Kornberg and co-workers (see Kornberg 1962), who observed the process in a cell-free system, and of Meselson and Stahl (1958), who followed the old and new strands through successive replications by means of isotope labeling. Meselson and Stahl showed that the parental DNA single chains remain intact during the replication process. I should emphasize, however, that not all the details of the process are understood, especially the manner of action of the enzymes necessary for the process.

Kornberg and associates have shown that under certain conditions artificial DNA of two kinds can be formed *in vitro* in the absence of primer molecules: one in which adenine and thymine nucleotides alternate in the two chains in complementary manner, and a second in which one chain consists of guanine nucleotides only and its partner of cytosine complements. Both types appear to replicate in the manner of native DNA.

Bacterial nuclei of *Escherichia coli* and their DNA viruses both contain single chromosomes consisting of a single giant molecule of DNA, circular in some stages and in some viruses a single rather than a double chain. The single-chain forms replicate by complement formation. The smallest known DNA-containing virus has a chromosome of approximately 5500 nucleotides. A T4 bacterial virus head contains a DNA molecule of about 200,000 nucleotides. A human cell has DNA distributed among 46 chromosomes totaling about five billion nucleotides, or enough to specify perhaps as many as a million different kinds of protein molecules. The precise organization of the chromosomes of higher plants and animals is not understood, but it is known from tritium labeling and radioautography that the DNA components replicate in the manner of bacterial DNA.

For years many of us were convinced that, if we could learn enough about crossing over in higher organisms by classical genetic methods, we would understand the details of the mechanism by which it occurs. We were discouragingly unsuccessful. At the DNA level in bacterial viruses the story seems simple. By heavy nitrogen (^{15}N) labeling and density-gradient separation techniques, it has been possible to show that genetic recombination occurs by exchange of homologous segments of DNA molecules in the double helix state, and, furthermore, that this apparently can occur in the absence of DNA replication (Watson 1965).

Just as Emerson suggested over fifty years ago, crossing over does indeed result in cross contamination of alleles in hybrids of viruses, bacteria, and multicellular organisms. Whether or not this is always by the mechanism revealed in bacterial viruses we cannot yet say.

Dramatic progress has been made in the last decade in the understanding of how DNA molecules direct the synthesis of specific proteins —so much so that all essential steps in the process can now be carried out experimentally in cell-free systems.

Although much of the detailed chemistry is known (Watson 1965), the several steps of the process will be briefly described for a single gene as follows:

(1) From one of the two chains of a double DNA helix, always the same one, a complementary RNA chain is constructed, presumably in the same manner as a complementary DNA chain is formed during DNA replication. This RNA is called messenger RNA or mRNA. What determines that the complement will be mRNA rather than DNA remains unknown.

(2) Messenger RNA moves from the nucleus to the cytoplasm where it associates with a number of submicroscopic ribosomes constructed of ribosomal protein and a second kind of RNA called ribosomal RNA or rRNA.

(3) The twenty amino acid building blocks are labeled with specific small RNA molecules (for example, the one combining with alanine having 77 nucleotides). This third kind of RNA is called variously soluble RNA (sRNA), transfer RNA (tRNA), or adapter RNA. I shall refer to it as transfer RNA.

(4) Like messenger RNA, both ribosomal and transfer RNA are synthesized against DNA templates—that is, are genetically specified.

(5) The labeled amino acids are arranged linearly along the mRNA template, progressing in the $5'-3'$ direction of the messenger. Thus, one by one, the amino acids are joined through peptide linkages beginning with the NH_2-terminal amino acid and ending with a COOH-terminal one.

Amino acids are coded in DNA and RNA by nucleotide triplets. Thus a DNA triplet for glycine is CCA and its complementary triplet (code word or codon) in RNA is GGU. (In this naming system A, T, C, G, and U specify adenine, thymine, cytosine, guanine, and uracil nucleotides respectively. In RNA the thymine nucleotide is replaced with a uracil counterpart. Thus U of RNA is complementary to A of either DNA or RNA.)

RNA code words have now been determined experimentally for all twenty amino acids, an achievement that is a brilliant chapter in molecular genetics. This decoding was done with RNA triplets of known sequence being used as templates for binding corresponding labeled amino acids. Marshall Nirenberg and co-workers (1965) have combined the separate triplet messengers with ribosomes and then, by isotope labeling of amino acids, determined the correspondence between amino

Table 17.1

Experimentally determined nucleotide sequences of RNA codons for specific amino acids, as reported by Nirenberg *et al.* (1965). The symbols U, C, A, and G designate uracil, cytosine, arginine, and guanine nucleotides. The order in which they are written, left to right, is in the 5′ to 3′ orientation of nucleotides. Amino acid abbreviations are *Ala*, alanine; *Arg*, arginine; *Asp*, aspartic acid; *Asp-NH₂*, asparagine; *Cys*, cysteine; *Glu*, glutamic acid; *Glu-NH₂*, glutamine; *Gly*, glycine; *His*, histidine; *Ileu*, isoleucine; *Leu*, leucine; *Lys*, lysine; *Met*, methionine; *Phe*, phenylalanine; *Pro*, proline; *Ser*, serine; *Thr*, threonine; *Trypt*, tryptophane; *Tyr*, tyrosine; *Val*, valine; and *Non*, nonsense. The systematic arrangement of the table permits the designation of predicted codons not tested at the time the table was prepared.

UUU		UCU		UGU		UAU	
	Phe		Ser		Cys		Tyr
UUC		UCC				UAC	
				UGA		UAA	
	Leu		Ser		Non or Trypt		Non
UUG		UCG				UAG	
CUU		CCU				CAU	
	Leu or Non		Pro		Arg		His
CUC		CCC		CGC		CAC	
		CCA		CGA		CAA	
	Leu		Pro		Arg		Glu-NH₂
CUG						CAG	
AUU		ACU		AGU		AAU	
	Ileu		Thr		Ser		Asp-NH₂
AUC		ACC		AGC		AAC	
		ACA		AGA		AAA	
	Met		Thr		Arg or Non		Lys
AUG		ACG				AAG	
GUU		GCU		GGU		GAU	
	Val		Ala		Gly		Asp
						GAC	
						GAA	
	Val		Ala		Gly		Glu

acids and single RNA coding triplets. The code is degenerate in the sense that more than one triplet may code for a specific amino acid. Nirenberg *et al.* (1965) have recently reported the coding significance of all 64 triplets, as now understood. These are given in Table 17.1.

Evidence confirming the code as shown comes from many sources: Of

27 mutations from normal to abnormal hemoglobins in man, all but one are accounted for by single nucleotide changes. Beale and Lehman (1965) have reported that this one exception, involving hemoglobin I, is only an apparent exception that resulted from an error in amino acid sequence determination (a case in which genetic data were used to detect an error in determining protein structure). Nitrite-induced mutations in tobacco mosaic virus are also consistent with the proposed code (Watson 1965). Furthermore, both mutations and intracodon recombinations which lead to amino acid alterations in the A protein of tryptophan synthetase are generally consistent (Guest and Yanofsky 1965).

How is a continuous RNA molecule read when no "spaces" exist between codons? For each protein counterpart there must be a signal for reading to begin and another to stop. By a most ingenious approach Brenner, Stretton, and Kaplan (1965) and Weigert and Garen (1965), working with bacterial virus and *E. coli* mutants, have determined what kinds of "sense" DNA triplets can be derived from "nonsense" triplets, that is, from those triplets that do not code for any amino acid and therefore could be chain-terminating codons in protein synthesis. There is evidence that the UAG and UAA triplets of RNA are such codons, at least in some virus and bacteria strains. These, however, may not be normal chain-terminating code words.

Evidently, the mRNA code is read simply as a succession of nonoverlapping triplets, regardless of starting point, for, when a nucleotide is omitted by mutation, the triplets distal to it, reading in the 5′–3′ direction, become scrambled and thereby specify an incomplete or "nonsense" protein. In fact, it was through such experimentally produced shifts in the genetic reading frame that Crick and co-workers produced the first solid evidence that DNA and RNA codons are triplets (Crick 1963).

The classical genetic test for allelism is known to break down sometimes if two different mutant forms of the same gene in hybrid combination give rise to a nonmutant phenotype. Intra-allelic complementation of this sort between glutamate dehydrogenase mutants in *Neurospora crassa* has now been shown by Coddington and Fincham (1965) to be the result of interaction between two types of protein chains in an enzyme molecule consisting of probably eight subunits. Normally the eight subunits are identical, but in complementation they are made up of eight mutant chains, four of each type.

It has long been obvious that not all of the genetic information in a cell is used at any one time. As an extreme example, mammalian red blood cells specialize in synthesizing hemoglobin molecules. Many other examples are known in which enzymes—so-called inducible enzymes—are formed by cells only in response to the presence of their substrate molecules and are suppressed by the end product of the reaction chain with which they are associated.

Such delicate and remarkable regulatory mechanisms are beginning to be understood, in large part through the highly imaginative work of Jacob, Monod, and associates (Watson 1965). In the case of the enzyme β-galactosidase in *E. coli,* it is postulated that the regulatory system consists of at least four units: regulatory gene, operator, β-galactosidase structural gene, and galactoside permease structural gene. The regulatory gene produces a repressor, presumably protein, conceivably an RNA-histone complex (Bonner 1965). In the absence of β-galactoside or other inducer, the repressor interacts with the operator in such a way that the information of the two structural genes is not transcribed into its RNA equivalent. Thus, neither of the two enzymes is produced. If β-galactoside is present, it combines with the repressor and inactivates it. The operator then operates, and the two enzymes necessary to utilize β-galactoside are produced. There is evidence that the mRNA for the two enzymes is formed from the operator end of the structural gene for galactosidase.

In contrast to inducer systems, there are systems in which the end product serves as a co-repressor, combining with the regulator-produced repressor in a manner that activates the repressor and inhibits gene function via the operator.

A second and independent regulatory system, known as feedback or end-product inhibition, involves inhibition of the activity—not the formation—of the first enzyme in a metabolic chain, with the result that all reactions in the sequence are stopped. This is presumed to involve a union of the end-product with a site on the enzyme other than that concerned in substrate binding, thus changing the state of the enzyme in a manner that interferes with substrate binding. Enzyme proteins of this kind are called allosteric proteins.

Much progress is being made in understanding gene action in terms of changes at the chromosome level, as is evident from Beermann's chapter in this volume (Ch. 11). He is personally responsible for much of the exciting work now being done.

There are many aspects of genetics which I have not discussed. For example, I have omitted all mention of cytoplasm except as a medium in which protein synthesis occurs. I know that it must be related to the nucleus in a highly specific way, for the nucleus of a frog's egg will not function in the cytoplasm of a closely related species. And I know that Sonneborn has shown in a most elegant fashion that there are cytoplasmic organelles that cannot be produced *de novo,* as though there were a cytoplasmic model-copy mechanism at work. I shall not consider this important part of heredity because my space and knowledge are limited, and also because Sonneborn has done so himself. Moreover, the subjects of population genetics, mutation, and radiation genetics have been thoroughly discussed elsewhere in this book. Finally, concerning prelife and early life evolution a great deal is being learned, to which I wish I might address myself, but space limitations again intervene.

I do want, however, to say a few words about genetics and cultural inheritance, for it is a subject with which I am much concerned. I do not need to point out that we are unique among species on earth in the degree to which we supplement biological inheritance with cultural inheritance, nor need I mention that the latter would be impossible without the former. This unilateral dependence of the nervous system on DNA instructions is sometimes used fallaciously as an argument that human populations with less developed cultures must be so because of genetic limitations—that since the peoples of such and such a continent have never developed a significant culture or civilization, they must be genetically incapable of doing so.

I suggest that, since more than ninety-nine per cent of our cultural inheritance has accumulated in less than one per cent of our time on earth as species of *Homo,* chance and opportunity must have played far larger parts in where and when it began to speed up than did genetic competence. Once started, it grows autocatalytically through transmission laterally among contemporary members of the species and longitudinally from generation to generation. The parent-to-child component of the latter type of transmission and the earliness with which it operates are far more important than most of us have realized.

Civilization after civilization has waxed and waned over time periods so short that genetic change almost certainly could not have been responsible.

When one realizes that it is theoretically possible for our species to revert in a single generation to the barbaric state of a hundred thousand years ago and for the entire process to be reversed in a second generation (if one assumes an adequate mechanism for reindoctrinating the children of the lost generation—say, an unreverted segment of the original population), a very simple conclusion is suggested—namely, that it is far easier and enormously quicker to raise the general cultural level of our species than it is to change its genetic composition. It is also far safer, for if a mistake is made in accomplishing the former, the process is easily and quickly reversed. I therefore advocate that we concentrate on improving our cultural heritage, at least for the fore-seeable future.

Although I recognize that they are not mutally exclusive and that we should be concerned with both, I prefer that we exhaust the possibili-ties of Lederberg's euphenics—or perhaps I should say cultural euphen-ics—before we resort in any large way to Muller's eugenics.

Literature Cited

AVERY, O. T., C. M. MacLEOD, AND M. McCARTY, 1944. Studies on the chemi-cal nature of the substance inducing transformation in pneumococcal types. J. Exp. Med. **79:** 137–158.

BEADLE, G. W., 1945. Biochemical genetics. Chem. Rev. **37:** 15–96.

BEADLE, G. W., AND B. EPHRUSSI, 1936. The differentiation of eye pigments in *Drosophila* as studied by transplantation. Genetics **21:** 225–247.

BEADLE, G. W., AND E. L. TATUM, 1941. Genetic control of biochemical re-actions in *Neurospora*. Proc. Nat. Acad. Sci. U.S. **27:** 499–506.

BEALE, D., AND H. LEHMAN, 1965. Abnormal hemoglobins and the genetic code. Nature **207:** 259–261.

BEER, G. DE, 1965. Mendel, Darwin, and the centre of science. The Listener, March 11: 364–366.

BONNER, J., 1965. *The Molecular Biology of Development.* The University Press, Oxford.

BRENNER, S., A. O. W. STRETTON, AND S. KAPLAN, 1965. Genetic code: The "nonsense" triplets for chain termination. Nature **206:** 994–998.

CODDINGTON, A., AND J. R. S. FINCHAM, 1965. Proof of hybrid enzyme for-mation in a case of intra-allelic complementation. J. Mol. Biol. **12:** 152–161.

CRICK, F. H. C., 1963. On the genetic code. Science **139:** 461–464.

DOBZHANSKY, TH., 1965. Mendelism, Darwinism and evolutionism. Proc. Amer. Phil. Soc. **109:** 205–215.

DUNN, L. C., 1965. Mendel, his work, and his place in history. Proc. Amer. Phil. Soc. **109:** 189–198.

EMERSON, R. A., 1911. Coupling *vs.* random segregation. Science **34:** 512–513.

FISHER, R. A., 1936. Has Mendel's work been rediscovered? Ann. Sci. **1:** 115–137.

GARROD, A. E., 1923. *Inborn Errors of Metabolism,* 2nd ed. Frowde, Hod-der & Stoughton, London.

GLASS, B., 1965. A century of biochemical genetics. Proc. Amer. Phil. Soc. **109:** 227–236.

GUEST, J. R., AND C. YANOFSKY, 1965. Amino acid replacements associated with reversion and recombination within a coding unit. J. Mol. Biol. **12:** 793–804.

HALDANE, J. B. S., 1942. *New Paths in Genetics.* Harper & Bros., New York.

HERSHEY, A. D., AND M. CHASE, 1952. Independent functions of viral protein and nucleic acid in growth of bacteriophage. J. Gen. Physiol. 36: 39–56.

HOPKINS, F. G., 1913. The dynamic side of biochemistry. Rept. Brit. Ass. Reprinted in *Hopkins and Biochemistry*. Heffer & Sons, Cambridge, England.

KORNBERG, A., 1962. *Enzymatic Synthesis of DNA*. Wiley & Sons Inc., New York.

KÜHN, A., E. CASPARI, AND E. PLAGGE, 1935. Über hormonale Genwirkungen bei *Ephestia kühniella*. Z. Nachr. Ges. Wiss. Göttingen 2: 1–29.

MESELSON, M., AND F. W. STAHL, 1958. The replication of DNA in *Escherichia coli*. Proc. Nat. Acad. Sci. U.S. 44: 671–682.

MORGAN, T. H., 1909. What are "Factors" in Mendelian explanations? Amer. Breeders Ass. 5: 365–368.

NIRENBERG, M., P. LEDER, M. BERNFIELD, R. BRIMACOMBE, J. TRUPIN, F. ROTTMAN, AND C. O'NEAL, 1965. RNA code words and protein synthesis, VII. On the general nature of the RNA code. Proc. Nat. Acad. Sci. U.S. 53: 1161–1168.

SCOTT-MONCRIEFF, R., 1936. A biochemical survey of some Mendelian factors for flower color. J. Genet. 32: 117–170.

STURTEVANT, A. H., 1965. *A History of Genetics*. Harper & Row, New York.

WATSON, J. D., 1965. *Molecular Biology of the Gene*. Benjamin, New York.

WEIGERT, M. G., AND A. GAREN, 1965. Base composition of nonsense codons in *E. coli*. Nature 206: 992–994.

WRIGHT, S., 1927. The effects in combination of the major color-factors of the guinea pig. Genetics 12: 530–569.

———, 1941. The physiology of the gene. Physiol. Rev. 21: 487–527.

———, 1942. The physiological genetics of coat color of the guinea pig. Biol. Symp. 6: 337–355.

18

Genetics and Medicine

James F. Crow

Paper number 1061 from the Genetics Laboratory, University of Wisconsin. Part of the work discussed in this paper was done with the support of the National Institutes of Health (GM-08217 and GM-07666).

The first half of the twentieth century was also the first half-century of Mendelism as a recognized science. During this period the major beneficiary of genetic knowledge has been agriculture. Selection, inbreeding, hybridization, artificial fertilization, and the use of pedigree information are now routine techniques of animal breeding. The plant breeder in addition can utilize haploidy, polyploidy, cytoplasmic factors, and various forms of asexual propagation. As a result, high-yielding, disease-resistant crop varieties are commonplace, and strains of plants and livestock have been made to order for particular environments and for specialized human needs.

In contrast, the major practical contribution of genetics in its second half-century is likely to concern man more directly, especially through its effects on medicine. The beginning of this period, from 1950 to 1965, has already produced some outstanding discoveries, and more are likely to follow at an accelerating pace.

That Mendel's discovery would ultimately have great influence on man's knowledge of and view toward himself was stated early by R. C. Punnett, among others. In the eleventh edition of the *Encyclopædia Britannica,* which was published in 1910–11, he wrote:

Increased knowledge of heredity means increased power of control over the living thing, and as we come to understand more and more the architecture of the plant or animal we realize what can and what cannot be done towards modification or improvement. The experiments of Biffen on the cereals have demonstrated what may be done with our present knowledge in establishing new, stable and more profitable varieties of wheat and barley, and it is impossible to doubt that as this knowledge becomes more widely disseminated

351

it will lead to considerable improvements in the methods of breeding animals and plants.

It is not, however, in the economic field, important as this may be, that Mendel's discovery is likely to have most meaning for us: rather it is in the new light in which man will come to view himself and his fellow creatures. Today we are almost entirely ignorant of the unit-characters that go to make the difference between one man and another. A few diseases, such as alcaptonuria and congenital cataract, a digital malformation, and probably eye colour, are as yet the only cases in which inheritance has been shown to run upon Mendelian lines. The complexity of the subject must render investigation at once difficult and slow; but the little that we know today offers the hope of a great extension in our knowledge at no very distant time. If this hope is borne out, if it is shown that the qualities of man, his body and his intellect, his immunities and his diseases, even his very virtues and vices, are dependent upon the ascertainable presence or absence of definite unit-characters whose mode of transmission follows fixed laws, and if also man decides that his life shall be ordered in the light of this knowledge, it is obvious that the social system will have to undergo considerable changes.

Soon after Mendel's work came to be generally recognized, there were reports of human characteristics showing Mendelian inheritance. Naturally, traits that were easily visible, such as those affecting the fingers, and that were expressed in the heterozygote would be most easily studied. It is not surprising, therefore, that the first convincing demonstration of Mendelian inheritance in man was Farabee's report on brachydactyly in 1905 (Stern 1960).

It was also recognized early by Garrod (1909) that alkaptonuria was inherited as if caused by homozygosity for a recessive gene. The evidence came from the inheritance pattern and the high frequency of consanguineous marriages among parents of affected persons. Soon after X-chromosome inheritance was understood, it was realized that color-blindness and hemophilia followed an X-linked pattern of inheritance.

The discovery of new inherited phenotypes has continued steadily for the past 50 years (see, for example, Becker 1964). The number of diseases known to be inherited as single gene differences has now grown to several hundred, the exact number depending on the rigor of the criteria used in admitting a disease to the list. Most of these are individually very rare, although collectively they add up to something like one per cent of all children born. A list of many such diseases, with their approximate incidences, has been published in a United Nations report (1958: pp. 197–200).

Human chromosome studies, until recently, were concerned mainly with establishing the chromosome number and identifying the X and Y chromosomes. The Y chromosome, being small, was overlooked in some early studies; but for two or three decades it has been generally recognized that there is a Y chromosome, identifiable during meiosis by the unequal synaptic pair that it makes with the X.

A most striking feature of human chromosome studies was the long period of time during which 48 was accepted as the correct diploid number. To the surprise of almost everyone the number was shown by Tjio and Levan in 1956 to be 46.

New techniques in chemistry and cytology plus new concepts from molecular biology and medicine have led to striking advances in the past decade and a half. Genetics has become one of the most active parts of medicine. I should like to discuss genetics and medicine from three viewpoints: genetics in the service of medicine, some contributions of medicine to genetics, and some genetic consequences of advances in medicine and public health. I want especially to emphasize the reciprocal relationship between genetics and medicine, the extent to which each has benefited from the other in the past, and the expectations for continued mutual benefit in the future.

Genetics in the Service of Medicine

One contribution genetics is making to medicine is in providing a deeper insight into disease-producing mechanisms. The recent developments in human cytogenetics furnish an example: Complete mystery suddenly changed to deep understanding with the discovery by Lejeune, Turpin, and Gautier (1959) that mongolism, or Down's syndrome, is caused by a chromosome anomaly. The previously known facts, familiar to students of the disease, were (1) mongoloid children practically always came from normal parents; (2) recurrence in a sibship was very rare; (3) concordance in one-egg twins was practically 100 per cent, but two-egg concordance was nearly zero; (4) on those rare occasions when a mongoloid person did reproduce, about half the children were affected; (5) the disease produced a number of seemingly unrelated anomalies; and (6) there was a striking increase in incidence with maternal age. The first five are immediately explained as predictable consequences of autosomal trisomy arising through nondisjunction. The sixth is not necessarily expected, but it is not particularly surprising; the D_1, 18, and XXY (Klinefelter's) types all have a maternal age effect. The original papers reporting these discoveries have been reprinted (Boyer 1963).

The hypothesis that trisomy is the cause of mongolism was suggested several times prior to 1959, but cytological techniques were then inadequate. In an early paper Haldane (1932) argued that nondisjunction and attached-X chromosomes exist in man. His reasoning about the latter was based on what we now realize was a wrong hypothesis of human sex determination; he was assuming, by analogy with *Drosophila,* that the Y chromosome was unimportant in sex determination. Speaking of *Drosophila,* Haldane said, "For example, primary nondisjunction both of the X and of the fourth chromosome occurs about once in 2000 individuals. We might therefore expect cytological abnormality to be reasonably frequent in man." Later in the same paper he said prophetically, "It seems possible that satisfactory mitoses might be observed in a culture of leukocytes. If so, the development of human cytology in relation to genetics will become possible."

As soon as human trisomy was discovered, it could be predicted that partial trisomy would be found, caused by half-translocations and other well-understood cytological mechanisms. One might also expect mosaicisms, caused by mitotic nondisjunction or chromosome loss. These predictions have been abundantly confirmed. In many instances cytological analysis has been useful in identifying otherwise normal persons with a high probability of having abnormal children.

It might be expected that there would be primary trisomic types for all the chromosomes, as in *Datura.* However, the phenotypes would not necessarily be predictable and many would probably be lethal. That many are indeed lethal is demonstrated by the finding of trisomic types among miscarried fetuses. Recently a specific deletion syndrome has been recognized, the "cri-du-chat" (Lejeune *et al.* 1963), and a somatic deletion is invariably associated with chronic myelogenous leukemia (Nowell and Hungerford 1960). Human cytogenetics is becoming an analytical tool comparable in precision to the cytogenetics of maize and is now a standard part of medical pathology. (For a recent review of techniques and some of the results, see Yunis 1965.)

Another area where genetic knowledge, this time together with biochemistry, has led to a deeper understanding of medical problems started in 1908 with Garrod's descriptions of "inborn errors of metabolism." For many years only a few additional cases were discovered, but since 1950 there have been dozens of new types found (see Stanbury, Wyngaarden, and Fredrickson 1965). In contrast to the chromosomal anomalies, where the understanding is deep but where not much can be done to prevent or repair the damage, the inborn errors can sometimes be corrected by supplying or withholding an appropriate dietary element. A dramatic example is the prevention of much, if not all, of the brain damage in phenylketonuria by early initiation of a diet low in phenylalanine. Another example is galactosemia, where the substitution of glucose for lactose in the diet prevents the symptoms. Heterozygous carriers of a typical recessive disease caused by an enzyme deficiency may be expected to have the enzyme in reduced amount. Thus carrier detection is possible, once an appropriate method for assaying the enzyme is developed.

Detailed chemical knowledge is not always necessary for some of the methods of biochemical genetics to be applied. Beadle and Tatum exploited the possibilities of organ transplants in order to determine the mode of action of some genes affecting *Drosophila* eye pigments. Similarly, much has been learned about factors affecting blood coagulation from the patterns of repair when transfusions are given among various persons with superficially similar genetic coagulation defects (Biggs and Macfarlane 1962).

An area of medicine where genetics has had a major influence is immunology. Shortly after their discovery, the ABO blood groups were found to be inherited, although it was some time later when the exact inheritance was understood. An important landmark in immunogenetics was the association of Rh incompatibility with hemolytic disease of the newborn. Previously the inheritance of erythroblastosis fetalis had been obscure. For example, in 1941 Snyder suggested, "The condition is apparently dependent upon a recessive gene with variable expression including icterus gravis, generalized congenital hydrops with or without jaundice, and severe congenital anemia." At the time this was a reasonable hypothesis, since the disease frequently recurs in sibships but shows no obvious association between parent and child. Once again, an understanding of the mechanism brought order out of the previous confusion. The pattern of maternal-fetal incompatibility could now be sought in other systems, and the rapid discovery during the 1950's of new blood group systems was the result. (For a general review, see Race and Sanger 1962.)

As early as 1916 Little and Tyzzer showed that the genotype has a great deal to do with acceptance or rejection of tissue transplants. They showed that a tumor from an inbred strain of mice could be transplanted to other members of the same strain and to the F_1 hybrids between this and other strains, but only very rarely to the F_2. Later these results were generalized to transplants of normal tissues in mice and by Loeb and Wright (1927) in guinea pigs. The rule is that a graft will not be accepted if the donor carries any histocompatibility gene not possessed by the recipient. From the frequency of acceptances by the F_2 generation of grafts from the original parents, from the F_1 generation, and from other F_2's, the minimum number of independent histocompatibility loci involved in the differences between mouse strains could be estimated at about a dozen. Roughly this number has now been found at the Jackson Laboratory.

The fundamental identity of graft rejection and antigen-antibody reaction was long suspected and finally proved in a number of ways. One kind of evidence, contributed by the study of a genetic disease in man, was the poor rejection of grafts by persons who had agammaglobulinemia, an X-linked recessive disorder manifested by a deficiency of plasma cells and poor antibody formation (Good and Zak 1956).

The study of blood groups in cattle by Irwin and his students led to another important development in immunogenetics. Out of this study grew Owen's discovery in 1945 that cattle twins whose blood vessels had interconnections during their prenatal life each had two kinds of blood cells, corresponding to the two kinds that the twins would have had separately had the mixture not occurred. Furthermore, both twins failed to produce antibodies to either kind of cell. This observation and later work by Medawar and others led to the discovery of immune tolerance, whereby under certain conditions an animal cannot make antibody against antigens to which he was exposed early in life.

The understanding of the genetics of histocompatibility has already led to the successful transplantation of organs between identical twins. Various methods of minimizing immune response have permitted partially or temporarily successful transplants between persons not of identical genotypes. Fuller understanding of the way tolerance can be achieved and antibodies selectively suppressed should make possible a wider range of successful transplants. The prediction that the surgery of the future can replace as well as repair may then be fulfilled. Donors might some day be from nonhuman primate strains which are bred for genetic homogeneity and to which the human recipients are made immunologically tolerant, as suggested by Lederberg (Wolstenholme 1963). Or perhaps, if the conditions leading to immunological tolerance in man were better understood, a child could be made tolerant to both parents, in which case he could receive grafts not only from either parent, but also from any of his sibs, since no child in the family would have genes not possessed by one of the parents.

It is interesting that in the history of immunogenetics, from Landsteiner's discovery of blood groups until quite recent times, the emphasis has been on the genetics of antigens. There are now a number of theories of antibody formation, most of them based on genetic models. Human medicine has once again provided some critical material in the form of Bence-Jones proteins from patients with multiple myeloma. Since each patient produces a single type of "antibody" protein, a full-scale chemical attack on each type is possible. By amino acid sequence analysis of proteins produced in this and similar disorders, one may hope to determine the chemical basis for the various antibody globulins. The future control or prevention of human disease through either stimulation or suppression of appropriate clones of antibody-producing cells is an exciting possibility.

A major medical trend of the past century has been the decrease in infectious disease, with the result that a larger fraction of medical problems are now constitutional diseases. Most of these probably have a substantial genetic component, so the importance of genetics in medical practice and public health is correspondingly increased. Genetic knowledge can aid the practicing physician and his patient in several ways, of which I shall discuss three.

Genetics as an aid to diagnosis

An inquiry into the family history is, of course, a standard part of medical diagnostic procedure. Whether the disease is genetic, environmental, or, as is frequently the case, both, the previous occurrence of the disease in a relative alerts the physician to the possibility of a genetic cause and increases the probability of an early and correct diagnosis.

If a disease is caused by an X-linked gene or by an autosomal dominant, the pattern of inheritance is usually clear if the pedigree is large enough. One can then determine which infants have a high risk of developing the condition. Separation of low-risk from high-risk individuals in the population may permit the employment of complicated or expensive screening procedures that would be impractical on a wide scale.

On the other hand, with a recessive disease the value of pedigree information is far less, for there are usually no ancestors or collateral relatives (except sibs) who show the condition. Once a child with a recessive disease has been born, all subsequent sibs are suspect and should be carefully watched. Consanguineous marriages, although extremely rare in the general population, are by no means unusual among the parents of persons with rare recessive diseases; therefore any instance of a consanguineous marriage should alert the physician to the possibility of a recessive disease in children. Similarly, some population isolates may have a high frequency of some gene, often one that is virtually unknown elsewhere.

Prevention of disease

The function of genetics in disease prevention is not completely distinct from that in disease diagnosis; the value of finding persons with a high probability of developing the disease is the same, whether it be for preventive or curative measures. If the disease is understood and can be predicted, it may be possible to create an environment in which the genetic damage is minimized or the limited genetic potential is maximized. An example is the special diet for galactosemia, mentioned before.

Genetic counseling

Genetic counseling has been practiced on a small scale for several decades (Hammons 1959). Now it is becoming a more widely recognized part of medicine. The rapid acquisition of new knowledge means an increase in the number of known inherited diseases. Most of these are rare, but collectively they account for a great deal of human misery. The United Nations (1958) report, previously mentioned, lists more than a hundred supposedly monogenic, severe traits with a total incidence of somewhat more than one per cent of all births.

In some instances genetic knowledge is very firm. For a dominant gene with full penetrance the geneticist can give an exact risk figure, usually 50 per cent. The recurrence risk—the risk that a second child will be affected—with a recessive disease from normal parents is safely taken as 25 per cent in most cases, since the probability that the first child resulted from a new mutation is very small. Improved methods of carrier detection, such as that for galactosemia, will eventually make possible the identification of carriers of many diseases before they produce affected children.

In some cases, as mentioned, valuable information is obtained from biochemical analysis. But I should like to emphasize also that an important source of information of a more routine type is the study of pedigrees. A great deal of knowledge about the inheritance of eye defects, for example, has been gathered mainly through pedigree studies (François 1961).

Another area of great progress in the past few years has been in cytogenetic analysis. Persons who carry chromosomes with balanced rearrangements (usually translocations) have a high probability of producing unbalanced gametes which, when fertilized, become nonviable or abnormal zygotes. For example, some instances of mongolism are known to be caused by a translocation. A cytogeneticist can sometimes identify those sibs or other relatives of the affected person who are carriers of the translocation and therefore have a high risk of producing abnormal children.

As knowledge increases, the number of diseases about which the counselor can give precise and useful information will increase correspondingly. At present the number is regrettably small, but fortunately accurate information is accruing rapidly.

It seems to me that one aspect of counseling has lagged behind.

There are many conditions for which the heredity is not simple and not understood—indeed, it may not even be known whether the disease is primarily genetically caused—but for which there is substantial clustering within families or pedigrees. For many such conditions empirical risk figures could be obtained. Parents who have had a severely impaired child would often like to know the risk of recurrence. They do not care whether a 25 per cent risk is based on genetic knowledge or past experience, as long as both risk figures are equally reliable.

With more attention to preventive medicine, better systems of medical record keeping, and more precise vital statistics, we could advise better than we now do without waiting for improvement in fundamental knowledge. We need not only more accurate but more specialized risk figures. For example, the recurrence risk following the birth of a child with cleft palate is usually given as about five per cent. But this is a composite value, undoubtedly an average of a quite heterogeneous collection. It might well be that the recurrence risk differs greatly depending on whether there are half a dozen previous normal sibs or whether the affected child is the only child. It certainly changes if one of the parents is affected or if there were two affected children rather than one. By analogy with life insurance rate calculations, we could have risks adjusted for age, sex, other relatives affected, relevant environmental factors, maternal age, race, or anything else that has a measurable modifying effect—whether the basis for this modification is understood or not.

A particularly useful summary of empirical risks was prepared by Fraser (1954). But this is a small beginning. With better systems of reporting and recording diseases and with computer systems for collating and analyzing, the genetic counselor could provide useful information in far more cases than he now can. Risks can be made more accurate and refined as additional risk-modifying factors are discovered. Collection of risk data has not yet attracted the amount of serious work that it might have. New fundamental knowledge is always welcome, of course, and in the long run it is far more desirable. But my point here is that much could be done now, with what is already known or obtainable, to make genetic counseling a more precise art.

As a single example, the information given by a genetic counselor regarding mongolism prior to 1959 might seem now to be hopelessly outdated. But as far as risk information is concerned, it would have been quite good. The great majority of cases are ordinary trisomy; the recurrence risk is very low; the maternal age effect is striking enough to take seriously; and the probability of its occurrence in the rare offspring of a mongoloid female is very high. The number of mistakes made by reliance on empirical information would have been relatively few. Now, of course, a good cytological analysis can help to detect the few cases that are the result of chromosome breakage. Those relatives who carry balanced rearrangements, and thus have a higher risk of producing abnormal children, can be identified. It must be stressed, however, that even in such cases the actual risk figures can only be empirical; indeed, the risk may differ in the two sexes. It has been found that females with balanced heterozygous translocations transmit unbalanced gametes far more frequently than do males. It is true that experiments with *Drosophila* and various plants have shown that alternate segregation from translocation heterozygotes is frequently higher in one sex than the other, but this information is not sufficient to permit predictions about the situation in man. Furthermore, the mechanism for the unequal transmission may be of other, less likely sorts; for example, possibly not all of the sperms function regularly, as may be the case in *Drosophila,* or there may possibly be gamete selection. In any case one has to rely on the empirical information.

These instances in which genetics has made a major impact on medicine are only a small sample, and a biased one. In particular, I have said nothing about the ramifications of the new knowledge of the gene and its action coming from molecular genetics and the study of microorganisms. Most of this is too new to have made its great impact, but that it eventually will is as certain as any future prediction can be.

There is a possibility that genetic defects can be repaired at more fundamental levels, cellular or intracellular, rather than at levels more distantly removed from the primary gene action. One can hope to repair agammaglobulinemia by stimulating or introducing competent plasma cells, or to cause the endogenous production of antihemophilic globulin, or to repair the defective enzyme in phenylketonuria rather than prescribing a diet that is unsatisfactory in many respects. A large part of the developmental engineering that is being discussed as a future possibility (e.g., Wolstenholme, 1963) can be expected in the realm of repair of gene deficiencies.

I should like to end this section by saying that to me it seems the greatest contribution genetics can make to medicine is to increase the ever-deepening chemical and biological knowledge of the human organism on which rational prevention, diagnosis, and treatment of disease must rest.

Some Contributions of Medicine to Genetics

Contributions of medicine to genetics can be conveniently divided into two categories. One contribution is to the formal genetics of man

—the extending to man of the kinds of genetic knowledge that already exist for such organisms as *Drosophila*. The second is more basic: It is the contribution of medicine to our understanding of genetic principles. There are so many ways that man is unsuited for genetic research that it is something of a surprise and a testimony to the ingenuity of the various workers that so much has been learned.

The formal genetics of man

Genetic analysis depends on gene markers, and most of man's phenotypic differences on which genetic research depends have been learned from medicine. As already mentioned, a large number of inherited traits and their mode of inheritance are known. In distinction to the mouse or *Drosophila*, in which most of the known genes are recessive, most of the known monogenic traits in man are dominant. This difference is readily understandable, for inbreeding is a part of the routine methodology of mouse and *Drosophila* genetics. But it means that most of the recessive genes in man are yet to be discovered; many may come to expression only very rarely, or never, because of elimination through heterozygous selection before they have a chance to become homozygous.

The human linkage map is still in a primitive state. Most known genes are very rare, so the probability that two of them will be found segregating in the same family is vanishingly small. As a consequence, the only known linkages depend on associations with a few markers with high frequencies, such as blood group genes.

The seeming synapsis of the X and Y chromosomes during spermatogenesis appeared to provide a possibility for crossing over between the X and Y, as was known to occur in some fishes. Haldane (1936) pointed out that this crossover might be taking place and that traits determined by genes located on the homologous parts of the X and Y chromosomes would have a characteristic pattern of inheritance. For example, the sex of a child with a dominant trait inherited through the father should be correlated with that of the affected paternal grandparent. Any exceptions would be attributable to crossing over between the gene and the end of the homologous region. Thus the geneticist would have a possible basis not only for identifying genes in this region but also for mapping their location without having to find families segregating simultaneously for two rare genes. For recessive genes similar, but more indirect, procedures were given.

On the basis of such studies, several maps of the human X and Y chromosomes were made (e.g., Snyder 1941). The situation soon became one of an embarrassment of riches, as too many traits seemed to satisfy

Haldane's criteria. It gradually came to be realized that various sex-biases in the disease manifestation could simulate this mode of inheritance, and none of the cases has since stood up under rigorous analysis. So it now appears that Haldane's suggestion was an ingenious failure.

Another way in which genes may be identified as being on a particular chromosome is by the examination of phenotypic frequencies in a population trisomic for this chromosome. Such an approach has been applied to the analysis of blood group phenotypes in individuals with mongolism, and a possible association of the ABO locus with the mongolism chromosome was reported (Shaw and Gershowitz 1963). As new protein polymorphisms are discovered, this procedure could be applied to them. It is likely that, with electrophoretic or gel-diffusion methods, two protein types (say, A and B) could be resolved into three phenotypes. These could be AA, BB, and AB in diploids and AAA, BBB, AAB, and ABB in trisomics. Even if the last two cannot be distinguished, one could easily compute the expected frequencies of $AAB + ABB$ in terms of the gene frequencies, p_A and p_B, and compare them with the expectations in diploids. If the gene is near the centromere and nondisjunction is at the second meiotic division or is postzygotic, the proportion of heterozygotes will be the same in triploids as in diploids, namely, $2p_A p_B$. This result is formally equivalent to endosperm inheritance in maize. On the other hand, if the nondisjunction is at the first meiotic division, the frequency of $AAB + ABB$ types can be shown to be $3p_A p_B$, or 50 per cent greater than that in diploids. Finally, if the gene is far from the centromere, the frequency approaches $8p_A p_B/3$ with either first or second division nondisjunction, a 33 per cent increase.

Thus, with enough data, one might hope to identify a gene as being on the mongolism chromosome, except for the unlikely possibility that the gene is very close to the centromere and nondisjunction hardly ever occurs at the first meiotic division. Conversely, a 50 per cent increase would show not only that the gene is near the centromere but also that, as in *Drosophila* (Merriam and Frost 1964), meiotic nondisjunction is mainly, if not exclusively, at the first division.

Both of these methods are applicable only to the chromosomes that produce viable trisomic types, and are thus very restricted. Deletion mapping has been useful in *Drosophila* and even more successful, though without the cytological correlation, in microorganisms. Some possible instances of autosomal hemizygosity in individuals carrying a recessive gene on one chromosome and a deletion including the corresponding locus on the homologous chromosome have been reported (see Elmore *et al.* 1966). By the accumulation of such information one may hope, in cytologically favorable cases, to associate known genes with specific chromosome regions.

One of the products of the study of human disease and abnormalities has been the elucidation of the sex-determining mechanism in man. For many years it had been assumed that man would follow the same rules as *Drosophila* and that the Y chromosome would be unimportant; although if human geneticists had taken the silk moth as a model, the role of the Y chromosome would have been appreciated. Not only were the discoveries of the XXY (Klinefelter) type and the XO (Turner) type important medically as explanations of the etiology of these two well-known but little-understood syndromes; they also showed unambiguously the role of the Y chromosome in human sex determination.

The discovery of the XO mouse and later the XXY mouse and XXY cat suggested that the Y chromosome may have general importance in the mammals. The XO mouse is a phenotypically normal and fertile female; the XXY male is normal, though sterile. Thus the male sex seems to be determined entirely by the presence or absence of the Y chromosome. That this is not the whole story in man is clear from the fact that the XO and XXY types are not fully normal females and males.

A surprise has been the discovery of persons with more than three sex-chromosomes. Individuals with as many as five have been found, with various combinations of X's and Y's. In the first place it is not clear what mechanism leads to such wholesale increases in chromosome number for the sex chromosomes. In the second place, it was surprising that such extreme examples of aneuploidy would be viable.

A reason for their viability was suggested by the discovery of the single active X principle (Lyon 1962). The observed fact that the maximum number of Barr (chromatin) bodies in the human interphase nucleus was always one less than the number of X chromosomes led to the proposal that the Barr bodies represent inactive X chromosomes. It has now been convincingly demonstrated that, within a particular clone of somatic cells, only one X chromosome is fully functioning. This provides not only an explanation of how a person with genotype XXX, XXXX, or XXXXX can be viable but also a totally new explanation for the phenomenon of dosage compensation (Muller 1950). Muller has presented evidence for the existence in *Drosophila* of genes whose function is to adjust the action of X-chromosome genes such that the phenotype is the same with one X chromosome as with two. The single active X in mammals accomplishes exactly the same purpose, namely, assuring that the male and female have the same phenotype for sex-linked but not sex-related characters. The mechanism, however, is totally different from that in *Drosophila*.

Contributions to basic genetics

The single active X hypothesis is of interest as an example of formal human genetics. It is of far greater genetic interest, however, as a case where the study of man (plus some very important related findings in the mouse) has demonstrated a new mechanism of dosage compensation. It provides an excellent example of how medicine has made an important contribution to basic genetics.

There are others. One is the association between genes and enzymes implied by Garrod's early studies on inborn errors of metabolism, already mentioned. In this case a deep insight into the nature of gene action was gained by the study of persons with diseases resulting from metabolic errors. Another example is agammaglobulinemia. This X-linked disease has shown the importance of genetic control over the development of plasma cells and the synthesis of gamma globulins, and the study of this "experiment of nature" has aided the understanding of immune mechanisms (Good and Zak 1956).

One of the greatest single contributions of medicine to basic genetics has been through the study of diseases caused by abnormal hemoglobins. That sickle cell anemia is an inherited disease has been known for some time. Pauling's suggestion that there was a defect in the hemoglobin molecule led eventually to the demonstration by Ingram that the difference between S-hemoglobin and normal hemoglobin lay in the substitution for valine of glutamic acid at a specific position in the molecule. This first demonstration that a mutation can lead to a single amino acid substitution, at a time when the nature of the gene was beginning to be understood, provided a key part of the story of the role of the genes in protein synthesis (see Ingram 1963).

Many more hemoglobin variants are now known that depend on an amino acid substitution in the alpha or the beta chain. With this chemical knowledge comes a greater understanding of the wide variety of hemoglobinopathies.

With improved methods for analysis of the amino acid sequence of proteins, it is possible to study in detail the hemoglobins and other proteins from various animals. Thus the comparative molecular structure of related species can be studied, and for the first time the rate of evolution of the amino acid composition of proteins can be estimated. Studies of hemoglobin, cytochrome-C, and ribonuclease have shown that the rate of change is roughly one amino acid change per ten million years (for a recent review, see Epstein and Motulsky 1965). Most

changes are consistent with there having been a single nucleotide substitution, so the rate probably represents only a slight underestimate of
the number of mutations that have been incorporated into the species.

We can try to relate this estimate to other estimates of the rate of
evolution given by population genetics theory. Haldane (1957) showed
that the number of gene substitutions that a species can make with a
certain total intensity of selection depends almost entirely on the initial frequency of the mutant and hardly at all on the selective advantage of the mutant. Using this principle and making what he considered reasonable assumptions about the relevant numerical quantities,
he concluded that a species could probably make a gene substitution
every 100 to 1000 generations. If there are 10,000 genes per genome,
then the number of changes incorporated per gene would be one per
million to ten million generations. So the rates of evolution of hemoglobins and cytochrome are not unexpected, if Haldane's principle is
an important factor in determining evolutionary rates.

One great advantage of man as a subject for genetic research is that
we know a great deal about human morphology, physiology, and behavior, and therefore small differences are noticed. Another advantage,
of particular importance for epidemiological and population research,
is that many relevant records are already available. We can expect still
more information in the future from better medical record-keeping systems, computerization, record linkage, and census records. Excellent
material for combined medical and genetic study has been isolated
populations, such as the Amish and Hutterites.

One way in which available data can be used takes advantage of the
fact that a person's surname is inherited as if the appropriate gene
were carried on the Y chromosome with a delay of one generation in
its expression. By exploiting this, one can estimate the inbreeding
coefficient from the proportion of marriages of persons with the same
name. There are a number of obvious pitfalls, but in some circumstances the method may be useful (Crow and Mange 1965).

Through the study of gene frequencies in different populations,
medical genetics has helped bring about a better understanding of the
way in which genetic variability is maintained. The best understood
human polymorphism is sickle cell anemia, where the S gene has been
maintained in some parts of the world by the heterozygote's advantage
of a greater resistance to falciparum malaria, as established by both epidemiological and physiological studies. The interrelationships of the
hemoglobins involved are complicated, but it is already clear that a
number of other hemoglobin abnormalities have also been maintained
because of resistance to malaria. Haldane was the first to emphasize the

importance of disease resistance as a factor in human evolution. Recent findings, such as those above, have apparently borne out Haldane's thesis and, furthermore, suggest that some contemporary polymorphisms are relics of disease-resistance mechanisms that were once important but are no longer relevant because of the virtual eradication of the disease.

Two decades ago it was fashionable to explain the frequencies of seemingly neutral genes (such as blood group factors) in different populations as determined primarily by random drift. However, after Fisher (1939) had analyzed Nabours' data on grouse locusts, he and Ford were inclined to attribute most such differences to differences in selection intensities in different populations. There have been a number of recent reports of very strong selection at a number of loci, particularly those concerned with the hemoglobins and ABO compatibility. Although intense selection at a few loci is possible, every animal breeder knows that he cannot select intensively for a great many characters at the same time. Thus the number of strongly selected polymorphisms is limited.

It has been apparent for some time that medical studies of large populations living under primitive conditions should provide some of the best information on the way in which selection is acting in man and some insights as to how it has operated in the past. Morton (unpublished) has recently completed a study of over 1000 Brazilian families chosen from a group characterized by high fertility, genetic variability, consanguinity, and infant mortality. Such a population maximizes the possibility that evidence for selection will be found. Included in the study were analyses of all the blood groups for which suitable sera are available, haptoglobins, transferrins, and the Gm and Inv factors, as well as tests of phenylthiocarbamide tasting. The general result was that no evidence of intense selection was found for any of these factors, except the previously known selection against incompatible ABO types. Thus it would appear that most of these polymorphisms at present are not associated with large selective differences, although differences too small to be detected even with this large population sample could still be responsible for maintenance of polymorphism through heterozygote advantage, selection for rarity, or other known mechanisms.

Origin of new genes by duplication has been recognized by *Drosophila* workers for many decades; in particular the phenomenon was emphasized by Bridges, who noticed many "repeats" in salivary gland chromosomes. Smithies, Connell, and Dixon (1962) have provided convincing chemical evidence that in human haptoglobins the Hp^2 allele is an almost complete duplication, combining Hp^{1F} and Hp^{1S} which differ from each other probably by only a single amino acid. The analogy with the Bar duplication is close, and the predicted triplication that would arise from unequal synapsis in an Hp^2 homozygote has been found. Presumably this triplication is selectively disadvantageous, for it is very rare. Nance (1963) has suggested a mechanism for maintenance of the haptoglobin polymorphism that differs from the usual assumption of heterozygote advantage. He suggests that, for some unknown reason, Hp^2 has a slight selective advantage, but that the two Hp^1 alleles are recurrently produced by unequal synapsis and crossing over in Hp^2 homozygotes, an event complementary to that which produces the triplication. Such recombination is probably not extremely rare; by analogy with Bar reversion, it would be expected to occur occasionally although it has not yet been directly demonstrated. However, if selection is very slight at the haptoglobin loci, unequal synapsis and crossing over might be sufficient to account for the presence of Hp^{1F} and Hp^{1S} in the population. If this hypothesis turns out to be correct, it will be an instance in which human genetics has demonstrated a new type of polymorphism-maintaining mechanism.

More examples could be given, but those mentioned are illustrative of the fact that medical genetics, in addition to its role in medical research and practice, has made substantial contributions to basic genetics. As cell and molecular genetics continue to develop new techniques, more and more of these will be applicable to the study of human genetics, and we can expect the interaction between basic genetics and medical genetics to become stronger.

Some Genetic Consequences of Medical Advances

The path connecting genetics and medicine, once narrow and rarely traveled, is now a busy highway. It is probably inevitable that there are some collisions.

One problem, which has long been foreseen but which becomes greater in proportion to the success of medicine and other forms of environmental improvement, is the perpetuation of diseases and abnormalities that were once ruthlessly eliminated by a rigorous environment. Clearly many persons who in an earlier period would have died or been so incapacitated as to lower their fertility are surviving and having children. To the extent that these conditions are heritable, they are being transmitted to future generations, adding to the already heavy burden of disease.

From studies of consanguineous marriages, it has been estimated that the average person carries some four or five hidden recessive genes that, if made homozygous, would produce recognizable and reasonably serious diseases. Despite the fact that the average person carries several such genes, the number of different kinds is so great, and the individual mutant types are so rare, that it is very unlikely that two unrelated persons have even one severe recessive gene in common. As carrier detection becomes cheaper and more accurate, such rare occurrences when two persons carry the same hidden gene can be discovered. Two persons who know that they carry the same gene may, depending on the nature of the disease and many other factors, choose not to marry or not to have children.

If such marriages are avoided, how much will it restrict the range of marriage partners? From the incidence of any given disease the carrier frequency can be estimated. With random mating, if p^2 is the incidence, then $2p(1 - p)$ is the carrier frequency, and the probability that two unrelated persons share the gene is the square of the carrier frequency, or about $4p^2$. This is four times the incidence. Summing the probabilities for all known recessive genes gives a value of only one or two per cent; so the restriction on marriage partners would be quite small. But if such a practice only altered the choice of mate and not the average number of children, there would be a corresponding additional contribution of harmful genes to future generations.

How may we assess the extent to which the gene frequency may be changed by avoidance of marriage in certain cases? To make the discussion concrete, I shall use phenylketonuria (PKU) as an example. With low phenylalanine diets many persons with PKU will grow up normally and may be expected to have children of their own. (I shall ignore the complications that may ensue when a mother who cannot metabolize phenylalanine has a child. It may well be that special diets will be required during pregnancy, or that wholly unforeseen difficulties may appear.)

No one knows the factors responsible for the present incidence of PKU, which is roughly one per 10,000 live births. It may be that the gene is completely recessive, in which case a mutation rate of 10^{-4} would be required to account for the present incidence, if it is assumed that the population is at equilibrium and that the fitness of homozygotes is zero. If the amount of inbreeding in the past has been appreciable or if there has been some selection against heterozygotes, a higher rate must be postulated. On the other hand, there may be or may have been in the past some selection in favor of heterozygotes. To account for the present incidence by heterozygote advantage would require only a one per cent selective advantage, a value too small to be measured. However, we can still assess the impact on the next few generations of relaxed selection against homozygotes without knowing how the gene frequency is maintained.

Let us assume the successful repair of all homozygotes for the harmful gene. This means that a fraction of the population, equal to p^2, which would otherwise not reproduce now do so, and therefore p^2 recessive genes are contributed to the next generation above the number that would be there otherwise. If p' is the frequency of mutant genes that would otherwise be present in the next generation, the proportion will be approximately $p' + p^2$. If p and p' are nearly the same, and there is no reason to think that the gene frequency is changing rapidly, the frequency has been increased by a fraction p; that is, it is $p(1 + p)$ instead of p. If p is 1/100, as it is for PKU, the gene frequency in the next generation, if complete repair has resulted in normal fertility of the present generation, would be increased by one per cent of its former value.

An increase of one per cent in the gene frequency means that the frequency of homozygotes would be multipled by a factor $(1.01)^2$, which is about a two per cent increase. With a two per cent increase per generation, it would require about 40 generations, or 12 centuries, to double the incidence. In comparison with the rate at which knowledge is changing, that is a long time.

In general, if p is the gene frequency and s is the selective disadvantage of the homozygote before treatment, a completely successful treatment will cause an increase in gene frequency sp and, with random mating, the genotype will increase by about $2sp$. With less than a complete restoration of fertility, the increase would, of course, be correspondingly less. This formula also makes it clear that the rarer the trait (i.e., the smaller p is) the less is the proportional increase in incidence in future generations.

I conclude that the successful treatment of rare recessive genes will not cause any great problem for the foreseeable future. Compared with the great alleviation of suffering in this generation by prevention or cure, the cost to the next few generations (who presumably will have the same or better cures available) seems small.

With a dominant gene the story is quite different. If I again let s stand for the amount by which the fitness is impaired in the untreated condition, a complete repair or at least restoration of normal fertility will increase the incidence of the disease in the next generation by a fraction s. For example, a dominant disease that reduces the expectation of children by 35 per cent would increase in incidence by about this amount in the next generation if all cases were to become fully fertile. This principle is easily seen for the case of a dominant gene that is lethal or sterilizing ($s = 1$). For such a gene, the entire incidence in this generation is the result of new mutations. If the disease is repaired and full fertility restored, the mutations from this generation are added to those that occur next generation, so the incidence would be doubled.

An example of a disease whose heredity is not known exactly, but which depends at least in part on one or more dominant genes, is pyloric stenosis. Prior to World War I this condition was nearly always fatal, but with the development of Rammstedt's operation many cases were repaired surgically. These persons have in many cases reached the age of reproduction and have now produced a number of children. About one in five of the sons of a parent who has had the operation is affected. Thus the incidence is increased by this amount beyond those cases that would have occurred anyhow.

Thus, we see that the cure of a dominant disease has a far larger effect on the next generation than the cure or prevention of a recessive disease. On the other hand, the consequences for society may not be so greatly different, at least if the person so treated is aware of the heredity of his condition. A person with a dominant disease that has been successfully treated knows that, if he has children, each of them has a 50 per cent chance of having the same condition. If the cure is complete, nontraumatic, and inexpensive, there is little reason to fear the disorder, and the parent would probably have little hesitation in subjecting his children to the risk. However, if the disease is severe, and if the treatment is only partially satisfactory, he would probably prefer not to subject his children to the 50 per cent risk. So the situation for the next generation would have a certain tendency to adjust itself to the perpetuation mainly of those diseases that are most effectively treated. The interest of society in lowering the incidence of disease is matched by the deep interest of the parent in his own children.

Again, a person who has been successfully treated for a recessive disease has little reason to fear for his own children. For example, a man who has been treated for PKU would have about one chance in 50 of marrying a woman who carried the same gene. Thus, unlike the one who has survived a dominant disease, he has little reason to be concerned over his own children. The concern is primarily one of society for an increased average incidence. But as we have seen, the percentage increase for recessive diseases is very slight unless the gene is common.

Thus the situation does not call for immediate grave concern. The repair of dominant conditions creates a problem only to the extent that parents are uninformed or choose to have children subject to the same risk that they themselves had. With rare recessives there is only a small increase, though a permanent and cumulative one.

But what about common conditions—weak hearts, diabetes, various constitutional disorders, mental disease? Here the answers are far harder. We need to know at least the following for each condition: (1) Is the repair or environmental advance affecting the reproductive pattern? (2) How complete is the repair? And, hardest, (3) How heritable is the trait? At present only the crudest guesses can be made.

One thing is abundantly clear: An environmental improvement must be permanent. Any return to the old conditions ordinarily brings back the original incidence, plus any increase gained by the perpetuation of genes that would otherwise have been eliminated. So we are certain to have to devote an increasing fraction of our economic resources to making up for one another's genetic deficiencies.

The question then becomes, how soon and to what extent should man start to intervene in his genetic future?

There is a wide measure of agreement that prospective parents are entitled to the best information available about the risk of their having diseased or defective children. Considerable human suffering would thereby be eliminated, but it is probably a small fraction of the total.

There seems to be no hesitancy on the part of society to improve the environment. This may mean cultural and educational improvements, as emphasized previously by Beadle (Ch. 17). It also can mean the most sophisticated kinds of developmental engineering as envisaged in the word euphenics (Wolstenholme 1963).

A recent symposium (Sonneborn 1965) presented several possible uses of molecular and cell biology to influence heredity. There were a number of suggestions for removal, addition, or replacment of genes based mainly on procedures developed for microorganisms. Indeed the potential possibilities are enormous. However, all such suggestions have one thing in common: They are not now practical, and one doesn't yet have to worry about the possible consequences of their misuse or accept any responsibility for having advocated them.

H. J. Muller, writing in that same symposium (Sonneborn 1965), fears that too much discussion of such possibilities as cell transplants, DNA transformations, directed mutation, or suitably designed episomes may result in escapism and postponement of practical genetic manipulation. In his words, "It would be intellectually dishonest and morally reprehensible of us to exploit the hope of mankind's eventual success in this enterprise as an excuse for not giving our support to the great re-educational process that could make possible, by means now physically available, a most significant advance in the genetic constitution of our species." He is referring, of course, to artificial insemination.

Genetic engineering, if it becomes practical, will probably be most effective for single gene traits. But the hereditary components of many of the most important human traits, intelligence, general health, emotional stability, unselfishness—to the extent that they are genetic—are likely to be polygenic. The principle that like begets like is the best guide to prediction for some time to come, and selection the most effective means of change. If we really want to change the human population by genetic means, Muller's method is the most likely to succeed.

But it is much less clear what society or the individuals comprising it want to do. There is no groundswell of public opinion in favor of doing anything by way of positive eugenics.

The rate of increase in knowledge is high and accelerating. To the next generation many of our beliefs of today will seem quite primitive, and any attempts at genetic manipulation of the population may seem similarly crude. On the other hand, to wait for complete knowledge is to do nothing forever.

Will future generations regard our generation somewhat as we do the pioneers who destroyed our forests and wildlife—as geneticists without the wisdom and courage to look to the future? Or, on the other hand, will they regard this generation as one which prudently refrained from rushing to act too soon in ignorance?

I have one conviction; it is high time that the social implications of our expanding genetic knowledge be discussed. Early eugenics was crude, oversimplified, and got confused in various dubious (and in some cases disastrous) political movements. I hope we are ready for a more mature consideration of eugenics and euphenics as complementary possibilities. It may well be that the second century of Mendelism will mark the beginning of a serious and informed consideration of the extent to which man can and should influence his biological future, with full deliberation on both the opportunities and the risks.

Literature Cited

BECKER, P. E., 1964. *Humangenetik. Ein kurzes Handbuch in fünf Bänden.* Georg Thieme Verlag, Stuttgart.

BIGGS, R., AND R. G. MACFARLANE, 1962. *Human Blood Coagulation and its Disorders.* F. A. Davis, Philadelphia.

BOYER, S. H., 1963. *Papers on Human Genetics.* Prentice-Hall, Inc., Englewood Cliffs, New Jersey.

CROW, J. F., AND A. P. MANGE, 1965. Measurement of inbreeding from the frequency of marriages between persons of the same surname. Eugen. Quart. **12**: 199–203.

ELMORE, S. M., W. E. NANCE, B. J. MCGEE, M. ENGEL-DE MONTMOLLIN, and E. ENGEL, 1966. Pycnodysostosis, with a familial chromosome anomaly. Amer. J. Med. **40**: 273–282.

EPSTEIN, C. J., AND A. G. MOTULSKY, 1965. Evolutionary origins of human proteins. Progr. Med. Genet. **4**: 85–127.

FISHER, R. A., 1939. Selective forces in wild populations of *Paratettix texanus*. Ann. Eugen. **9**: 109–122.

FRANÇOIS, J., 1961. *Heredity in Ophthalmalogy*. C. V. Mosby Co., St. Louis.

FRASER, F. C., 1954. Medical genetics in pediatrics. J. Pediat. **44**: 85–103.

GARROD, A. E., 1909. *Inborn Errors of Metabolism*. Reprinted 1963, Oxford University Press, Oxford.

GOOD, R. A., AND S. J. ZAK, 1956. Disturbances in gamma globulin synthesis as "experiments of nature." Pediatrics **18**: 109–149.

HALDANE, J. B. S., 1932. Genetical evidence for a cytological abnormality in man. J. Genet. **26**: 341–344.

———, 1936. A search for incomplete sex-linkage in man. Ann. Eugen. **7**: 28–57.

———, 1957. The cost of natural selection. J. Genet. **55**: 511–524.

HAMMONS, H. G. (ed.), 1959. *Heredity Counseling*. Hoeber-Harper, New York.

INGRAM, V. M., 1963. *The Hemoglobins in Genetics and Evolution*. Columbia Univ. Press, New York.

LEJEUNE, J., J. LAFOURCADE, R. BERGER, J. VIALATTE, M. BOESWILLWALD, P. SERINGE, AND R. TURPIN, 1963. Trois cas de deletion partielle du bras court d'un chromosome 5. Compt. Rend. **257**: 3098–3102.

LEJEUNE, J., R. TURPIN, AND M. GAUTIER, 1959. Le mongolisme, premier example d'aberration autosomique humaine. Ann. Génét. Hum. **1**: 41–49.

LITTLE, C. C., AND E. E. TYZZER, 1916. Further experimental studies on the inheritance of susceptibility of a transplantable tumor. J. Med. Res. **33**: 393–453.

LOEB, L., AND S. WRIGHT, 1927. Transplantation and individuality differentials in inbred families of guinea pigs. Amer. J. Pathol. **3**: 251–283.

LYON, M. F., 1962. Sex chromatin and gene action in the mammalian X-chromosome. Amer. J. Hum. Genet. **14**: 135–148.

MERRIAM, J. R., AND J. N. FROST, 1964. Exchange and nondisjunction of the X chromosomes in female *Drosophila melanogaster*. Genetics **49**: 109–122.

MULLER, H. J., 1950. Evidence for the precision of genetic adaptation. Harvey Lect. **43**: 165–229.

NANCE, W. E., 1963. Genetic control of hemoglobin synthesis. Science **141**: 123–130.

NOWELL, P. C., and D. A. HUNGERFORD, 1960. A minute chromosome in human chronic granulocytic leukemia. Science **132**: 1497.

OWEN, R. D., 1945. Immunogenetic consequences of vascular anastomosis between bovine twins. Science **102**: 400–401.

PUNNETT, R. C., 1910-11. Mendelism. Encyclopædia Britannica (11th ed.).

RACE, R. R., AND RUTH SANGER, 1962. *Blood Groups in Man* (4th ed.). F. A. Davis Company, Philadelphia.

SHAW, M. W., AND H. GERSHOWITZ, 1963. Blood group frequencies in mongols. Amer. J. Hum. Genet. 15: 495–496.

SMITHIES, O., G. E. CONNELL, AND G. H. DIXON, 1962. Chromosomal rearrangements and the evolution of haptoglobin genes. Nature 196: 232–236.

SNYDER, L. H., 1941. *Medical Genetics*. Duke Univ. Press, Durham, North Carolina.

SONNEBORN, T. M. (ed.), 1965. *The Control of Human Heredity and Evolution*. Macmillan, New York.

STANBURY, J. B., J. B. WYNGAARDEN, AND D. S. FREDRICKSON, 1965. *The Metabolic Basis of Inherited Disease*. McGraw-Hill, New York.

STERN, C., 1960. *Principles of Human Genetics* (2nd ed.). W. H. Freeman and Co., San Francisco.

TJIO, J. H., AND A. LEVAN, 1956. The chromosome number of man. Hereditas 42: 1–6.

UNITED NATIONS, 1958. Report of the United Nations Scientific Committee on the Effects of Atomic Radiation. General Assembly, Official Records, 13th Session, Supplement 17 (A/3838).

WOLSTENHOLME, G. (ed.), 1963. *Man and His Future*. Little, Brown, Boston.

YUNIS, J. J., 1965. *Human Chromosome Methodology*. Academic Press, New York.

19

The Evolutionary Integration of the Genetic Material into Genetic Systems

T. M. Sonneborn

Contribution No. 781 of the Zoology Department, Indiana University. The work in this paper was supported by contract COO-235-21 of the Atomic Energy Commission and grant E-81H of the American Cancer Society.

The successes of viral, bacterial, and molecular genetics have profoundly divided geneticists, indeed all biologists. In passionate reaction, one eminent physiologist declared, "Anything really simple is not biology at all; it is physics or chemistry. The very essence of biology is complexity." Such declarations by the far right are matched by credos of the extreme left. A distinguished viral geneticist has maintained that we should all restrict ourselves to the simplest phenomena in the simplest materials, viruses and bacteria; that there is nothing to be gained and much to be lost by squandering time and thought now on more complicated problems or materials. Another has said that these problems should be approached step by step—little steps for little feet.

The views of the extreme left are of course not shared by all microbial geneticists or by all molecular geneticists; nor are the views of the extreme right shared by all other geneticists and biologists. Many geneticists are at or not far from the center. They recognize, indeed almost worship, the new revolutionary microbial and molecular genetics of the last decade or two, and they appreciate that the most fundamental aspects of genetics are best studied in microbes. But they also recognize that higher organisms, while retaining the fundamental features observable in microbes, have evolved new genetic phenomena that do not occur at all in microbes. This needs stressing because microbial geneticists often seem to take for granted that all important genetic phenomena observable in higher organisms will be found also in microbes where they are stripped to essentials and most amenable to analysis at

375

the deepest molecular level. This is apparently the main reason of some for considering investigation of complicated higher organisms (except when it can be carried out at the molecular level) to be less rewarding and even unnecessarily wasteful of effort. Geneticists near the center, of whom I count myself one, on the contrary hold that investigation of genetic phenomena found only in higher organisms is not only highly rewarding but essential to genetic understanding, even when the investigations are limited to nonmolecular approaches. We maintain that understanding biology, precisely because its chief feature is evolution, depends not only on understanding the fundamentals applicable to all organisms but also on understanding the levels of evolutionary advance, including, in the case of genetics, advances in genetic systems.

Indeed, our attempt to assess where we now stand a century after Mendel's epoch-making discoveries would be lacking a very important feature if we failed to put into perspective both the limitations of microbial genetic systems and the innovations evolved by higher organisms. I propose therefore to compare some highlights of the genetic systems shown by four major evolutionary levels. The topic is complicated and vast, far too vast to be considered exhaustively here. I shall therefore set some arbitrary limits to my survey. I shall say very little about population genetics but shall concentrate on genetic systems as they are seen to operate in individuals, selecting examples to illustrate my central theme of the evolution of novelty in genetic systems. Much that I shall discuss will be familiar, as an assessment of the present state of knowledge is bound to be to an informed readership; but there may be some value in trying to put even the familiar into perspective.

Bacterial Systems

So much has been published about the genetic material and genetic system in the simplest existing complete organisms, the bacteria, that I need do little more than recount briefly their main features. The genetic material is simply a single thread or ring of double-stranded DNA. Sometimes part of a second thread is transiently present. The DNA includes regulator genes and operons. DNA episomes, with their own regulator genes and operons, can enter and leave the DNA thread and can replicate independently when free in the cell.

The bacterial genetic system, through which the DNA operates, has both direct and indirect aspects. Directly, it functions in the main through transcription of the DNA into complementary RNA, some of which is translated into polypeptides by means of the genetic code and the protein-synthetic machinery and some of which is not known to be translated but is otherwise converted into parts of the protein-synthetic machinery. Possibly parts of the DNA are not even transcribed but function as operators, promoters, and the like. In performing its functions, some of the DNA thread is locally and transiently combined with transcribed RNA, with enzymes, and with repressors presumed to be protein. Genic circuits, operating through repressors and inducers, regulate genic activity to yield rapid adaptation to environmental changes. Simultaneously needed products are supplied by multicistronic operons or functionally linked regulatory circuits. Such circuits can also be geared to yield in succession the products needed for internally programmed developmental sequences such as those associated with division, mating, sporulation, and germination. Virtually all of the classic modes of genic interactions occur: complementary factors, epistasy, pleiotropy, and so on. These interactions are expressions of the linearity, forking, and circularity of gene-controlled metabolic pathways, each step of which depends on an enzyme produced by genic action. Recombination by a crossing-over-like process, following conjugation, transduction, and direct transfer of free DNA, together with mutations, yields systems of population genetics.

The indirect aspects of the bacterial genetic system, more remote from DNA, can best be appreciated by a consideration of the whole bacterial cell. The cell is the essential vehicle for maintaining, replicating, spreading, and varying bacterial genetic material as well as for carrying out the syntheses of other needed cellular components. In these processes the limiting plasma membrane plays a role second only to that of DNA. It not only regulates the egress and ingress of molecules but also confines genic products to a volume small enough to permit at least some of them by mere diffusion to collide, interact, and assemble themselves into structures. The membrane also bears the adenosine triphosphate generating system and extends inward as enigmatic structures such as the mesosome. The membrane and its appendages may also serve in segregating the products of DNA replication into daughter cells (Ryter and Jacob 1964). Unfortunately, very little is known about how the genetic system controls the construction, growth, and functioning of its chief operational organelle, the plasma membrane.

Somewhat more is known about two other organelles, the wall (Landman and Halle 1963) and the flagellum (Abram and Koffler 1964; Asakura, Eguchi, and Iino 1964). This knowledge may be applicable, by analogy, to the plasma membrane. The wall can be removed, and though the DNA continues to make all of the molecular constituents, they diffuse out, failing to be assembled into wall. Assembly can, however, be induced—slowly, precariously, inefficiently—by growth on certain semisolid media, which perhaps merely provide mechanical, nonspecific barriers to loss of the building blocks. Retention of a little piece of wall serves the same end; the entire wall is regenerated. In other media, cells without wall do not make wall; but they can grow and multiply irregularly.

Flagella are chemically simpler than wall. Analysis of their formation, though still incomplete, is already instructive. Each flagellum consists of several closely packed fibers. Each fiber is a homopolymer of a protein monomer. The monomer differs somewhat in composition according to genotype and species; but the general name, flagellin, designates the class of flagellar monomers. (In some species, the repeating unit may include carbohydrate.) Abram and Koffler (1964) report that flagellin extracted from *Bacillus pumilis* spontaneously aggregates into different structural forms under different conditions, the form being indistinguishable from flagella under certain conditions. This aggregation is a nonenzymatic, nonenergy-requiring, reversible reaction; it appears to resemble crystallization. Asakura, Eguchi, and Iino (1964) and Iino (1964) have carried out similar studies on differently prepared flagellins from *Salmonella*. Unlike Abram and Koffler, they report that "flagella" are formed promptly only when seeded with fragments of flagella and that the number of flagella formed is the same as the number of fragment seeds present. The two reports have led to two different theories of the development of flagella: independent self-assembly of monomers into a polymer *vs.* dependence of assembly upon a like-structured "seed." Both laboratories are very much aware of the possible role of the flagellar basal granule (Glauert, Kerridge, and Horne 1963) either as a local concentration of flagellin (in the theory of Abram and Koffler) or as a seed for "crystallization" of flagellin (in the theory of Asakura, Eguchi, and Iino). Iino and co-workers are using a number of flagellar mutants to permit further penetration into the mechanism of flagellum origin and development. This is indeed the prototype of a problem we shall encounter repeatedly. As matters now stand, it looks as if flagellin or certain kinds of flagellin can be self-assembled into flagella without need for a pre-existing assembly of monomers under certain conditions; but under other conditions or with other kinds of flagellin, presence of some assembled monomers is required for the separated monomers to achieve assembly in solution. Thus existing assemblies of genic products—wall, flagella, and presumably plasma membrane—serve indispensably under some conditions as supplementary parts of the genetic system, directing their own further elaboration.

The genetic material of bacteria, its organization, and its direct and indirect integration into an operational genetic system are indeed impressively comprehensive. These achievements were not lost during further evolution. Higher organisms have the same genetic material, DNA; their genetic code is either identical or almost so; their protein-synthetic machinery and mechanisms appear to be essentially identical; comparable genic interactions have been found in them; and, as we shall see, even the more indirect aspects of the bacterial genetic system have their counterparts in higher organisms. If genetic novelty evolved after the bacteria, it is not evident in these fundamental respects. Besides, the story of microbial genetics is not finished. New episodes, through important discoveries and ideas, are being added year by year. Nevertheless, it is already clear that evolution did lead to genuinely new and theoretically important features of the direct and indirect operation of genetic systems. A viewer of genetic systems who sees only those of bacteria and viruses is like a viewer of a magnificent old European cathedral who sees only the underground sparse remains of a feebler ancient production.

Genetic Systems in Eucaryotic Unicellular Organisms

The next higher evolutionary level is that of the unicellular organisms which, like multicellular organisms but unlike bacteria and bluegreen algae, possess true membrane-bounded nuclei. This major distinction among organisms has long been recognized by the classification into eucaryotes and procaryotes (Chatton 1925). Eucaryotic unicellular organisms exhibit many new cytological features. They possess true, microscopically visible and chemically complex chromosomes. The chromosomes have centromeres; some bear nucleoli. Coiling cycles, as well as locally differential coiling, occur. Centrioles are often present. The genome is partitioned into more than one chromsome, the number and size of the haploid set of chromosomes varying greatly from species to species. There are haploid, diploid, and polyploid species. The nuclei undergo mitosis, meiosis, and fertilization. This array of new features speaks clearly for the magnitude of the gap between procaryotic and eucaryotic unicells. Thus far, it has been reduced only by studies on dinoflagellates which seem to possess an intermediate nuclear organization (Giesbrecht 1958, 1962, 1965; Ris 1962; Kellenberger 1962; Kubai 1965).

This abundance of new cytological developments brought with it many new features for genetic systems. Obviously, for example, partitioning the genes among more than one chromosome, along with meiosis and fertilization, added a basically new mechanism of recombination—chromosomal reassortment—denied to procaryotes with their genome in a single DNA thread. Most of the new features of genetic systems associated with the cytogenetic inventions of eucaryotic unicells have been retained in multicellular organisms. They have been much more fully investigated in multicellular organisms and are well known to geneticists. I shall therefore not attempt to summarize them here but shall limit my discussion to a few less familiar but highly important features, starting with some that seem to be correlated with the deceptively simple matter of increased cell size, for these features appear to put much of the evolutionary development into a reasonably understandable framework.

Eucaryotic unicells are larger, usually by one or more orders of magnitude in linear dimensions and three or more in volume, than the procaryotes, whose size is roughly of the order of one micron. This great increase in cell size could hardly have become established without correlated changes in the genetic system; without such changes the large cells would probably have been so physiologically inefficient as to be unable to compete successfully with small cells. Mere diffusion of genic products suffices for those products to interact effectively in cells as small as procaryotes; it becomes rapidly less satisfactory and efficient as cell size increases and is quite inadequate for cells as large as eucaryotes (Stern and Nanney 1965). One step toward alleviation of the difficulty in eucaryotic cells was the innovation of cytoplasmic streaming and other forms of cytoplasmic mobility, which, in contrast to the cytoplasmic immobility of procaryotes, constitutes an important difference between the two groups, as Stanier (1964) has emphasized. But stirring and diffusion together are apparently insufficient because eucaryotic unicells consistently show one or both of two developments of genetic systems that seem to serve the needs imposed by large cell size. On the one hand, they developed means of enormously increasing the amount of genic activity per cell. On the other hand, they perfected means of concentrating genic products where they were to be used in the cell. Each of these important developments merits further exposition.

Greater genic activity per cell could conceivably be achieved in various ways, but, so far as we know, only one general method was and is actually employed. There is to my knowledge no clear and unambiguous evidence for a uniformly greater activity of RNA obtained by its increased stability or replication. On the other hand, an increase of genic activity by an increase in the number of gene replicas per cell is well authenticated. The beginnings of a correlation between genic dosage and cell size appear even in bacteria: In *Salmonella typhimurium,* the number of discrete "nuclear bodies" per cell increases with cell size (Schaechter, Maaløe, and Kjeldgaard 1958). In eucaryotic unicells with persistently large size, high genic dosage is often a regular species character, not, as in *Salmonella,* a mere physiological variation. In different species, high genic dosage takes different forms, for example, polyploidy, polygenomic nuclei, and multiple nuclei per cell.

These solutions to the problem posed by increased cell size usually sacrificed to a considerable degree the efficiency of fixation of expressible genetic variability and so reduced the advantage of sexuality. The quantitative theoretical basis for estimating the effect of high genic dosage on the fixation of genetic variability is provided by Schensted's (1958) analysis of the specific case of the polyploid macronucleus of ciliates, in which the chromosomes of each diploid set are apparently held together as a unit. She derived formulae to measure the rates at which pure nuclear types segregate during the course of amitotic divisions of such polygenomic nuclei when they contain more than one type of genome. At the levels of polygenomy commonly encountered, 50 to 500 diploid genomes per nucleus, hundreds of cell generations are required to segregate pure types from nuclei containing two genomic types in equal proportions, the condition expected if two such polygenomic nuclei were to fuse in a sort of fertilization. Larger numbers of cell generations are of course required to obtain purity for a new type arising by mutation in one genome, even if the genomes were haploid. On the other hand, if both products of replication of a genome tend to go to the same daughter nucleus, purity of type is achieved less slowly, as expected in multinucleate species with a lower ploidy level per nucleus. The Schensted formulae also lead to comparable results when applied, with the necessary minor adjustments, to organisms like certain amoebae believed to possess highly polyploid nuclei in which the individual chromosomes are not united into genome sets. Under all of these conditions, therefore, the fixation of genetic variability by mutation or recombination at sexual reproduction becomes inefficient, if not impracticable. For this and possibly other reasons, sexual processes are conspicuously lacking in many eucaryotic unicells. However, some of them, the ciliates, have succeeded in combining high genic dosage with sexuality by maintaining two kinds of nuclei per cell, a diploid nucleus for meiosis and fertilization and a polygenomic nucleus which is sacrificed at fertilization and replaced by a new one derived from the fertilization nucleus. In other Protozoa, for example, certain Radiolaria, large polygenomic nuclei can form small "secondary" nuclei, suspected of being haploid or diploid (Grell 1953). Whether these "reduced" nuclei function in fertilization remains unknown, but they apparently provide a means of segregating and fixing genetic variability even if sexuality is absent.

High genic dosage was not the only solution to the problems raised by large cell size or the only one pertinent to genetic material and genetic systems. Another genetically significant solution, universally used by eucaryotes, was the evolution of functionally specialized, intracellular compartments or organelles about the size of bacteria, that is, small enough for efficient diffusion of molecules within them. Such organelles would spare high genic dosage only if they could trap and concentrate the genic products needed for their specialized functions, of if they could produce and confine their own needed molecules, or if they could do both—perhaps producing those used nowhere else and trapping their share of those participating also in other cellular activities.

Very little is known concretely about how organelles actually acquire their molecules. However, some long-known facts, familiar to geneticists, are relevant. These facts indicate that at least some organelles reproduce themselves and mutate, but that mutations in the nuclear genome also affect the organelles (see Rhoades 1955, for a critical review). Dual genetic control of the organelle by the nucleus and by the organelle itself suggests, but does not prove, that some species of molecules in an organelle may be formed by nuclear genic action while others may be produced in the organelle itself. This interpretation, indeed the whole situation, is now being re-evaluated in the light of recent discoveries of DNA and DNA-related activities in a number of organelles.

The exciting new story unfolding with these discoveries has old beginnings. In the first decade of the century, a puzzling minute structure in certain flagellated Protozoa—the so-called kinetonucleus or kinetoplast—was observed to divide regularly at cell division, to be irreplaceable when destroyed or lost, and to stain both with nuclear dyes and with Janus Green B. These early indications that it had both nuclear and mitochondrial properties have now been confirmed in detail by modern methods. Kinetoplasts contain and synthesize DNA (Cosgrove and Anderson 1954; Steinert, Firket, and Steinert 1958). Their DNA has a different buoyant density from that of the nuclear DNA (Du Buy, Mattern, and Riley 1965). The kinetoplast was also shown to have typical mitochondrial structure (e.g., Clark and Wallace 1960) and to develop this structure along with mitochondrial enzymes in response to certain cultural conditions (Vickerman 1962; Rudzinska, D'Alesandro, and Trager 1964; Trager 1965).

Meanwhile, DNA and DNA synthesis were found in ordinary mitochondria (reviewed by Swift 1965), in chloroplasts (reviewed by Gibor 1965), in kinetosomes, that is, the basal granules of cilia and flagella (Sukhanova and Nilova 1965; Randall and Disbrey 1965, who also review earlier reports), and in the free nucleoli of amphibian oocytes (Miller 1964). Whether improved methods of detecting very small quantities of localized DNA would reveal its presence elsewhere in the cytoplasm remains to be seen.

What then is the genetic significance of DNA in organelles? Does it, as is often held, explain the capacity of the organelle to grow and divide? However natural such an interpretation may seem at first thought, it does not hold up on more careful examination. Strictly speaking, DNA replicates nothing but itself. It intervenes only indirectly, through its agents RNA and protein, in the reproduction of the cell and its organelles, including even chromosomes and nuclei. In principle, there is no reason why DNA has to be *in* a reproducing organelle; its functions can be carried out at a distance. Even the histone of that central organelle, the chromosome, was shown by Bloch and Brack (1964) to be synthesized in the cytoplasm in the grasshopper, *Chortophaga*. Loss of most or all of the DNA of the kinetoplast does not prevent persistence and reproduction of the residue of the organelle (e.g., Mühlpfordt 1963). The DNA that codes for some molecules used during growth and division of cytoplasmic organelles appears not to be in the organelle, and there is no reason why the DNA for *any* of the organellar molecules must be in the organelle, although its being there could well increase operational efficiency.

Viewed from the other side, division is not always a property of organelles that contain DNA. The kinetosome, as we have seen, contains DNA, but it does not divide (Ehret and de Haller 1963). In some cells, to be sure, each new kinetosome arises in close association with an existing kinetosome. Dippell (1965 and unpublished) has shown that this occurs in *Paramecium* by accumulation of microtubules which then organize into the typical kinetosomal ring of nine triplet-tubules. In other cells such as the amoebo-flagellate *Naegleria* (Schuster 1963) and the fern *Marsilea* (Gall and Mizukami 1963), microtubules organize into kinetosomes (or centrioles) in the absence of existing kinetosomes. Both observations warn against the conclusion that the presence of DNA in an organelle automatically accounts for or leads to growth and division.

On the other hand, there is much to indicate that organellar DNA codes for at least some molecular species in the organelle and is the basis of at least some of its hereditary traits. Chloroplasts contain the complete protein-synthetic machinery (Kirk 1964). They contain ribosomes, and in *Euglena* the chloroplast ribosomes are reported to have a composition different from that of the ribosomes outside the chloroplast (Brawerman 1962). In agreement, chloroplasts synthesize RNA and proteins, and this synthesis is blockable by actinomycin D. Thus, within the chloroplast, DNA appears to be transcribed into RNA and the RNA to be translated into protein. Similar evidence has been reported (Kroon 1963; Luck and Reich 1964; Swift 1965) for DNA-dependent RNA synthesis, the presence of ribosomes, and protein synthesis in mitochondria. The DNA of chloroplasts and mitochondria thus appears to function like the DNA of nuclei. Tentatively, it may be supposed that the same is true for the DNA of kinetoplasts and kinetosomes. Taken in connection with the well-known existence of hereditary diversities in mitochondria and chloroplasts (see reviews by Rhoades 1955; Gibor and Granick 1964), the demonstrated role of organellar DNA in protein synthesis strongly suggests that the proteins produced play a part in determining hereditary characters of these organelles, as has often been pointed out (e.g., Kislev, Swift, and Bogorad 1965). One may imagine a number of ways in which the proteins could play this part, for example either as structural or functional components of the organelle or as parts of a system which communicates with the nucleus and regulates the activity of certain nuclear genes. The facts thus indicate that the DNA of organelles is an extension of the genetic material beyond the nucleus and that DNA-bearing organelles constitute genetic subsystems of the cell.

This conclusion is independent of the answer to the question of whether some organelles, particularly mitochondria and chloroplasts, are descendants of procaryotes that became symbionts of eucaryotes very early in the course of evolution. The idea of the symbiotic nature of organelles is very old (e.g., Mereschkowski 1905; Wallin 1927) and has recently been revived by Ris and Plaut (1962) and others (see discussion by Nass, Nass, and Afzelius 1965); it doubtless will be much discussed as more is discovered about organelles. In the present context, however, it is necessary to note only that some DNA-bearing organelles, especially kinetosomes, seem not to fit this interpretation at all. Aside from the question of symbionticism, all DNA-bearing organelles are fully integrated into the genetic system of the cell. Mutational analysis of the hereditary characters of mitochondria (Sherman and Slonimski 1964) and of chloroplasts (reviewed by Rhoades 1955) and experimental recombinations between nuclear genomes and plastid types, especially in *Oenothera* (Stubbe 1964; review by Cleland 1962), show that both sources of genetic information, nucleus and organelle, cooperate in only dimly perceived ways to determine the character and functioning of an organelle.

Finally, it should be emphasized that organellar DNA, regardless of the dosage of its "genes" per organelle, permits high dosage per cell for the genes simply by the multiplicity of each organellar type. Thus a large cell like *Paramecium* has thousands of mitochondria and thousands of kinetosomes, each with its own supply of genes. This therefore relieves the nucleus of the need of having those genes in high dosage. Organellar DNA may indeed be regarded as an adaptive measure permitting cells to restrict the ploidy level in the nucleus to a level favorable for sexual processes. On the other hand, high gene dosage within a single organelle or high multiplicity of a given organelle would result in the applicability of the Schensted type of analysis (discussed previously) to organelles that are randomly distributed at cell division and would help explain why mutations of such organelles have on the whole been more difficult to find than mutations of chromosomal genes. We thus can begin to see not only how the evolution of organelles is related to increase of cell size but also how, in the course of evolution, parts of the cell outside the central nucleus assumed important places in the genetic system of the cell (see also Sager 1965).

Further light on the operation of the extranuclear parts of the genetic system is shed by additional studies, new and old, which may not be directly concerned with DNA at all. These are little known or appreciated, yet theoretically important. I shall recount two of them, the first being an analysis of the reproduction and determinism of the pattern of surface structure in *Paramecium*. The surface of this giant cell, more than 100 μ long, consists solely of about 75 generally longitudinal rows of repeated units of structure (Fig. 19.1), most rows containing something like 100 units. Because these units will be at the focus of attention, their structure and the positions and orientations of their parts, as shown in Figure 19.1, need to be stressed. Each unit is itself complex, although it has dimensions of only about one micron. It contains one or two cilia and kinetosomes, a long fiber arising to the right on one kinetosome and extending anteriorly, a blind (parasomal) sac on the right of the fiber, membranous vesicles, and other structures. Trichocysts are inserted in the transverse anterior and posterior boundaries of the unit. Covered by a membrane which is continuous over the whole cell, the units are open internally and are continuous with the internal cytoplasm.

When two cells arise from one at fission, the number of units is of course doubled, but most of the new units arise in the equatorial zone of the cell where nearly all new growth occurs. Dippell (1965 and unpublished) has discovered that new units arise by the appearance, *within* an existing unit, of the components for one or more additional units. The "parent" unit elongates and then divides into two, or simultaneously into several, units. Most important is the precise localiza-

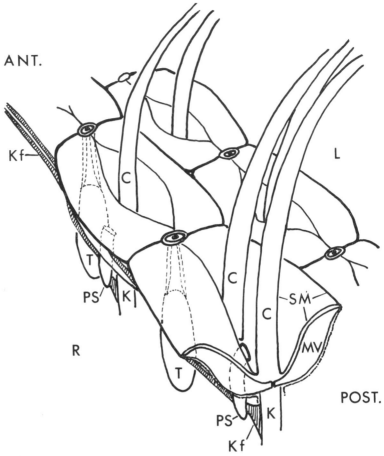

Fig. 19.1.—Diagram of the repeating unit of surface structure in *Paramecium aurelia* viewed from outside the cell, showing two units in each of two contiguous antero-posterior rows; the unit on the lower left is cut near the middle to show more of the internal structure. The *cell's* anterior, posterior, right, and left are indicated by *ANT., POST., R,* and *L,* respectively. *C,* cilium; *K,* kinetosome; *Kf,* kinetosomal fiber; *MV,* membranous vesicle; *PS,* parasomal sac; *SM,* surface membrane; *T,* trichocyst.

tion of each new part. New kinetosomes appear immediately anterior to existing kinetosomes, new fibers arise on the right side of kinetosomes and extend forward, new blind sacs arise on the right and anterior to their associated kinetosome, new subsurface vesicles arise in their usual place, and new trichocysts appear in the new transverse boundaries. Some of these new structures, such as the kinetosomes, fibers, and blind sacs, arise within the units; others, such as trichocysts (Ehret and de Haller 1963), arise deep in the cell and migrate to their proper places.

Regardless of where the component parts arise and how they are formed, the information for their assembly into the typical unit pattern clearly lies entirely within the existing unit. Beisson and Sonneborn (1965) proved this by "grafting" a small patch of units in upsidedown orientation. These upside-down units reproduced their orientation; all of their descendent units were upside down as long as followed, through about 800 cell generations and numerous fertilizations. Neither the nuclear genome nor the polarity of the cell nor the adjacent normally oriented rows of units in the same cell prevented the inverted units from reproducing their inverted pattern of parts. Figure 19.2 diagrams a row of inverted units flanked by rows of normally oriented units.

What is the source and nature of the hereditary information in the surface unit which determines the location and orientation of all newly formed parts? The reported occurrence of DNA in kinetosomes, of course, raises the question of the extent to which this, or possibly other, DNA in the unit orders the arrangement of new parts. Conceivably the DNA could code for structural proteins which then orient other molecular species, resulting eventually in the organization of visible structures. If so, the problem is still unsolved. How is the hypothetical structural protein located and oriented? In the last analysis, it is difficult if not impossible to avoid the conclusion that the structure of the existing unit, not merely its DNA, determines where new parts will be located and how they will be oriented. That even gross existing structural pattern can indeed determine the pattern of new products is strikingly shown by the next example.

The shells or tests of certain amoebae (Figure 19.3) have a single hole, the so-called mouth, through which the pseudopodia protrude during feeding and locomotion. In many species, such as *Euglypha* or *Difflugia corona*, the mouth is bordered by a circlet of projections of the test, called teeth. In each species the spaces between the teeth are the same size and shape as the teeth, but inverted. The number, size, and shape of the teeth and spaces differ from species to species, and even to some extent among different lines of descent within the same species, but are inherited with great constancy in a clone (Jennings 1916). In the process of cell division (Figure 19.3), about half of the body protrudes through the mouth, a new test forms on the protruding part, *the teeth of the new test forming in the inter-tooth spaces of the old test,* and the two cells then separate. This clear indication that the

ANT.

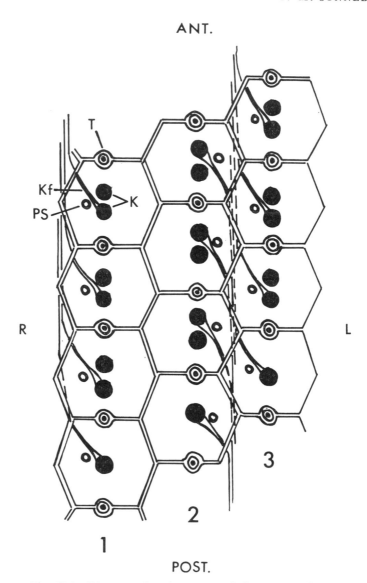

POST.

Fig. 19.2.—Diagram of a short part of three rows of surface
units on a cell of *Paramecium aurelia* possessing one inverted
row, all other rows being normally oriented. Row 2 is the
inverted row; rows 1 and 3 are adjacent, normally oriented
rows. Symbols, the same as in Fig. 19.1.

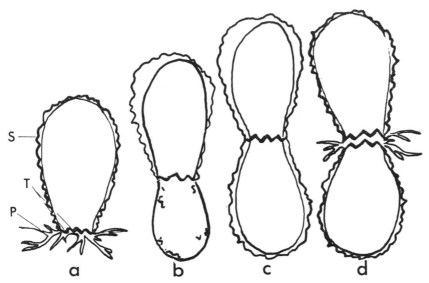

Fig. 19.3.—Diagram of a shelled (testate) amoeba, *Euglypha: a,* vegetative animal showing shell (*S*), teeth (*T*), and pseudopodia (*P*) emerging from mouth; *b,* an early stage of fission with naked half of cell protruding through mouth; *c,* later stage of fission, with new shell formed, its teeth fitting into the spaces between the teeth of the "parent's" shell; *d,* the two products of fission separating. (Redrawn after Schewiakoff 1887.)

inheritance of tooth characters is mediated by a template mechanism was confirmed experimentally by Jennings (1937). He broke off some of the teeth along with an adjacent piece of the test and observed the tooth characters of the descendants of the operated cells. The results were striking. The daughter tests were also incomplete, lacking or almost wholly lacking teeth in a region of the mouth corresponding to that of the broken area in the parent. The parent circlet of teeth clearly acted as a template for tooth formation. However, other factors are also involved, for successive generations showed a gradual repair of the damage. When a complete circlet of teeth was finally restored after several successive generations, the new tooth number was often different from that of the operated ancestor. And the new number was thereafter strictly inherited. In effect, the operation induced a "mutation" by permitting the development of a different template.

The reproduction of the surface unit in *Paramecium* and the tooth characters in *Difflugia* shows that extranuclear structures can direct their own reproduction, mutate, and perpetuate the mutations. In these cases, there can be no reasonable suspicion that the reproducing parts are symbionts or indeed that their features discussed above directly derive from DNA, foreign or domestic. We may assume that DNA codes for enzymes and proteins that participate in construction of the kinetosome and its fiber, the other diverse structures of the surface unit of *Paramecium,* and the test of *Difflugia.* Yet neither the inherited mutation of tooth number in *Difflugia* nor the inherited mutation in orientation of rows of surface units in *Paramecium* can be attributed to a mutation in DNA. The inheritance of these mutant traits results from fixed spatial relations between existing and newly formed parts at both the molecular and supramolecular levels. The same sort of determinism, the details and principles of which are now a challenge to investigation, may underlie the mechanism of "growth by intussusception" and may apply, for example, to growth of membranes with diverse, perpetuated specific properties, such as plasma membranes and the membranes of mitochondria, plastids, and other structures. We should not therefore be lulled, by the presence of DNA in organelles, into assuming that it alone accounts for their reproduction and for the inheritance of all of their properties and mutations. Other genetic mechanisms exist in eucaryotic unicells.

These mechanisms, exploiting possibilities in the cytoplasm, served to render the nuclei of eucaryotic unicells largely free from the need for high gene dosage, as mentioned above. Repeats in the haploid or diploid nuclei could be limited to certain genes, such as those functioning in the protein-synthesizing system. With such nuclei, mitosis, meiosis, and sexual processes would have a selective advantage that was minimized or denied to highly polyploid amitotic nuclei. The further course of evolution could thus be channeled through the nuclear system. The cytoplasmic job was largely finished.

Genetic Systems in Multicellular Organisms

The transition from eucaryotic unicells to multicellular organisms is gradual. Correspondingly, the genetic material and systems show no abrupt discontinuity, nothing like the gap between procaryotes and eucaryotes. Chromosome structure, for example, appears to be essentially identical, as emphasized by the recent discovery of typical banded polytene chromosomes in developing macronuclei of certain ciliates (Ammermann 1964; Alonso and Pérez-Silva 1965). What was set forth above for the cellular organelles of unicells holds also for those of multicells; indeed, the discussion of them in the preceding section drew on both. Genetic properties of the cell surface comparable to those found in *Paramecium* have also been reported in Amphibia (Curtis 1960, 1962). Some of the most distinctive features of operation of the genetic systems of multicells—those features expressed through cellular interactions—have their beginnings in unicells. Limited cellular differentiation occurs in colonial forms; aging changes accumulate progressively during clonal reproduction; stimuli are transmitted by cell contact in conjugation and by diffusing hormones in the sex signaling of Suctoria; and directed cell movements take place in the formation of slugs from free amoebae in *Dictyostelium*. Multicellular organisms, of course, exploited and further developed such cellular interactions to a very high degree. They also evolved, as will now be set forth, what seem to be new forms of behavior of chromosomes, more varied developmental possibilities of cytoorganelles, and new modes of inter-individual communication and organization.

Heterochromatin, which plays an important role in chromosome behavior in multicells, is seldom mentioned in studies on unicells. This, in my opinion, is no oversight. While I do not doubt the occurrence of heterochromatin in unicells, it seems to be a much more significant feature of genetic systems that are expressed in multicellularity, complex development, and cellular differentiation. In fact, many of the peculiarly multicellular features of chromosome behavior are known or believed to be associated with heterochromatin and are obviously related to development and differentiation. More concretely, genes in or close to heterochromatic regions are repressed, apparently by being mechanically inaccessible to de-repression (Brink 1964). However, the heterochromatic state of a region can be relieved; the region can become euchromatic (e.g., Cooper 1959). Heterochromatin production is thus a means of *temporary* genic repression and, under certain conditions to be considered later, provides a means of potentiating the pattern, in space and time, of the genic activities needed for complex development and cellular differentiation. Brink (1964) has reviewed in this connection variegated position effects, meiotic drive, the largely inactive and heterochromatic X chromosome of mammalian females, and unstable loci in flowering plants. However, the heterochromatic state is also correlated with regular aberrancies in the movements of chromosomes, resulting in their elimination or loss from nuclei at definite times and places in the developmental sequence. Such regularities could hardly occur without a system of signal sending and receiving among the chromosomes. A few examples will serve to illustrate and validate these general comments.

Among the many remarkable and instructive aspects of chromosome behavior in the fungus gnat *Sciara,* as summarized by Metz (1938), certain aspects of the X chromosome are of special interest. The X chromosomes of the father are eliminated from the nuclei of the offspring at various definite stages of development, different for somatic and germ lines. Also the pattern of elimination is different in the sons and daughters. Meiosis is normal in the daughters, but the sons transmit via sperm only the X chromosome received from the mother. By a study of translocations, Crouse (1960a) proved that this very definite but unorthodox behavior of paternal X chromosomes in males depends on a small heterochromatic segment at the end of the short arm of that chromosome. X chromosomes lacking this region are not eliminated; autosomes possessing it (even when it is far away from a centromere) are eliminated. One further fact is significant: Sex is determined by the chromosomal complement of the mother; usually a female produces either all sons or all daughters. In other words, the mother's genotype determines whether the male or female pattern of X chromosome elimination will take place in her offspring (Crouse 1960b). We can now begin to see how the decisive heterochromatic tip of the X chromosome fits into the genetic system. Apparently it receives a signal, determined by the male genotype, which modifies it so that it responds in the sons to another signal determined by the genotype of the mother and carried over into the offspring. The response is aberrant behavior of the whole chromosome, leading to its elimination at prescribed times and places.

In certain coccids, comparable behavior is shown by the whole haploid set received from the father (Brown and Nur 1964). This set becomes heterochromatic in males shortly after the onset of development, remains so throughout most of life, and is eliminated during spermatogenesis. The heterochromatic chromosomes fail to make messenger RNA (Berlowitz 1965), and their genes fail to come to expression. In this case, there seems to be no one localized region of a chromosome controlling its heterochromatinization or loss. The chromosomes have diffuse centromeres, so that the behavior of fragments, resulting from X-irradiation of the mother or father, can be followed. All fragments of chromosomes of the same set behave alike: In the sons, those from the mother are euchromatic and transmitted at spermatogenesis; those from the father become heterochromatic and are not transmitted through sperm. The male thus seems to modify the whole of all the chromosomes it transmits via sperm in such a way that they respond by heterochromatinization and elimination at prescribed times and places. This does not happen, however, in exceptional cells that lack chromosomes from the mother. Heterochromatinization is lost, apparently in the absence of continual signals that would have been sent by chromosomes derived from the mother. Again, therefore, heterochromatin is integrated via signal systems into the rest of the genetic system.

The fact that chromosomal material can shift back and forth between the heterochromatic and euchromatic states makes this mechanism suitable for gene repression in cell lineages in which the action of the repressed genes will later be needed. Nonuse of a chromosome or chromosomal segment in a given cell lineage after a certain point in development could be accomplished perhaps more efficiently, by its loss instead of by heterochromatinization. This alternative also takes place. Loss of parts of chromosomes or whole chromosomes has long been known to occur during the early development of somatic cells in some organisms. S. Beermann (1959) has observed this in *Cyclops*, and Stich (1962) showed, as expected, that much DNA is lost in the process. In some coccids, the haploid set received from the father is eliminated from both the somatic and germ lines early in the development of males (Brown and Nur 1964), instead of undergoing early heterochromatinization and loss during spermatogenesis, as happens in other coccids. In various insects, one or more chromosomes are normally lost from somatic cells but retained in the germ line (e.g., Bauer and Beermann 1952; Beermann 1956).

Both heterochromatinization and loss of chromosomal material affect simultaneously the action of groups of contiguous genes. This seems to imply that genes are to some extent locally grouped with regard to the time and place of their activity. In this connection, Beermann (1956) suggested that germ-line limited chromosomes may perform functions essential only in the germ line. Geyer-Duszyńska (1959) found that oocytes of *Wachtliella* fail to mature if the female lacks the germ-line limited chromosomes, and Bantock (1961) found the same in *Mayetiola*. Nicklas (1960) has some indications that chromosomes which are normally limited to the germ line are lethal to somatic cells of *Mycophila*. Chromosomes of the haploid set that remains condensed and inactive during most of development in certain coccids become active and essential during spermatogenesis (Nur and Chandra 1963). Both haploid sets seem to be active and necessary very early in development before one haploid set condenses in the male. Apparently in female mammals both X chromosomes operate in primary sex determination before all but one of them condense. All of these observations, as well as the concentration of sex-associated genes in the sex chromosomes and pseudoallelic gene clusters, bespeak the concentration in certain chromosomes of genes that act in concert at certain stages of development or in certain cells. Grant's (1964) book, *The Architecture of the Germ Plasm,* assembles much evidence largely, but not exclusively, from higher plants for the juxtaposition of genes that have temporally or spatially related functions. Efficiency would appear to favor grouping such genes together. They could then be repressed or activated together by a single signal-response circuit operating at a level of structure higher than that of a single gene.

Before leaving the chromosomal part of the genetic systems of multicellular organisms, I come back to the matter of genic dosage discussed extensively above in connection with unicells. With the evolution of multicellularity and its concomitant cellular differentiation, one might suppose that in certain cells some genes would have to exert a degree of activity beyond the capacity of the usual duplex dosage. If so, the dosage of these genes alone might be increased, when and where it would be useful. Relatively little that bears on this possibility is known, but there are some scattered suggestive observations. Breuer and Pavan (1955), Rudkin and Corlette (1957), Stich and Naylor (1958), Swift (1962), and others have observed disproportionate increases of DNA at definite loci in polytene chromosomes of *Rhynchosciara* and other insects.

If extra DNA is indeed produced locally, as is indicated, what becomes of it? The relatively meager information pertaining to this question suggests that at least some of it may be released from the chromosomes. The DNA found by Miller (1964) in the multitude of free nucleoli in the germinal vesicle of amphibian oocytes probably consists of one or more replicas of the DNA of the nucleolus-organizer region. During oogonial divisions in the crane fly, *Tipula,* an enormous amount of Feulgen positive material appears at the nucleolar region (Bayreuther 1956); the amount of DNA in that region is roughly equal to the total DNA in the remainder of the chromosomes (Lima-de-Faria 1962). The fate of this DNA is still unknown. The extra ring of chromatin which appears in oogonia of the water beetle, *Dytiscus,* has been found to be Feulgen positive (Bauer, unpublished; mentioned in Bauer and Beermann 1952). The puzzling facts of antibody formation have led Smithies (1965) to suggest, among other possibilities, that replicas of the DNA of antibody-forming genes may be liberated and may multiply like episomes. Sampson *et al.* (1963), Sampson, Clarkson, and Davies (1965), and others claim to have found a so-called metabolic DNA that is not conserved but is rapidly turned over. These are only hints that much remains to be learned about the chromosomal part of the genetic system of multicellular organisms.

Other parts of the genetic system, more remote from nuclear DNA, also may show new developments in multicells. Multicellular plants possess a considerable array of plastid types that develop from colorless proplastids, instead of reproducing directly by division, and exhibit various specialized functions. So far as I know, plastids other than chloroplasts have not yet been examined for possession of DNA. Whether each type of mature plastid develops from a different kind of proplastid or whether a single proplastid type has the capacity to develop into all types of mature plastids remains obscure. Even less is known in this regard about mitochondria—for example, the nature of their development and the possibility of heterogeneity among them. Nevertheless, the little that is known about cytoorganelles of multicellular organisms suggests that the organellar part of the genetic system is more complex and varied in its functioning than it is in unicells.

Still more remote from nuclear DNA are the most characteristic aspects of genetic systems in multicellular animals. In them, the genetic material maintains and multiplies itself by means of integrated genetic systems that operate not only by determining the development of complex individuals but also by endowing these individuals with means of intercommunication via varied signal systems involving motions, odors, tastes, feels, and sounds. Complex behavior patterns evolved, including home building and the nurture, protection, and training of the young. Families and societies appeared with functional specialization of individuals. They are all aspects of the operation of the genetic system, for persistence is rooted in genetic transmission.

This increasing indirectness and remoteness of aspects of the genetic system from nuclear DNA reaches its culmination in man. In him, not only are comparable remote aspects still more complex, but a distinctive and entirely new genetic system appears. Information is stored outside the organisms and transferred across the generations. The individual learns both from remote contemporaries and from predecessors long since dead. Ideas and activities are copied and mutated. They undergo an evolution of their own. This new genetic system permits and fosters foresight and planning, and raises the possibility of directed control of development, functioning, heredity, and evolution. Beadle and Crow, in Chapters 17 and 18, have commented on the feasibility, efficiency, and relative desirability of various kinds of planning and attempted control; these matters have been dealt with extensively in recent publications (Wolstenholme 1963; Sonneborn 1965; Smith 1965; Dobzhansky 1965). The central point for my thesis is not what decisions should be made, but that man's genetic systems permit him to debate and make decisions that can deliberately affect the maintenance, spread, well-being, and character of his genetic material.

In brief, the course of evolution of genetic material into genetic systems from procaryotes to man is marked not only by the appearance of new features of organization and operation of chromosomes but also by other increasingly important parts or aspects of the genetic system that are increasingly more indirect and more remote from DNA. From the part played by the membrane, wall, and flagellum of bacteria, to the cytoorganelles and surface units of eucaryotic unicells, to the integrated development and operation of the multicellular body, to the interindividual communication and social organization of higher animals, to the extraorganismic, second genetic system of man with its potential for foresight and planned directiveness, is a long and marvellous progression of evolving integrated genetic systems. In short, DNA has evolved systems embracing euphenics and planned parenthood in the broadest sense.

Were we to follow the extreme dicta or opinions of those I quoted at the start, how much more limited would be our knowledge, how narrow our views, how distorted our vision. Studies of procaryotes have, as everyone knows, revolutionized genetics. In them, molecular genetics has had most of its main triumphs. Continuation of such studies and further extensions of the molecular approach to higher organisms doubtless will continue to be tremendously fruitful as far into the future as we can foresee. Exclusion of such "simplicity" as nonbiological is absurd and would deprive genetics of a major source of insight. But neither should we wait for little feet to make little steps one by one up the ladder of genetic materials and problems. As Lewis remarked in Chapter 3, there are scientific rewards for investigating higher organisms by both molecular and nonmolecular methods. To that, many chapters in this volume bear witness. Those chapters, as well as my attempt here to discern and point out some of the basic genetic novelties that emerged in the progression up the few major evolutionary levels, show that each level has its own special contribution to make to the attainment of genetic understanding. Concurrent attack at every biological level and by every potentially fruitful approach is clearly called for.

Literature Cited

ABRAM, D., AND H. KOFFLER, 1964. *In vitro* formation of flagella-like filaments and other structures from flagellin. J. Mol. Biol. **9**: 168–185.

ALONSO, P., AND J. PÉREZ-SILVA, 1965. Giant chromosomes in Protozoa. Nature **205**: 313–314.

AMMERMANN, D., 1964. Riesenchromosomen in der Makronukleusanlage des Ciliaten *Stylonychia* spec. Naturwissenschaften **51**: 249.

ASAKURA, S., G. EGUCHI, AND T. IINO, 1964. Reconstitution of bacterial flagella *in vitro*. J. Mol. Biol. **10**: 42–56.

BANTOCK, C., 1961. Chromosome elimination in Cecidomyiidae. Nature **190**: 466–467.

BAUER, H., AND W. BEERMANN, 1952. Der Chromosomencyclus der Ortho-cladiinen (Nematocera, Diptera). Z. Naturforsch, **7b**: 557–563.

BAYREUTHER, K., 1956. Die Oogenese der Tipuliden. Chromosoma **7**: 508–557.

BEERMANN, S., 1959. Chromatindiminution bei Copepoden. Chromosoma **10**: 504–514.

BEERMANN, W., 1956. Nuclear differentiation and functional morphology of chromosomes. Cold Spring Harbor Symp. Quant. Biol. **21**: 217–232.

BEISSON, J., AND T. M. SONNEBORN, 1965. Cytoplasmic inheritance of the organization of the cell cortex in *Paramecium aurelia*. Proc. Nat. Acad. Sci. U.S. **53**: 275–282.

BERLOWITZ, L., 1965. Correlation of genetic activity, heterochromatization and RNA metabolism. Proc. Nat. Acad. Sci. U.S. **53**: 68–73.

BLOCH, D. P., AND S. D. BRACK, 1964. Evidence for the cytoplasmic synthesis of nuclear histone during spermiogenesis in the grasshopper *Chortophaga viridifasciata* (de Geer). J. Cell Biol. **22**: 327–340.

BRAWERMAN, G., 1962. A specific species of ribosomes associated with the chloroplasts of *Euglena gracilis*. Biochim. Biophys. Acta **61**: 313–315.

BREUER, M. E., AND C. PAVAN, 1955. Behavior of polytene chromosomes of *Rhynchosciara angelae* at different stages of larval development. Chromosoma **7**: 371–386.

BRINK, R. A., 1964. Genetic repression in multicellular organisms. Amer. Natur. **98**: 193–211.

BROWN, S. W., AND U. NUR, 1964. Heterochromatic chromosomes in the coccids. Science **145**: 130–136.

CHATTON, É., 1925. *Pansporella perplexa*. Ann. sci. natur. Zool. **8**: 5–84.

CLARK, T. B., AND F. G. WALLACE, 1960. A comparative study of kinetoplast ultrastructure in the Trypanosomatidae. J. Protozool. **7**: 115–124.

CLELAND, R. E., 1962. The cytogenetics of *Oenothera*. Advance. Genet. **11**: 147–237.

COOPER, K. W., 1959. Cytogenetic analysis of major heterochromatic elements (especially Xh and Y) in *Drosophila melanogaster,* and the theory of "heterochromatin." Chromosoma **10**: 535–588.

COSGROVE, W. B., AND E. ANDERSON, 1954. The kinetoplast of *Crithidia fasciculata*. Anat. Rec. **120**: 813–814.

CROUSE, H., 1960a. The controlling element in sex chromosome behavior in *Sciara*. Genetics **45**: 1429-1443.

———, 1960b. The nature of the influence of X translocations on sex of progeny in *Sciara corprophila*. Chromosoma **11**: 146–166.

CURTIS, A. S. G., 1960. Cortical grafting in *Xenopus laevis*. J. Embryol. Exp. Morphol. **8**: 163–173.

———, 1962. Morphogenetic interactions before gastrulation in the amphibian *Xenopus laevis*—the cortical field. J. Embryol. Exp. Morphol. **10**: 410–422.

DIPPELL, R. V., 1965. Reproduction of surface structure in *Paramecium*. Excerpta Medica Foundation Int. Congr. Ser. 91, Progress in Proto-zoology: 65.

DOBZHANSKY, TH., 1965. Mendelism, Darwinism, and Evolutionism. Proc. Amer. Phil. Soc. **109**: 205–215.

DU BUY, H. G., C. F. T. MATTERN, AND F. L. RILEY, 1965. Isolation and characterization of DNA from kinetoplasts of *Leishmania enriettii*. Science **147**: 754-756.

EHRET, C. F., AND G. DE HALLER, 1963. Origin, development, and maturation of organelles and organelle systems in the cell surface in *Paramecium*. J. Ultrastructure Res. (suppl.) **6**: 1–42.

GALL, J., AND I. MIZUKAMI, 1963. Centriole replication in the water fern *Marsilea*. J. Cell Biol. **19**: 26*A*.

GEYER-DUSZYŃSKA, I., 1959. Experimental research on chromosome elimination in Cecidomyiidae (Diptera). J. Exp. Zool. **141**: 391–441.

GIBOR, A., 1965. Chloroplast heredity and nucleic acids. Amer. Natur. **99**: 229-240.

GIBOR, A., AND S. GRANICK, 1964. Plastids and mitochondria: Inheritable systems. Science **145**: 890–897.

GIESBRECHT, P., 1958. Vergleichende Untersuchungen über einige Reaktionen den Chromosomen von *Bacillus negativans* und *Amphidinium elegans*. 4th Int. Conf. Electron Microscopy, Berlin (Springer Verlag): 251–255.

———, 1962. Vergleichende Untersuchungen an den Chromosomen des Dinoflagellaten *Amphidinium elegans* und denen der Bakterien. Zentralbl. Bakteriol. **187**: 452–458.

———, 1965. Über die Tertiärstruktur der DNS in den Chromosomen lebender Zellen. Z. Naturforsch. **20***B:* 927–928.

GLAUERT, A. M., D. KERRIDGE, AND R. W. HORNE, 1963. The fine structure and mode of attachment of the sheathed flagellum of *Vibrio metchnikovii*. J. Cell Biol. **18**: 327–336.

GRANT, V., 1964. *The Architecture of the Germ Plasm*. John Wiley & Sons, New York.

GRELL, K. G., 1953. Die Chromosomen von *Aulacantha scolymantha* Haeckel. Arch. Protistenk. **99**: 1–54.

IINO, T., 1964. Genetical studies of *Salmonella* flagella. Jap. J. Genet. **39**: 313–335.

JENNINGS, H. S., 1916. Heredity, variation and the results of selection in the uniparental reproduction of *Difflugia corona*. Genetics **1**: 407–534.

———, 1937. Formation, inheritance and variation of the teeth in *Difflugia corona*. A study of the morphogenic activities of rhizopod protoplasm. J. Exp. Zool. **77**: 287–336.

KELLENBERGER, E., 1962. The study of natural and artificial DNA-plasms by thin sections. Symp. Int. Soc. Cell Biol., vol. I: *The Interpretation of Ultrastructure*, pp. 233–249. Edited by R. J. C. Harris. Academic Press, New York.

KIRK, J. T. O., 1964. Studies on RNA synthesis in chloroplast preparations. Biochem. Biophys. Res. Commun. **16**: 233–238.

KISLEV, N., H. SWIFT, AND L. BOGORAD, 1965. Nucleic acids of chloroplasts and mitochondria in Swiss chard. J. Cell Biol. **25**: 327–344.

KROON, A. M., 1963. Protein synthesis in heart mitochondria. I. Amino acid incorporation into the protein of isolated beef-heart mitochondria and fractions derived from them by sonic oscillation. Biochim. Biophys. Acta 72: 391–402.

KUBAI, D. F., 1965. Cytochemical and electron microscope studies of the nucleus of dinoflagellates. M.A. Thesis, Univ. Wis., Madison.

LANDMAN, O. E., AND S. HALLE, 1963. Enzymically and physically induced inheritance changes in *Bacillus subtilis*. J. Mol. Biol. 7: 721-738.

LIMA-DE-FARIA, A., 1962. Metabolic DNA in *Tipula oleracea*. Chromosoma 13: 47–59.

LUCK, D. J. L., AND E. REICH, 1964. DNA in mitochondria of *Neurospora crassa*. Proc. Nat. Acad. Sci. U.S. 52: 931–938.

MERESCHKOWSKY, C., 1905. Ueber Natur und Ursprung der Chromatophoren im Pflanzenreiche. Biol. Centralbl. 25: 593-604.

METZ, C. W., 1938. Chromosome behavior, inheritance and sex determination in *Sciara*. Amer. Natur. 72: 485-520.

MILLER, O. L., 1964. Extrachromosomal nucleolar DNA in amphibian oocytes. J. Cell Biol. 23: 60A.

MÜHLPFORDT, H., 1963. Uber die Bedeutung und Feinstrucktur des Blepharoplasten bei parasitischen Flagellaten. Z. Tropenmed. u. Parasitol. 14: 357–398; 475–501.

NASS, M. M. K., S. NASS, AND B. A. AFZELIUS, 1965. The general occurrence of mitochondrial DNA. Exp. Cell. Res. 37: 516–539.

NICKLAS, R. B., 1960. The chromosome cycle of a primitive Cecidomyiid *Mycophila speyeri*. Chromosoma 11: 402-418.

NUR, U., AND H. S. CHANDRA, 1963. Interspecific hybridization and gynogenesis in mealy bugs. Amer. Natur. 97: 197–202.

RANDALL, SIR J., AND C. DISBREY, 1965. Evidence for the presence of DNA at basal body sites in *Tetrahymena pyriformis*. Proc. Roy. Soc. B 162: 473–491.

RHOADES, M. M., 1955. Interaction of genic and non-genic hereditary units and the physiology of non-genic inheritance. Handbuch Pflanzenphysiol. 1: 19–57.

RIS, H., 1962. Interpretation of ultrastructure in the cell nucleus. Symp. Int. Soc. Cell Biol., vol. I: *The Interpretation of Ultrastructure*, pp. 69–88. Edited by R. J. C. Harris. Academic Press, New York.

RIS, H., AND W. PLAUT, 1962. Ultrastructure of DNA containing areas in the chloroplast of *Chlamydomonas*. J. Cell Biol. 13: 383-391.

RUDKIN, G. T., AND S. L. CORLETTE, 1957. Disproportionate synthesis of DNA in a polytene chromosome region. Proc. Nat. Acad. Sci. U.S. 43: 964-968.

RUDZINSKA, M. A., P. A. D'ALESANDRO, AND W. TRAGER, 1964. The fine structure of *Leishmania donovani* and the role of the kinetoplast in the leishmania-leptomonad transformation. J. Protozool. 11: 166–191.

RYTER, A., AND F. JACOB, 1964. Étude au microscope électronique de la liaison entre noyau et mésosome chez *Bacillus subtilis*. Ann. Inst. Pasteur 107: 384–400.

SAGER, R., 1965. On non-chromosomal heredity in microorganisms. XV Symp. Soc. Gen. Microbiol. 324–342.

SAMPSON, M., D. CLARKSON, AND D. D. DAVIES, 1965. DNA synthesis in aluminum-treated roots of barley. Science 148: 1476–1477.

SAMPSON, M., A. KATOH, Y. HOTTA, AND H. STERN, 1963. Metabolically labile deoxyribonucleic acid. Proc. Nat. Acad. Sci. U.S. 50: 459–463.

SCHAECHTER, M., O. MAALØE, AND N. O. KJELDGAARD, 1958. Dependency on medium and temperature of cell size and chemical composition during balanced growth of *Salmonella typhimurium*. J. Gen. Microbiol. 19: 592–606.

SCHENSTED, J. V., 1958. Model of subnuclear segregation in the micronucleus of ciliates. Amer. Natur. 92: 161–170.

SCHEWIAKOFF, W., 1888. Ueber die karyokinetische Kerntheilung der *Euglypha alveolata*. Morph. Jahrb. 13: 193–258.

SCHUSTER, F., 1963. An electron microscope study of the amoebo-flagellate *Naegleria gruberi* (Schardinger). I. The amoeboid and flagellate stages. J. Protozool. 10: 297–313.

SHERMAN, F., AND P. P. SLONIMSKI, 1964. Respiration-deficient mutants of yeast. II. Biochemistry. Biochim. Biophys. Acta 90: 1–15.

SMITH, J. M., 1965. Eugenics and Utopia. Proc. Amer. Acad. Arts, Sci. 94: 487–505.

SMITHIES, O., 1965. Antibody induction and tolerance. Science 149: 151–156.

SONNEBORN, T. M. (ed.), 1965. *The Control of Human Heredity and Evolution*. Macmillan, New York.

STANIER, R. Y., 1964. Towards a definition of bacteria. *The Bacteria*, vol. V, ch. 10. Edited by I. C. Gunsalus and R. Y. Stanier. Academic Press, New York.

STEINERT, G., M. FIRKET, AND M. STEINERT, 1958. Synthèse d'acide désoxyribonucléique dans le corps parabasal de *Trypanosoma mega*. Exp. Cell. Res. 15: 632–635.

STERN, H., AND D. L. NANNEY, 1965. *The Biology of Cells*. J. Wiley & Sons, New York.

STICH, H. F., 1962. Variations of the deoxyribonucleic acid (DNA) content in embryonal cells of *Cyclops strenuus*. Exp. Cell Res. 26: 136–143.

STICH, H. F., AND J. M. NAYLOR, 1958. Variation of desoxyribonucleic acid content of specific chromosome regions. Exp. Cell Res. 14: 442-445.

STUBBE, W., 1964. The role of the plastomes in evolution of the genus *Oenothera*. Genetica 35: 28–33.

SUKHANOVA, K. M., AND V. K. NILOVA, 1965. An autoradiographic study of nucleic acid synthesis in the life cycle of *Opalina ranarum* Ehrbg. Excerpta Medica Foundation Int. Congr. Ser. 91, Progress in Protozoology: 202.

SWIFT, H., 1962. Nucleic acids and cell morphology in Dipteran salivary glands. *The Molecular Control of Cellular Activity*, pp. 73–126. Edited by J. M. Allen. McGraw-Hill, New York.

———, 1965. Nucleic acids of mitochondria and chloroplasts. Amer. Natur. 99: 201–228.

TRAGER, W., 1965. The kinetoplast and differentiation in certain parasitic protozoa. Amer. Natur. **99**: 255–266.

VICKERMAN, K., 1962. The mechanism of cyclical development in trypanosomes of the *Trypanosoma brucei* subgroup: An hypothesis based on ultrastructural observations. Trans. Roy. Soc. Trop. Med. Hyg. **56**: 487–495.

WALLIN, I. E., 1927. *Symbionticism and the Origin of Species.* Williams and Wilkins Co., Baltimore.

WOLSTENHOLME, G. (ed.), 1963. *Man and His Future.* Churchill, London.

20

Genetic Principles Applied to the Breeding of Crop Plants

H. Kihara and K. Tsunewaki

Contribution No. 588 from the National Institute of Genetics, Japan.

Mendel stated in the introduction to his classical paper, "Experiments in plant hybridization," that the experience with artificial fertilization, which had been attempted with ornamental plants in order to obtain new color varieties, led him to his experiments with peas. He investigated seven varieties of peas, differing from one another in one character, and found that alternative characters segregated in the hybrid offspring. By repeated hybridization, he showed that all seven differentiating characters recombined freely. He actually obtained all possible combinations, namely, 2^7 or 128, of the seven characters by repeated crossing. Thus he proved that the parental characters can be combined in offspring according to the mathematical law of combination.

Characters which segregate from each other in hybrid offspring were called "allelomorphs" by Bateson. Naturally, they were assumed to be the units of inheritance, and plant breeders adopted the concept of unit characters as a guiding principle. Actually, even today, as in the early days of Mendelism, breeders are eager to obtain new varieties by combining the characters of the parents.

The unit character hypothesis was abandoned because each character was found, in general, to be controlled by more than one element, these elements later being called "genes." Also it became clear that not all genes segregate freely but that some are linked in several groups.

Genetics has expanded very rapidly. We know now how to induce hereditary changes which can be of use to mankind, and we are able to apply modern genetic principles to the breeding of crop plants. Because many of the applications are known, we will restrict our discussion to the utilization of sterility, induced artificially by triploidy, by reciprocal translocations, and by the introduction of specific nuclei of

403

crop plants into alien cytoplasm by successive backcrosses. Although sterility is usually detrimental to crop plants when they propagate only by seeds, even such a character can be utilized in plant breeding, as we shall show. We will also compare the varieties obtained artificially by new methods with those established in ancient times and inherited by contemporary man.

Genomic Sterility

Two kinds of sterility can be distinguished, genomic sterility and cytoplasmic sterility. Genomic sterility can be caused by genes and also by deficiencies or duplications of whole chromosomes or chromosome segments. Although there are many examples of the use of genomic sterility, we shall describe only two: The first involves sterility caused by triploidy; the second, sterility caused by reciprocal translocations.

Triploidy

Autotriploid plants ($3x$) are sterile because gametes having chromosome numbers intermediate between x and $2x$ are usually not functional. Sterility thus caused has been used to obtain seedless fruits: Triploid watermelons are a good example. In the meiotic metaphase of triploid watermelons, we find eleven trivalents. Disjunction to the poles of the components of the trivalents is at random, so we can expect gametes with 11 or 22 chromosomes only once among $(1 + 1)^{11}$ or 2048 combinations. The remaining gametes, having intermediate chromosome numbers, are not viable. Therefore the percentage of sterile gametes amounts theoretically to 99.9 per cent. Investigation of the offspring obtained from backcrosses ($3x \times 2x$) and examination of pollen grains from the triploid plants support this conclusion.

Triploid watermelons are obtained easily by a cross of colchicine-induced tetraploids with normal diploids. However, since $3x$ melons do not set fruit without pollination, diploid plants must be planted with or adjacent to triploids. The pollen grains are supplied to the stigmas of $3x$ plants by insects or by hand pollination. The pollen grains grow on the stigmas and penetrate into the embryo sacs, but no embryos are produced because the female gametes are sterile. However, growth hormones supplied to the ovaries by the germinating pollen grains do induce the formation of fruits.

By use of this principle, triploid watermelons have been produced commercially (Kihara 1951b). However, there were many difficulties to be overcome. For example, triploidy was often accompanied by such unfavorable traits as poor seed germination, colored empty seeds, hollow heart, and triangular or tetrangular shape of fruits. Such drawbacks have been overcome partly by improvement of cultivation techniques and partly by use of suitable parents.

One drawback, which has not yet been eliminated, is the late maturing of $3x$ watermelons. In the early stage of development the growth of $3x$ plants is slow compared with that of the diploids. This is sufficient to retard maturity even though after about six weeks the growth rate of triploids overtakes that of the diploids.

The consumption of watermelons in Japan is at the highest point around the Buddhist Bon Festival (commemorating the souls of the deceased) which takes place in the middle of August. However, the maturity of the triploid melons is at its peak usually a little later. Nevertheless, in certain prefectures like Gifu, $3x$ watermelons are widely cultivated. The area grown at present covers 150 hectares.

In Taiwan, the late maturing of $3x$ melons has no significance. Two crops a year can be raised there, and the fruits are exported to Hongkong. Cultivation of triploid watermelons in Taiwan is quite recent. Nevertheless the area grown reached 300 hectares this year.

In America, too, lateness seems to have only a slight influence on seedless watermelon culture. Resistance to wilt and anthracnose is a more serious concern. Since 1949 intense breeding work has been conducted by O. J. Eigsti. Seedless watermelons are gradually acquiring a good reputation in the United States, and they will be marketed this year at numerous locations (Eigsti, unpublished).

Segmental interchange

To meet the need of farmers and consumers, a group of Japanese breeders is trying to obtain seedless watermelons by using reciprocal translocations of chromosomes to induce sterility. In this case both parental strains and hybrids are diploid. If the procedure is successful, there should be no need to worry about a maturity delay.

By X-ray treatment, Nishimura and Sakaguchi (1960) obtained, among others, one X_1 plant having ④ + 9_{II}, which was approximately 50 per cent pollen fertile (Table 20.1). If 50 per cent fertility is obtained by a single interchange, then two independent interchanges should give a fertility of 25 per cent, while two interchanges combined in one ring of six should result in 16.6 per cent fertility. Nishimura's pollen fertility of 15 per cent for No. 2 (⑥ + 8_{II}) fits well the expectation of 16.6 per cent (Table 20.1).*

Oka, who has carried out similar breeding work, had comparable re-

* The theoretical fertility of pollen grains with ⑥ was assumed to be equal to that of those with ④ + ④, namely 25 per cent. However, a more correct calculation may be obtained in a different way; it will be given elsewhere.

Table 20.1

Pollen fertility of a normal diploid melon variety, Asahi-Yamato, and its two
chromosomal mutants with reciprocal translocations induced by X-rays
(Nishimura and Sakaguchi 1960)

	Chromosome configuration	Pollen fertility (%)
Asahi-Yamato	11_{II}	98
No. 4	④$+ 9_{II}$	52
No. 2	⑥$+ 8_{II}$	15

sults with his material, as given in Table 20.2. Pollen fertility of plants
having one interchange was around 50 per cent, while for those with
two independent interchanges it was 32 per cent. In Table 20.2 the
number of seeds per fruit is given. All single interchange heterozygotes
had both plump and empty seeds in a ratio of approximately one to
one, that is, seed fertility of 50 per cent. It is noteworthy that the total
number of seeds was significantly higher in the heterozygotes than in
the normals. However, we have been informed that as far as fruit setting, sugar content, and size of fruits are concerned, the heterozygotes
were by no means inferior to the normals. To reduce further the number of seeds, still more segmental interchanges need to be added, and
this requires skill and time. According to our calculations, sterility will

Table 20.2

Pollen fertility and seed fertility and number of seeds per fruit in relation to chromosome configuration in melon hybrids between interchange homozygotes and normals
(Hiroyuki Oka, unpublished). Numbering of strains in the table is arbitrary. They
belong to the X_4-generation. According to their origin (X_1), they fall into two groups,
Nos. 1–4 and Nos. 5–7. No. 8 is a hybrid between the two groups.

	Chromosome configuration	Pollen fertility (%)	No. of seeds per fruit		
			Plump	Empty	Total
Control	11_{II}	95	212	22	234
Cont.×No. 1	④$+ 9_{II}$	52	152	141	293
Cont.×No. 2	"	52	153	145	298
Cont.×No. 3	"	49	154	159	313
Cont.×No. 4	"	54	135	137	272
Cont.×No. 5	④$+ 9_{II}$	51	140	149	289
Cont.×No. 6	"	53	149	143	292
Cont.×No. 7	"	51	137	145	282
No. 8	④$+$ ④$+ 7_{II}$	32	—	—	—

be sufficient when a translocation heterozygote is produced having two rings of eight and one ring of six. Thus, the breeding of seedless water-melons maturing simultaneously with the diploids still lags far from our goal.

Examples of seedless fruits in nature

Seedless bananas are comparable in the nature of their fruit to seed-less watermelons, although they are of spontaneous origin. All wild ba-nana species are diploid, and the basic chromosome number is eleven, just as in watermelons. The flowers of wild bananas must be effectively pollinated to form a fruit, and the fruits are filled with seeds. However, there are diploid banana varieties with edible fruits that are partheno-carpic and seedless (Cheeseman and Larter 1935). Their female gam-etes are highly sterile, but the male gametes are not. According to Dodds and Simmonds (1948), a diploid variety called Pisang Lilan is parthenocarpic and female sterile. But this variety does produce some viable pollen grains. The pollen fertility was estimated to be around 50 per cent, and the variety was found to be heterozygous for a single interchange. Cheeseman's (1932) finding of three rings of four, as well as five bivalents, in one diploid species (*Musa malaccensis*) suggests that segmental interchange is frequent in bananas (see also Dodds and Simmonds 1948).

Most edible bananas are triploid (Cheeseman and Larter 1935). They are both male and female sterile and set fruit by parthenocarpy. According to Cheeseman (1932), univalents, trivalents, and even multi-valents were observed in a $3x$ banana variety called Gros Michel.

Using Gros Michel, Wilson (1946) observed 0–8 trivalents (mode 2) in the meiosis of pollen mother cells. He found suppression of the first division, probably leading to the formation of unreduced gametes.

From more than 150 thousand pollinated flowers, using seven tri-ploid varieties as females and ten diploid varieties as pollen sources, Cheeseman and Dodds (1942) obtained several hundred hybrid progeny. From these, the chromosomes of 117 plants were counted: 97 offspring (83 per cent) were euploid, having $2x$, $3x$, $4x$, $5x$, and $8x$ chromosomes, and the remaining 20 were aneuploids. So it appears that the gametes of triploid bananas having intermediate chromosome numbers are func-tional on rare occasions.

Since diploid parthenocarpic bananas are not all completely female or male sterile, triploidy may have contributed toward the acquisition of complete seedlessness combined with vigorous vegetative growth. This may explain why most present commercial bananas are triploid.

We may assume that the diploid sexual ancestors of bananas have acquired genes for parthenocarpy and genomic sterility in the course of evolution under cultivated conditions. Nature has provided *Musa* with many kinds of genomic sterility. Our experience with bananas indicates that we should induce not only gametic sterility but also parthenocarpy.

Cytoplasmic Male Sterility

Heterosis is one of the most fruitful principles which have been applied to the breeding of crop plants, and nowadays hybrid varieties of a number of crops are commercially grown on farms. Hybrid corn is the best example. In the United States, hybrid corn occupied less than 5 per cent of the total corn acreage in 1936, while only nine years later the acreage had risen to 90 per cent or even higher.

In the early days hybrid corn seed was produced by detasseling of the maternal strain which had been grown beside another strain as the pollen furnisher. However, detasseling required considerable labor and, furthermore, reduced seed production somewhat because of damage to the plants. These problems were solved, however, when cytoplasmic male sterility was exploited, provided that a suitable combination of male-sterile cytoplasm and fertility-restoring genes could be found.

Heterosis also occurs in self-pollinated crops such as sorghum, wheat, and rice. In these crops, use of cytoplasmic male sterility is the only practical way to produce hybrid seeds on a large scale.

According to Poehlman (1959), the first commercial hybrid sorghum appeared in 1956, and by 1959 almost all ordinary varieties were replaced by hybrid sorghum. The success in sorghum also depended on the discovery of a working system of cytoplasmic male sterility and genic fertility restoration.

Stephens and Holland (1954) found that the cytoplasm of a milo variety of sorghum caused male sterility when its nucleus was replaced by that of kafir. Genes restoring fertility to this cytoplasm were found also among milo varieties. A number of inbred lines were produced, which possessed either the male-sterile cytoplasm or the restoring genes. Hybrid sorghum produced from a single cross between those inbred lines out-yields the standard commercial varieties by 25 to 40 per cent.

Stimulated by such success in corn and sorghum, hybrid wheat has become in recent years an object of great interest among wheat breeders in various parts of the world. As in sorghum, a cytoplasmic male sterility and fertility-restoration system had to be found before any actual breeding work for hybrid wheat could be started.

Caudata *cytoplasm*

In 1933, Kihara (1949, 1951*a*) produced a hybrid between *Aegilops caudata* (♀) and a common wheat, *Triticum aestivum* var. *erythrosper-*

mum (*T.v.e.*), as the male parent. The hybrid was twice backcrossed to the wheat, which was again used as the pollen parent. In the second backcross generation (B_2) two plants with black ears were selected, and their offspring were maintained for several years by self-pollination. Those B_2 plants and their descendants showed varying seed fertility (5—60 per cent) by self-pollination, according to environmental conditions (Kihara 1951*a*).

F_1 hybrids from the same cross combination were again produced in 1949. In order to introduce *caudata* cytoplasm into wheat, we have again backcrossed the hybrids successively, using wheat as pollen furnisher. By 1965 the sixteenth backcross generation had been attained. As already reported in 1959 (Kihara 1959), plants of SB_3 (third generation of the substitution backcross) showed very low pollen fertility but almost normal seed fertility when pollinated by the wheat parent. After SB_4, pollen fertility was always nearly zero, the plants being totally sterile under bagged condition. So far no recovery of pollen fertility has been noted. In contrast, F_1 hybrids from the reciprocal cross *T.v.e.* (♀) × *Ae. caudata* (♂) gave rise to fully fertile offspring when backcrossed as female parents to the wheat parent two or more times. It became evident from the results of these experiments that the sterility was caused by *caudata* cytoplasm.

The male-sterile line of *T.v.e.*, as donor of *caudata* cytoplasm, has been crossed to 12 varieties of common wheat, 13 of emmer, and two strains of synthesized hexaploids. For all cross combinations, substitution backcrossing has been continued since the F_1 hybrids were produced. The most advanced materials, except *T.v.e.* at SB_{16}, have reached SB_7; several are still in the SB_2 or SB_3 generation.

During the nucleus-substitution work, four fertility restorers for *caudata* plasma were discovered: P 168, Comp. 44, Elgin, and ABD-13. P 168 is a derivative of *T.v.e.*, whose chromosome 1D is replaced by a *caudata* chromosome, C-sat-2. Its origin was described in detail in 1959 (Kihara 1959). Comp. 44 is a strain of *T. compactum,* called No. 44, which has been maintained in our laboratory since 1920. Elgin is an American club wheat belonging also to *T. compactum*. ABD-13 is an artificial amphidiploid between *T. dicoccum* var. Vernal and *Ae. squarrosa* var. *strangulata,* and was produced by M. Tanaka (1961). Gene analysis of fertility restoration by Comp. 44 was carried out in detail, and it was concluded that a single gene controls fertility restoration (Tsunewaki 1962).

All four restorers are ineffective in the heterozygous condition, and F_1 hybrids between them and male-sterile *T.v.e.* are quite sterile. Accordingly, they are not suitable as breeding material. In order to improve the fertility, two restorers have been combined. Comp. 44 with *caudata* cytoplasm was crossed as the female parent to P 168, another restorer. In F_2 a great range of variation (0–85 per cent) was found in the seed fertility of self-fertilized plants. Some of the F_2 plants were totally fertile (above 80 per cent), while Comp. 44 and P 168, individually with the same *caudata* cytoplasm, were only partially fertile (about 50 per cent and 20 per cent, respectively). Thus two restorers seem to work better in combination than alone.

Ovata *cytoplasm*

Since 1950, Fukasawa (1953, 1959) has been working with the cytoplasm of *Ae. ovata*. He introduced this cytoplasm into wheat by successive backcrosses of wheat as the recurrent male parent to *Ae. ovata* or *Aegilotricum,* the latter produced from the cross *Ae. ovata* (♀) × *T. durum* (♂). He found that *ovata* cytoplasm causes male sterility in wheat, and has produced several male-sterile lines of emmer as well as of common wheat. Among these, male-sterile lines of *T. dicoccum* var. Khapli and *T. aestivum* var. Norin 26 have been given to us. Using them as donors of *ovata* plasma, we have developed many new male-sterile lines involving eight varieties of common wheat, nine varieties of emmer, and one strain of a synthesized hexaploid. From one to six successive backcrosses have been made.

During this work we found that P 168, crossed to male-sterile Norin 26 as the female parent, completely restores male fertility in the F_1 generation. Pollen fertility as well as seed fertility of bagged ears was investigated with F_2 plants from this cross. At the same time, the relationship between ear color and fertility was analyzed, since P 168 carries the genes for black ear and for fertility restoration on the same chromosome (C-sat-2). It was desirable to break the linkage between those two genes and to transfer, if possible, the restoring gene into a wheat chromosome. The results of this investigation are summarized in Table 20.3. Of 182 plants, 141 (77.5 per cent) showed seed fertility above 50 per cent, 26 (14.3 per cent) showed seed fertility varying between 50 and 0 per cent, and 15 plants (8.2 per cent) were completely sterile. Plants with fertility higher than 50 per cent when bagged may be fully fertile under open pollination. Since the F_1 plants between male-sterile Norin 26 and P 168 showed some meiotic irregularities, a certain reduction of fertility in some F_2 plants must be expected because of unbalanced gene combinations. In any case, the results presented in Table 20.3 indicate that there is a strong linkage between the genes for black ear and for fertility restoration. Many plants with yellow ears were more or less completely male-sterile, while a great majority of black-eared plants were fertile. However, four plants with

Table 20.3

Classification of F₂ plants from the cross MS-Norin 26 (yellow-eared, with *ovata* plasma) × P 168 (black-eared), based on their seed fertility and ear color

Fertility class	No. of plants		
	Black	Yellow	Total
Sterile (0.0%)	9	6	15
Almost sterile (0.1–10.0%)	2	4	6
Partially fertile (10.1–50.0%)	20	0	20
Fully fertile (50.1–100.0%)	137	4	141
Total	168	14	182

yellow ears were found to be almost totally fertile. In these plants the linkage of the genes for the two characters has supposedly been broken.

In this connection, it is worthwhile to note a peculiar transmission behavior of the black ear gene, *Bl*, or more properly that of the *Ae. caudata* chromosome carrying it. As mentioned already, this chromosome, called C-sat-2, bearing gene *Bl*, was incorporated, through replacement of chromosome 1D, into the chromosome complement of common wheat. P 168 and P 174 are two strains of *T.v.e.* with this replacement. P 174 differs from P 168 by possessing *caudata* cytoplasm, while the latter has the cytoplasm of wheat. The frequencies of black-eared plants in the F₂'s from several crosses in which wheat strains with different cytoplasms were used as the female parents are summarized in Table 20.4. No yellow-eared plants were recovered in F₂ when F₁ had *caudata* cytoplasm. In the cytoplasms of *Ae. ovata* and *T. aestivum,* a few yellow-eared F₂ plants had segregated, their percentage being significantly higher in the latter cytoplasm than in the former. Evidently the *caudata* chromosome, C-sat-2, is preferentially transmitted in all three cytoplasms, and the transmission rate is highest in *caudata* cytoplasm, followed by *ovata* and *aestivum* cytoplasms in that order. It seems to indicate that there is a closer relation of *caudata* cytoplasm to *ovata* cytoplasm than to that of wheat.

Another fertility restorer for *ovata* cytoplasm has been found in *T. timopheevi.* In this case restoration was not observed until the third backcross generation. The highest seed fertility recorded was only eight per cent.

Fukasawa (1955) reported that *T. dicoccoides* var. *kotschyanum* with *ovata* cytoplasm was pollen fertile. Accordingly, this variety can be used as a source of restoring genes. Among 124 varieties of common wheat

Table 20.4

Transmission of gene *Bl* (black ear) of *caudata* origin in three different cytoplasms; expressed by the frequency of black-eared and yellow-eared plants in F$_2$ (Kihara 1963, and unpublished). The F$_1$'s of the first cross combination gave black-eared and yellow-eared plants in a ratio of approximately one to one when they were backcrossed as female parents to normal *T.v.e.* In each cross combination the female parent possesses the cytoplasm of the species listed in the first column.

Cytoplasm	Cross combination	No. of F$_2$ plants			Yellow (%)
		Total	Black	Yellow	
Ae. caudata	P 174 (*Bl*) ♀ × *T.v.e.* (*bl*)	90	90	0	0.0
Ae. caudata	Comp. 44 (*bl*) ♀ × P 168 (*Bl*)	256	256	0	0.0
Ae. ovata	Norin 26 (*bl*) ♀ × P 168 (*Bl*)	199	183[a]	16	8.0
T. aestivum	*T.v.e.* (*bl*) ♀ × P 174 (*Bl*)	745	655	90	12.1
T. aestivum	*T.v.e.* (*bl*) ♀ × P 168 (*Bl*)	245	216	29	11.8

[a] Includes brown-eared plants.

tested, Wilson and Ross (1961) reported that five showed a certain degree of fertility restoration to *ovata* cytoplasm. Although some environmental effects seem to have been involved, Kawvale and C.I. 12511 were revealed to carry genes for partial fertility restoration.

Timopheevi *cytoplasm*

A third male-sterile plasma is now available for hybrid wheat. In 1953, Kihara crossed *T. timopheevi* var. *typicum* (♀) by *T. dicoccum* var. White Emmer (♂). The F$_1$ hybrid was backcrossed four times to *T. dicoccum*. No reduction of male fertility was observed. In 1958, this emmer strain with *timopheevi* cytoplasm was crossed as the female parent to two other emmer varieties, *T. dicoccum* var. Hokudai and *T. durum* var. *reichenbachii*. Since then substitution backcrosses have been carried out seven times. At SB$_4$ and later generations the latter variety started to show a high degree of male sterility (Kihara 1966*b*).

Independently of this work, Wilson and Ross (1962), at the Ft. Hays Branch of Kansas Agricultural Experiment Station, crossed *T. timopheevi* as the female parent to a common wheat variety, Bison. Successive backcrosses were made to place Bison's nucleus into *timopheevi* cytoplasm. All plants of SB$_2$, SB$_3$, and SB$_4$ generations became male-sterile. In the fall of 1961, seeds of the male-sterile line of Bison were released on request. Several fertility restorers for *timopheevi* cytoplasm were found by wheat workers in the Kansas as well as the Nebraska Agricultural Experiment Station. Among them, Cheyenne and Selkirk were found to carry genes for partial restoration of male fertility.

We obtained a seed sample of male-sterile Bison through J. W. Schmidt of the University of Nebraska, and crossed it to ten varieties (or strains) of hexaploid wheat and eight varieties of emmer. We performed similar crosses to our own emmer stocks with *timopheevi* cytoplasm. Through this work several new restorers for *timopheevi*-type sterility have been discovered. F_1 hybrids of *T. spelta* var. *duhamelianum* and a synthetic hexaploid, ABD-13, with male-sterile Bison were totally male fertile with respect to pollen and seed fertility. These two restorers, especially *T. spelta* var. *duhamelianum,* appear to be promising as the source of fertility-restoring genes for *timopheevi* cytoplasm. As to tetraploid wheats, all eight varieties of emmer restored male fertility to some extent. Among these eight, *T. polonicum* var. *vestitum* seems to be the most effective restorer. Because of the prevalence of restoring genes in emmer wheats, *timopheevi* cytoplasm is not a suitable male-sterile material for breeding hybrid emmer wheat.

Mechanisms of fertility restoration

It has become clear from the foregoing investigations that there is a specific interaction between a male-sterile cytoplasm and the "inoculated" fertility-restoring genes. A restorer gene effective in one male-sterile cytoplasm is not necessarily functional in another. This relationship is clearly shown in Figure 20.1. Breeders must look for the best restorer for each male-sterile cytoplasm.

There is another interesting phenomenon that might be of significance in breeding work. As you may see from Figure 20.1, the genotypes of wheats fall into two groups according to their behavior in F_1 and the following backcross generations. In one group, represented conveniently by Comp. 44 in *caudata* plasma, the self-fertilized F_1 shows very low male fertility, which is recovered, however, in the course of backcrosses. In contrast, the other group, represented, for instance, by *T. durum* var. *reichenbachii* in *timopheevi* plasma, shows in F_1 a complete recovery of male fertility, gradually diminishing in the course of continued backcrosses (Fig. 20.2). For the first group it may be assumed that homozygosity of the restoring gene or genes is required for recovery, while the presence of complementary genes which produce a heterotic effect is indicated for the second group.

Constancy of cytoplasm

Since the breeding work toward hybrid wheat is still in an early stage of development, only the basic investigations on cytoplasmic

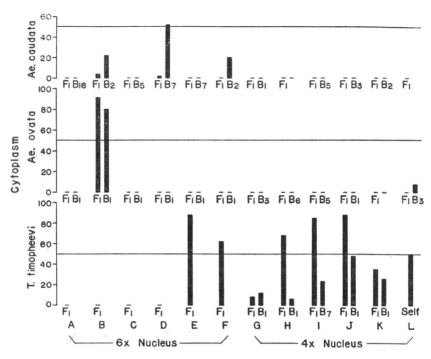

Fig. 20.1.—Seed fertility by self-fertilization in F_1 and most advanced backcross generations of crosses between three kinds of male-sterile wheats having *caudata, ovata,* or *timopheevi* cytoplasm and normal, fertile wheats as recurrent male parents. *A, T. aestivum* var. *erythrospermum* (*T.v.e.*); *B,* P 168, a derivative of *T.v.e.; C, T. aestivum* var. Salmon; *D, T. compactum* (Comp. 44); *E, T. spelta* var. *duhamelianum; F,* a synthesized 6*x* wheat (ABD-13); *G. T. dicoccoides* var, *spontaneo-nigrum; H, T. dicoccum;* var. Khapli; *I, T. durum* var. *reichenbachii; J, T. polonicum* var. *vestitum; K, T. turgidum* var. SNS; *L, T. timopheevi* var. *typicum.*

male sterility and fertility-restoration systems could be presented here. Relying on the results hitherto obtained, we are convinced that the cytoplasms of various species belonging to the same or a related genus are more or less differentiated from each other and that their hereditary plasmatic characters have not been modified by nuclear genes, at least, for thirty years or so. *Ae. caudata* was first crossed to wheat in 1933. Since then no detectable change of its cytoplasm in regard to the manifestation of wheat genomes has been noted. Furthermore, cytoplasms of the present-day emmer and common wheat do not show any detectable difference, even though they became phylogenetically separated more than 5000 years ago (see subsequent discussion). Such constancy of he-

reditary traits of the cytoplasm indicates that it may be possible to trace
the origin of the cytoplasm of a certain crop plant to its wild relative.

Hereditary characteristics of different cytoplasms are revealed only
when a series of nucleus substitutions have been carried out and a set
of different nuclei of more or less closely related species have replaced
their own. By such research the genetic differences among three cytoplasms—namely, those of *Ae. caudata, Ae. ovata,* and *T. timopheevi*—
have been disclosed, as shown in Table 20.5. The cytoplasm of *Ae. caudata* is characterized by its frequent formation of germless grains, production of haploid or twin seedlings in hexaploid wheat, and induction of pistillody in emmer wheat. In some cases, female fertility is reduced. P 168 and Comp. 44 act as partial fertility restorers. Characteristic of *ovata* cytoplasm is the induction of male sterility in most wheat
varieties and extremely prolonged vegetative growth in emmer wheat.
No pistillody is caused. P 168 restores male fertility completely. *Timopheevi* cytoplasm is different from the preceding two, because *T. spelta*
and all emmer varieties having it restore male fertility to different levels. This cytoplasm does not exhibit any other remarkable effect.

The cytoplasm of common wheat must have been derived from
emmer wheat, not from *Ae. squarrosa,* because their hybrids can never
be produced when *Ae. squarrosa* is used as the female parent; however,

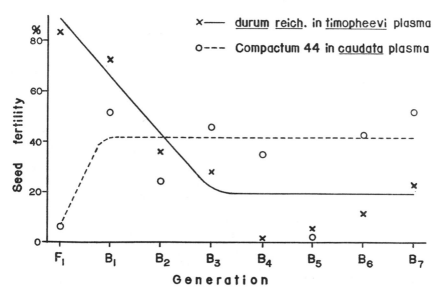

Fig. 20.2.—Behavior of two representative restorers in F₁ and backcross generations.

Table 20.5

Hereditary characteristics of three cytoplasms revealed by
substitution of a set of wheat nuclei

Nucleus	Cytoplasm		
	Ae. caudata	*Ae. ovata*	*T. timopheevi*
Hexaploid wheat			
T. aestivum	male-sterile, germless grains	male-sterile	male-sterile
T. aestivum P. 168	partially male-fertile	completely male-fertile	male-sterile
T. aestivum Salmon	male-sterile, haploid and twin seedlings	male-sterile	male-sterile
T. compactum Comp. 44	partially male-fertile	male-sterile	male-sterile
T. spelta duhamelianum	male-sterile, reduced female fertility	male-sterile	completely male-fertile
Tetraploid wheat			
T. durum reichenbachii	pistillody, abortive ovules	male-sterile, delayed heading	partially male-fertile
T. polonicum vestitum	pistillody	male-sterile, delayed heading	completely male-fertile
T. dicoccoides spontaneo-nigrum	pistillody	male-sterile, delayed heading	slightly male-fertile

not only hybrids but also many amphidiploids have been obtained when emmer was the female parent. The origin of emmer's cytoplasm is still obscure. It is suggested that the BB-analyser, probably a species of the Sitopsis section of *Aegilops,* may have been the maternal parent, whose cross to einkorn wheat gave the first emmer wheat (Kihara 1966a). This supposition is strongly supported by the fact that hybrids as well as amphidiploids were produced from the cross *Ae. speltoides* (♀) × einkorn wheat (♂), but not from the reciprocal combination. In order to prove this hypothesis, we must investigate the relation of the *speltoides* cytoplasm to that of polypoid wheats.

In certain plants, such as *Epilobium* (Michaelis 1954), the plasmon is mutable, changing cytoplasmic properties very frequently. Such a mutability of cytoplasm is known to be induced by certain nuclear genes (Du Buy and Woods 1959), for example, the iojap gene in corn. Fortunately, genes of this kind appear to be either lacking or rare in wheat and its relatives, which opens the possibility to reveal in the future the origin and differentiation of the cytoplasms of this group by the nucleus-substitution method.

Induction of cytoplasmic male sterility is a way of mass production of entirely female individuals in bisexual plants. In unisexual organisms, like most higher animals, the situation is much simpler, and man has unconsciously produced heterosis through hybridization in his economically important animals even in antiquity. For example mules (hybrid between mare and he-ass) have been used as draft and burden animals from ancient times, because they were found to be more vigorous, hardy, and disease-free than either parent. Heterosis was also known among the breeders of the silkworm in Europe and Japan in the middle of the nineteenth century. Systematic utilization of hybrid silkworms has been practiced since 1918 everywhere in Japan (Y. Tanaka 1943).

In the plant kingdom there are species whose hybridity is maintained permanently by a special mechanism, like that of *Oenothera lamarckiana*. If we could produce such systems, we would gain a powerful instrument to apply to plant breeding (see Burnham 1956).

Literature Cited

Burnham, C. R., 1956. Chromosomal interchanges in plants. Bot. Rev. 22: 419–552.

Cheeseman, E. E., 1932. Genetic and cytological studies of *Musa*. I. Certain hybrids of the Gros Michel banana. J. Genet. 26: 291–312.

Cheeseman, E. E., and K. S. Dodds, 1942. Genetic and cytological studies of *Musa*. IV. Certain triploid clones. J. Genet. 43: 337–357.

Cheeseman, E. E., and L. N. H. Larter, 1935. Genetic and cytological studies of *Musa*. III. Chromosome numbers in the Musaceae. J. Genet. 30: 31–52.

Dodds, K. S., and N. W. Simmonds, 1948. Sterility and parthenocarpy in diploid hybrids of *Musa*. Heredity 2: 101–117.

Du Buy, H. G., and M. W. Woods, 1959. Segregation of cytoplasmic particles in green plants. Proc. IX Int. Bot. Congr. 2A: 9–10.

Fukasawa, H., 1953. Studies on restoration and substitution of nucleus in *Aegilotricum*. I. Appearance of male-sterile *durum* in substitution crosses. Cytologia 18: 167–175.

———, 1955. Studies on restoration and substitution of nucleus in *Aegilotricum*. II. The interrelationships between *ovata* cytoplasm and fertility restoring factors. Cytologia 20: 211–217.

———, 1959. Nucleus substitution and restoration by means of successive backcrosses in wheat and its related genus *Aegilops*. Jap. J. Bot. 17: 55–91.

Kihara, H., 1949. Advances in genome-analysis of *Triticum*. Botanical Papers Dedicated to Prof. Kingo Miyabe in Celebration of his Ninetieth Birthday: 42–55.

———, 1951a. Substitution of nucleus and its effect on genome manifestations. Cytologia 16: 177–193.

———, 1951b. Triploid watermelons. Proc. Amer. Soc. Hort. Sci. 58: 217–230.

————, 1959. Fertility and morphological variation in the substitution and restoration backcrosses of the hybrids, *Triticum vulgare* × *Aegilops caudata*. Proc. X Int. Congr. Genet. 1: 142–171.

————, 1963. Nucleus and chromosome substitution in wheat and *Aegilops*. II. Chromosome substitution. Seiken Zihô 15: 13–23.

————, 1966a. Factors affecting the evolution of common wheat. Indian J. Genet. Plant Breed. 26A: 14–28.

————, 1966b. Nucleus and chromosome substitution in wheat and *Aegilops*. I. Nucleus substitution. Proc. II Int. Wheat Genet. Symp. (in press).

MICHAELIS, P., 1954. Cytoplasmic inheritance in *Epilobium* and its theoretical significance. Advance. Genet. 6: 288–401.

NISHIMURA, Y., AND S. SAKAGUCHI, 1960. Studies on the reciprocal translocations of chromosomes in watermelon. I. Three translocated strains in the variety Asahi-Yamato. Niigata Univ., Bull. Fac. Agr. 12: 22–29.

POEHLMAN, J. M., 1959. *Breeding Field Crops*. Henry Holt and Co., New York.

STEPHENS, J. C., AND R. F. HOLLAND, 1954. Cytoplasmic male-sterility for hybrid sorghum seed production. Agron. J. 46: 20–23.

TANAKA, M., 1961. New amphidiploids, synthesized 6x-wheats, derived from Emmer wheat × *Aegilops squarrosa*. Wheat Inform. Serv. 12: 11.

TANAKA, Y., 1943. *Sericultural Science*. Kobunsha, Tokyo.

TSUNEWAKI, K., 1962. Analysis of the fertility-restoring gene in *Triticum aestivum* ssp. *compactum*. Seiken Zihô 15: 47–53.

WILSON, G. B., 1946. Cytological studies in the *Musae*. I. Meiosis in some triploid clones. Genetics 31: 241–258.

WILSON, J. A., AND W. M. ROSS, 1961. Cross-breeding in wheat, *Triticum aestivum*. I. Frequency of the pollen-restoring character in hybrid wheat having *Aegilops ovata* cytoplasm. Crop Sci. 1: 191–193.

WILSON, J. A., AND W. M. ROSS, 1962. Male sterility interaction of the *Triticum aestivum* nucleus and *Triticum timopheevi* cytoplasm. Wheat Inform. Serv. 14: 29–30.

21

The Gene Material as the Initiator
and the Organizing Basis of Life

H. J. Muller

The View of Protoplasm's Primacy

The sharp polarization of views on our present topic can be better understood if we first briefly review the findings that seemed to justify T. H. Huxley's statement of 1853 (as cited by Wilson 1896), characterizing protoplasm as "the physical basis of life." Firstly, contrary to what Schleiden and Schwann shortly before that had concluded, it had become clear that it was the cells' contents, not their walls, that played the main role in life. Secondly, the bulk of the active material of these contents lay in the protoplasm (including under this term both cytoplasm and nucleoplasm). Thirdly, protoplasm was ubiquitous and seemed fundamentally alike in all then-known forms of life. Fourthly, the maintenance of active life was found by physiologists and chemists to depend, in all the diverse forms they studied, upon a turnover of materials in protoplasm called "metabolism." In metabolism, the building-up or "anabolic" processes, in living things that were maintaining themselves, balanced in the course of time the breaking-down or "catabolic" ones, but at some stages the former exceeded the latter sufficiently so that in the still longer run the former prevailed. Thus the anabolic processes resulted in the kind of growth and rather accurate reproduction so distinctive of all living, as compared with all nonliving, matter.

True, it was postulated by an increasing number of leading biologists that protoplasm was composed of or contained a host of smaller, perhaps invisibly minute, units, which themselves, when in their cellular setting, underwent metabolism that included "assimilation, growth, and division." Moreover, these particles were often thought to differ from one another and to carry along their respective characteristics through their multiplications. But since the body as a whole and the cell as a whole obviously did this, the specificity involved was usually taken for granted in the postulated smaller units and did not appear to raise any novel difficulties. All that seemed needed was the predominance of each object's special kind of anabolism, already determined by its special structure.

Thus, on the very rare occasions in the nineteenth century when the nonsupernatural origin of life was discussed, as by Haeckel (1866), it was thought to have been by aggregation, through random contacts and innate affinities, of varied organic molecules, especially proteins. These molecules had already been formed by the natural chemical processes occurring among nonliving substances. Some of the more enduring aggregates happened to become modified until a type had arisen which could continue adding suitable material and carried on a sufficient predominance of anabolic over catabolic processes. At last the object, thus enlarged, tended to fall apart into two. The essential difficulties involved in this conception were not realized.

In extenuation, it may be recalled that the view of the primacy in life of protoplasm and metabolism had gained favor even before Darwin's exposition of evolution by natural selection. Later in the nineteenth and early twentieth centuries, the subject of life's origin had seemed so taboo and speculative that there was little open questioning about how protoplasm and metabolism could have become established in the first place, starting with nonliving forms. It is a curious anachronism, however, that even today some of the most eminent biochemists and biologists, doing very valuable work in their respective fields, still adhere to this view and its corollary concerning life's origin. Unfortunately, it became much publicized and elaborated, beginning in the 1930's, by the Lysenkoist Oparin in his book, *The Origin of Life* (1938 *et seq.*), as a part of the attempt to downrate the significance of genetics. His part of that attempt was most subtly carried out.

The Rise of Recognition that There Is a Genetic Material

For a long time the alternative view was not very clearly separated from the one just discussed. Even Haeckel had proposed, in 1866, that the nucleus carried the inheritance. But our present conceptions had their main source in the observations on nuclear and chromosomal behavior, made in the early 1880's, that in 1884 led Weismann, O. Hertwig, Kölliker, and Strasburger, independently, to their great theory that the chromosomes are the basis of heredity, after Roux had in 1883 already concluded that the chromosomal determiners are manifold in number, quality, and effect and linearly arranged. Wilson's *The Cell in Development and Inheritance,* in its 1896 edition, made this clear to English-speaking readers, although since then these developments have often been neglected.

In the ensuing two decades (1883–1903), the chromosome theory received notable confirmation through varied observations and experiments, and was also freed of some extravagancies that Weismann and Roux had tried to attach to it. Before these two decades were quite over, it became joined both with the rediscovered Mendelian mechanism of heredity and, to some extent, with the uncouth rudiments of a chromosomal mutation theory, proposed by de Vries. After one more decade—that is, by 1913—crossing over, with its further confirmation of Roux's conclusion of thirty years earlier, had been discovered and demonstrated.

Reasons why all these developments were not yet clearly separated from the older view of protoplasm's primacy were the following. Many biologists were still uncertain whether Mendelian inheritance and discrete mutation represented general phenomena, especially since so-called blending inheritance and continuous genetic variation seemed often to occur and since de Vries' mutants seemed highly paradoxical in their inheritance. These matters, however, were soon to be largely cleared up, at least enough to gratify those tending to favor the primacy of the genetic material.

Gradually, an ever sharper distinction was deduced, and demonstrated, between most genetic material and the other material within protoplasm, together with a knowledge that the former played a guiding role over the structure and activities of the latter. Nevertheless, it was a long time before even geneticists in general realized that the genetic material must, at its deepest level at least, work by processes fundamentally different from those of the rest of the protoplasm, processes that could not be regarded as embodying "assimilation, growth, and division," that is, of "metabolism" as conceived for the protoplasm. It had long been known that continued life, at least in forms above bacteria, requires genetic material (we will here call it *gene material*), but it had not yet been proposed that this gene material by itself, in a nonplasmic form, had constituted the earliest ancestors of organisms. Certainly many biologists still assumed that protoplasm might first have evolved without this distinctive gene material, when they thought of the matter at all, and tended to believe that the gene material had differentiated later, within the protoplasm, or had arisen separately and then combined in a symbiotic relation with the protoplasm.

Troland's "Enzyme Theory of Life"

Although the observations and experiments for directly demonstrating the primacy, even in the origin of life, of the gene material *per se* are yet to be carried out, this is one of the cases in which a valid logical analysis of pre-existing facts has long since made the conclusion an extremely probable or even necessary one. The first really important and specific statements along these lines of which I am aware were made by Troland, who had entered biology from physics and chemistry. They were expressed in three largely disregarded papers of 1914–17, most notably in the one for biologists in *The American Naturalist* in 1917. In this article, Troland, referring to the findings of genetics—especially those of the *Drosophila* work that had proved the existence of numerous different chromosomal genes, capable of individual mutations—pointed out that these genes fell into the chemist's category of "autocatalysts." This term had been applied to them earlier by Hagedoorn (1911), although without the important inferences drawn by Troland; still earlier, W. Ostwald, in 1908, and others had applied the term "autocatalysis" to biological growth in general (e.g., W. Ostwald 1908, as cited by Troland 1917).

An "autocatalytic" molecule (or other structure) by definition had the effect of hastening some given reaction that results in the production of a molecule (or structure) having a composition identical with its own. Such an effect, at least to a small degree, must, as Troland said, be an extremely common one, since few substances fail to have some effect (plus or minus) on the speed of any given reaction, including that reaction by which they are produced, and "plus" effects must form no small proportion of them. It must even now be admitted that, by this broad definition, genes do in a sense act as autocatalysts in their eventual effect. The category was an exceedingly mixed one, however, and it even included the process of crystallization by which molecules are laid down from a solution onto a pre-existing crystal of the same chemical kind. It was this type of autocatalysis with which, Troland thought, gene reproduction had most in common.

In likening or identifying gene reproduction with crystallization, Troland made the important distinction that the gene, unlike an ordinary crystal, must be composed of a number of parts of different composition, having a definite pattern with regard to each other, that differed from one gene to a nonhomologous one. Each part, he proposed, selectively attached to itself an individual part, present in the medium, that had a composition corresponding to its own. What has here been advisedly termed a "corresponding" part was in Troland's view a part of identical composition, as it would be in an ordinary crystal. However, he also pointed out that some structurally "corresponding" things have a different relationship, "such as that existing between a body and its mirror image, or between a lock and a key," and that their attachments are sometimes even stronger.

By means of a matching of parts, a whole pattern of corresponding parts (here, like ones) became built up, having a pattern identical with that of the original gene. The parts of the daughter pattern also became attached to one another and were finally released from the mother pattern. Troland even discussed some of the physicochemical features of the energetics that would probably play a role in these changes of connection.

But Troland's thesis went much further. Bodies having this kind of "autocatalysis," after undergoing given chemical, and therefore discontinuous, changes of pattern as a result of chance encounters, should provide a basis upon which natural selection might work, among individual patterns and among any cohering groups of them. It was assumed then (as with genes today) that the differing patterns would somehow affect their own survival and multiplication differentially.

Troland's statement of this matter was that the genes would have not only autocatalytic properties but also "heterocatalytic" ones (which, as previously noted, he thought was true of many kinds of substances). Since biological catalysts are termed "enzymes," Troland also termed the genes "enzymes" (as Driesch in 1894 had termed the hereditary determiners "ferments"), and he designated his theory as "the enzyme theory of life." He pointed to the already existing evidence that given genes are determiners for (or may themselves be) given enzymes, and he generalized on this in accord with the then-prevalent view that practically every chemical reaction in a cell is controlled by a specific enzyme (e.g., Berzelius 1836, as cited by Loeb 1906). Troland gave reasons for believing these "enzymes" to be composed of nucleic acid. If one accepted all this and that the materials and conditions for these genes' multiplication could have been present before protoplasmic life existed, it followed, he argued, that processes could begin which finally did result in life as we know it. Moreover, the descendants of these gene-enzymes would in a sense still play the master role in life.

Muller's Concept of Gene Primacy

Troland's remarkable paper, which I read when it appeared in 1917, startled me, for it expressed a number of ideas very similar in essentials to some I had already formulated. However, there were several crucial differences in our conceptions (see my statements of 1912, 1921, and 1926, published in 1962, pp. 6–17, 1922, and 1929, respectively). For one thing, although believing in the importance and multiplicity of specific enzymes in protoplasmic reactions and the dependence of their presence on genes, I believed it illegitimate to *identify* genes with enzymes and too early to decide in what then-known category of chemical substances (if any) genes belonged. Even in sperm there was still an un-classified residuum of material, and known enzymes were widely thought to be proteins.

More important, the multiplication of genes had to be a quite different and much more peculiar process than "autocatalysis" of any kind (including crystallization) yet known to the physicochemical sciences. Even if the process were considered to be an effect merely on reaction *rates*, those rates in the absence of the promoter, in this case, the given gene, must be infinitesimal. Thus the promoters here, unlike those of ordinary inorganic catalysis (yet like enzymes in this respect), could more justly be said actually to *cause* the reactions rather than to hasten them.

It is true that, in agreement with Troland, I believed it likely that the daughter gene material was constructed by the piecemeal matching of part for part, mosaically (I, too, thought of them as identically formed parts). Otherwise the gene structure as a whole would be confronted with the impossible task of selecting, from a virtually infinite number of possible reactions (which would have been represented by all possible genes), the one particular very complex reaction or group of reactions that it must cause (or "catalyze"). And it would have to do this in spite of the limited number of different substrates available to all the genes alike. This difficulty was epitomized in the fact that mutated genes retained the faculty of causing or "catalyzing" their self-construction; that is, even after mutation, they succeeded in applying this faculty in such a way as to construct just the new pattern—the fact most crucial for all biological evolution.

Troland had seen no real difficulty here, if the construction process consisted of a mosaically occurring crystallization of like parts. But, as I pointed out, such specific "autocatalysis," even by way of crystallization, could not be the generalized property of matter that he thought it to be when he declared, "We have advanced definite reasons for believing that autocatalytic activity is a property of all chemical substances whatsoever, given the appropriate chemical environment." If one detail of the process is considered, how—without some special mode of construction—could just any *three*-dimensional structure always choose a partner that was like (or "corresponded" to) it, not only in the regions of its points of potential connection but even throughout its bulk? More generally speaking, if such "autocatalysis" were so widespread, reproduction of this kind, in which even the variations were reproduced, would be of common occurrence. In that case, evolution by natural selection and its eventual products, diverse forms of adapted "living things," would have been too easy to come by. They should be found to have arisen among the most varied materials and conditions.

For this reason I regarded the specific mode of construction which permits the gene material to reproduce not merely itself but its changes, even through an unlimited number of changes of cumulatively diverse types, to constitute the cardinal problem facing genetics, as well as biology in general, and also to carry the key to the origin of life. Although agreeing with Troland on the basic role in life played by this type of so-called autocatalysis, I was forced to conclude that he had vastly underestimated the very special nature of the process and the difficulty of finding out just what structure or structures carry it on.

In the paper of 1922, however, I still considered it possible that metabolizing protoplasm, or at least an early forerunner of it, other than actual gene material, might play a necessary role, or perhaps even the main role, in gene reproduction. For instance, it might act somewhat as a mimeograph does, causing the repeated production of any pattern of gene material that was presented to it. In that case the gene material itself might have to possess only a certain rather simple feature or features to be acceptable for reproduction, and the chief clue to the basic reproduction mechanism and to its mode of origin would lie in the protoplasm.

In the paper of 1929, however, I concluded that it would have been virtually impossible for the faculties here required to originate by natural processes occurring in nonliving matter whereas these faculties could have arisen in gene material capable of carrying on its own self-reproduction. Surely a faculty like accurate mimeographing requires a highly special, complicated structure. Moreover, the process of manufacturing just this structure must also be highly special, complicated, and accurate. It would be an almost impossible coincidence for a structure possessing both these faculties to have arisen except by a biological type of natural selection, involving the operations of a substance already capable of reproducing itself and its variants. In other words, we would have to attribute to this primitive protoplasm itself the capabilities of gene material. Yet there would then be no step-by-step advantages that led that protoplasm, in its evolution, to get in addition the capability of duplicating a totally different kind of gene material, represented by that in the chromosomes.

On the other hand, starting with the present kind of gene material or some primitive version of it, it would be provided from its inception with an evolutionary mechanism by which it could gain capabilities of utilizing increasingly the nonliving materials about it. It would tend to form them into surrounding structures that fostered its own and their own continuance and multiplication. This means that it would eventually evolve a protoplasm working, and therefore metabolizing, in ways that helped to preserve and multiply the given generative gene material.

Of course this by no means implies that no cooperating materials, including some fairly complicated although probably often imprecise ones, needed to be present in the medium if the reproduction of the primitive gene material was to take place. But it cannot be supposed that those cooperating materials themselves were capable of carrying on some kind of reproduction or metabolism on their own by which their substance was accurately enough replaced and augmented to allow their own increase and that of the gene material proper. Everyone who has at some time within the past hundred years thought rationally about the natural origin of life has realized that complicated organic molecules, including some having considerable potential chemical energy, must first have arisen without the intervention of life, and must not only have combined to form the ancestral reproducing bodies but also furnished them with the materials and energy they needed, in forms requiring the least reworking. That is, they were ready-made—prefabricated—and required little more than arrangement and binding into the pattern of the reproducing bodies, whatever those were, as the so-called "heterotroph hypothesis" has, in effect, so long maintained. Through selected mutational steps, progressively less ready-made forms could be utilized, as Horowitz (1945) spelled out over two decades ago in a form that the chemists could appreciate.

However, all this is a quite different matter from the concept of an evolution of nongenic bodies that could themselves grow. There could have been no gradual selection for the kind of accurate growth ability needed until the bodies selected had the highly special capability of causing materials about them to assume the very same forms that even their own *changes* had caused in them. And that capability is the one which (if accompanied by a versatile power of influencing other substances also) defines the gene material itself. This is the main point overlooked by those who seek life's origin in other material or who fail to realize how remarkable that capability is.

In both of those two papers I pointed out that there was already known to be gene material not only in the nuclear chromosomes but also in some cytoplasmic bodies, certainly the chloroplastids. In view of the remarkable properties and therefore structure that gene material must possess, I surmised (1941) that the gene material in these bodies may have had an ancestry common to that in the nuclear chromosomes and become separated from the latter when, at a level of evolution subsequent to that of bluegreen algae, a nuclear membrane became established. Doubtless its presence within those special bodies rather than outside them was in some way advantageous.

The reason why this gene material in the cytoplasm had remained relatively minor in inheritance was discussed in some detail in my paper of 1941, "The threads that weave evolution." There it was pointed out that this minor role was to be expected because of the much greater opportunity for evolutionary increase in number of qualitatively different parts that was afforded to the nuclear chromosomes. This had come about as a result of the mechanisms, evolved for those chromosomes, for qualitatively exact distribution at mitosis and fertilization and for precise recombination, including crossing over, at meiosis.

Further Concepts Concerning the Gene Material

Once it had been concluded that the gene material is probably unique and that it is primary in life and the origin of life, further conclusions concerning it could be drawn, and were presented in my paper of 1929 on the subject. The gene material must (so it was there concluded) be composed of two very different kinds of structural arrangements. Arrangements of the first kind were not highly complex and were probably similar in very early times to those of today (being the structures which had, as it were, happened to fall together, without benefit of prior natural selection). They must be the basic arrangements which lie behind the very generalized ability of the gene material to copy specifically any of the highly diverse possible arrangements of the second kind.

These arrangements of the second type have been the ones subject to modification by ordinary mutation, and in the long course of evolution some of them have become extremely complex. Figuratively at least, "and perhaps . . . even literally," the two kinds of arrangements lie in different "dimensions" from one another, it was said. Through the arrangements and rearrangements of this second kind, the argument continued, the gene material has come to influence other materials in diverse, often complicated ways. Thus eventually, by natural selection among different arrangements of the second type, adaptations of the neighboring nongene material have been produced that have served the multiplication of the given gene material itself.

In both of these papers the limits of *a gene* were taken as those mainly demarcated by tests of phenotypically expressed allelism, as shown in heterozygotes between independently arisen mutants. Recent recruits into genetics from physics and chemistry, not aware of this usage, have employed the same limit concepts although renaming them "cistron" and "noncomplementation," respectively. Even before these two papers, to be sure, I had reported that there was at least one case in *Drosophila*—that of the Truncate, dumpy, etc., series—in which this test was demonstrably invalid, but such a case was obviously exceptional. From data on the frequencies of origination of what I termed "non-overlapping" (i.e., nonallelic or "complementing") mutants versus the frequencies of different numbers of repetitions of overlapping (i.e., allelic or "noncomplementing") ones, it was calculated (although by an improvised, somewhat faulty "Poisson series" method) that in *Drosophila* the total number of different genes is at least on the order of a thousand, but is more probably several thousand, and that the bulk of one average-sized gene would certainly be submicroscopic.

It is true that the alternative concept—that the active gene material is uninterrupted along the chromosome—could in my opinion not yet be excluded. However, reasons, which I believe to be valid still, were presented that favored as more probable—despite position effects between chromosome parts of mainly different function which are not very far from each other—a "segmented" structure of the gene material, such that the junctions between genes differ in some way from those between parts within a gene (see also Muller 1940).

In this connection the following statement, which concludes the discussion in my 1940 article, should be of interest:

. . . we must be careful not to take it for granted that the chromonemal internodes demarcated by different criteria would necessarily coincide with one another. X-ray breakage, for example, might be possible at more points than crossing-over breakage, or *vice-versa,* and the points of crossing-over in turn might be different from the limits set by ultra-violet mutation or from the boundaries pertaining to certain types of gene-functioning, and there might be still different limits prescribed for the smallest amount capable of exerting auto-synthesis or auto-attaction. If then the different criteria gave different results we should have correspondingly different kinds of "genes," according to the definition of gene which we chose to follow. In fact, according to some criteria of their functioning genes are already known to occupy overlapping areas, in that they show the so-called position effect.

Thus we should beware of taking too simplified a view of the problem at issue. There may not merely be "wheels," but "wheels within wheels," in living matter, and if the recent studies of viruses by the X-ray diffraction method, as reported for instance by Astbury . . . and by Crowfoot . . . at the Seventh Genetics Congress, may be used as showing what structures might be found in the genetic material, according to the author's (1926 [1929]) conception of viruses as representing relatively free genes, then it is not unlikely that there are various grades of division and subdivision, each with its special kind of arrangement, between the relatively gross bodies [chromosomes] hitherto recognized by the biologist and the very much finer ones hitherto studied by the chemist. We cannot pretend to have answered such problems yet. They are, so far as geneticists are concerned, for the future, while for the present it is a step even to be able to recognize their existence. But that cannot, in my opinion, invalidate the fundamentals thus far established of what has been called "gene theory," even though many geneticists have in the past adopted a too hard and fast if not arbitrary conception of how much constitutes one gene. In this work of the future, it is to be hoped, the techniques of chemistry and physics will increasingly take part, along with those of genetics.

Perhaps the reader should be reminded here that, before the data to which we alluded above could be held applicable to problems of normal gene structure and evolution, the way had been cleared by the finding of evidence that the so-called mutations of *Oenothera* are atypical phenomena, not bearing directly on gene structure or on the usual process of evolution (see Muller 1917, 1918, 1923). Moreover, not only had Morgan and the other *Drosophila* workers noticed that the usual mutations they found affected individual genes, but evidence had also been adduced (e.g., Muller 1920) that they usually affected only one of of two identical genes of a diploid cell on a given occasion.

The latter result was, of course, to be expected of random encounters that have escaped cellular control—that is, expected under Troland's concept of "molecular chaos." It is to be noted that this is a very relative "chaos," however, much limited by the many factors which determine the nature, conditions, and positions of the gene material and the other substances present at the given place and time. It was also suggested (Muller 1928) that others of the pointwise mutations might be errors in the construction of a daughter gene, but the investigation of this possibility by a study of the relation of mutation frequency to number of cell generations elapsed, as influenced by "aging," ran into technical difficulties in the large-scale tests then conducted.

Shortly afterward, the study of mutations induced by ionizing radiation provided further evidence for the above-mentioned points concerning the gene material's segmentation and the spatial limitation of most of its mutations. It was also finally concluded, from the nonmosaic nature of *most* of the mutants, that, at least in *Drosophila* spermatozoa, the chromosome is composed of only one "chromonemal strand." Of course this has since been resolved into two, more elementary, strands of complementary structure. Hence, this evidence that nonmosaics are induced by radiation now means that if only one of the complements is changed at a given point, the influence of the other one tends somehow to effect the proper repair of the first before the change becomes a final one, or else—and much less likely to happen—a given change of the first tends to cause a complementary change in the other. Similar evidence, as yet unpublished, has not long ago been found by Rinehart and myself for certain of the so-called spontaneous mutations.

It should be noted in this connection that "hits" near enough together to damage two complementary strands at corresponding points coincidentally ought not to be too rare, but that there would be great difficulty in extending such coincidences to even more strands, of different but parallel chromonemas, and also in supposing a so-called domino effect on them. Thus the one-strand concept still appears valid, with the very important modification that a single chromonemal strand is on last analysis a double structure. It will be noted that Bonnevie's (1908) conception of a chromonemal basis of the chromosome had herein been accepted. In fact, it was accepted long ago (see Muller 1962: Article 1, citing a 1912 manuscript) by some of the younger *Drosophila* workers, as necessitated by the linkage evidence from that organism.

Troland's and my error in supposing that the self-specified reproduction of gene material leads directly to the construction of a like strand was caused, primarily, by the lesser complexity required by this method for the eventual production of like strands, which was known to be the ultimate result. Moreover, Troland had his comparison with crystallization in apparent support of this view, and I had that of synapsis —a phenomenon still to be deciphered in physicochemical terms. And in those times the relevant physics and chemistry were weak, and the personnel pursuing these subjects were with very rare exceptions, such as Troland himself, who died soon afterward, hard to interest in biology and reluctant to attempt an exposition of physics and chemistry to such novices as biologists. According to calculations of Jehle and his group (1950 *et seq.*), however, short-range specific attractions between like groups may after all play at least some subsidiary role in the reproduction and synapsis of gene material. On the other side, some quarter century ago several investigators, most notably Pauling and Delbrück (1940), independently advanced strong reasons why, on physicochemical grounds, a daughter strand should be complementary to the mother strand.

Physicochemical Discoveries Concerning the Gene Material

For well over half a century there had seemed no sound way of interpreting the faculties possessed by the gene material in terms of what had been learned by chemistry, even though some of the early chemists studying such nuclei as those of spermatozoa had had that object in mind. Nor could one soundly decide whether these faculties were attributable to the chromosome's nucleic acid, to a permanent portion of its otherwise variable protein, to these two in a necessary combination, or even to some of the small amount of unanalyzed residuum. Opinions varied accordingly.

This situation was improved by the finding of Stanley (1935) and his group in 1934 that tobacco mosaic virus, which obviously has the faculties of gene material, can be obtained in a viable, that is, infectious, form as a "crystallized" combination of (ribo)nucleic acid and protein. That the nucleic acid by itself could determine its specificity, although subsequently demonstrated by them, seemed at that time unlikely. The structure of nucleic acids was then thought to consist of monotonous repetitions of the same four nucleotides, always in the same arrangement—"tetranucleotides."

But a surprising discovery was forthcoming a decade later. This was the discovery by Avery, MacLeod, and McCarty (1944) that the material which Griffith (1928) had long previously found to carry over inherited traits from one strain of bacterium to another could still work effectively if freed of all or practically all constituents but its nucleic acid. Unfortunately, these investigators did not specify that the nucleic acid is by this result indicated to constitute the gene material. Instead they termed it "transforming substance," a term which would seem to imply that it induces directed mutations.

However, in my lecture "The gene" (1945, published 1947) I called attention to the remarkable genetic inference that could be drawn from their result. I also proposed that this gene material, in the form of a chromosome or chromosome part, penetrated the affected bacterium and there became implanted into its genome by crossing over. Lederberg (1947) meanwhile was discovering that conjugation and recombination can occur in bacteria. Moreover, the similar-seeming transformation just reported by Delbrück in phage, and still uninterpreted then, was, I suggested, probably an instance of crossing over in these so-called agents also. These interpretations were confirmed some time later.

It is true that certain biochemists had questioned whether the bacterial "transforming substance" had been completely freed of protein, but this objection was not long afterward eliminated. The time had come to question the validity of the tetranucleotide concept. Proceeding on the inference that it was invalid and that the specific, inherited arrangement of the nucleotides in line determined what specific effect on other materials in the cell any given portion of gene material has, one could ask how such an influence is possible for nucleic acids, since they have a composition so far different from that of known enzymes.

As a portion of the answer, Spiegelman (1945) and I (in "The gene"), independently and practically simultaneously, made the same suggestion. Taking into account the biochemical findings that had shown (since the work of Engelhardt and Ljubimova 1939) the exceedingly versatile roles played by nucleotide triphosphates in participating in so many cellular reactions in which a transfer of energy occurs and probably even (according to Lipmann 1941) in the linking together of amino acids into proteins, we each proposed that a chain of nucleotides having a given arrangement might somehow guide the course of this and their own linking and perhaps the course of other reactions also. Spiegelman, in fact, gave some experimental support, derived from yeast, to the conception. It still seems to me that there may be some truth in it. For, although the chained nucleotides are supposed ordinarily to have only one phosphate group, they should be able, on occasion, to become bound by their hydrogen bonds to individual triphosphate nucleotides, that is, to energy-carriers that can implement varied reactions.

Eight years after the paper by Avery, MacLeod, and McCarty, Hershey and Chase (1952) reported elegant investigations showing that the nucleic acid of phages, marked with radioactive phosphorus, became implanted in the bacteria which the phages infected. On the other hand, the protein of the phages, tagged with radioactive sulfur, gave no evidence of having entered. This seemed to clinch the argument for the nucleic acid constitution of the gene material.

Bearings of the Great Chemogenetic Integration and of "Prebiosis" Findings

As is now so well known, Watson and Crick (1953a,b) in the following year, thus guided as to choice of material, focused their study on chromosomal nucleic acid. Applying the X-ray diffraction findings of Wilkins, Stokes, and Wilson (1953) and other British physicists, especially Franklin and Gosling (1953), as well as the biochemists' data on relative nucleotide frequencies, and utilizing models to try out the varied spatial possibilities of atomic arrangement, they soon succeeded in inaugurating the great chemical revolution in basic genetics. Here at last was the concrete, detailed chemical structure of the gene material: nucleotides lined up into complementary strands, hydrogen-bonded with one another. And at once Watson and Crick pointed out how this structure would be able to guide the formation of copies of itself, next to itself, by piecemeal matching, no matter what the linear arrangement of the nucleotides happened to be. Moreover, even the main principle of mutation became clear. At its most "pointwise" (and probable) extreme, it would consist of the substitution, loss, or insertion, however accomplished, of a single nucleotide. Watson and Crick presented one way in which a single nucleotide substitution would be expected occasionally to occur.

It is evident that this linear arrangement of nucleotides constitutes, in actuality, what I had in 1926 ("speculatively," as some critics would consider) termed "the second kind of arrangement" in the gene material. At the same time, the individual nucleotides themselves, of their usually four types, constitute the first kind of arrangement, and this does in effect occupy other "dimensions."

It would be fatuous for me here to attempt to treat the flood of confirmations and extensions that since 1953 have been called forth by this breakthrough of genetics into biochemistry, or biochemistry into genetics—whichever one prefers to term it. The chemical identity of the gene material is no longer in doubt, its conformation has been worked out, and it is evident what main features of this conformation give the material its singular and truly fateful faculties—those of "reproducing itself" *and* its mutants, and of influencing other materials—the three faculties which, when in combination, underlie the possibility of all biological evolution.

Among the critical contributions of the new chemogenetics to the evidence that the gene material was the initiator and is still the organizing basis of life is of course the proof that even *in vitro* it can replicate itself—reproduce—if its aqueous medium is furnished with the following constituents: the four types of nucleotides composing the chain, in their high-energy (triphosphate) form, magnesium ions (usually), and just one enzyme. It is not a requirement that *in vitro* this enzyme be a specific one for the given arrangement of these nucleotides. However, the enzyme for DNA formation must, under most (not all) conditions studied, be different from that for RNA formation. Moreover, Haruna and Spiegelman (1965) have found the replication enzyme for certain viruses to be, under usual circumstances, species specific, as well as discriminatory against RNA fragments.

A still different enzyme is normally, but not always, needed to mediate the "transcription" (synthesis) of complementary RNA from a DNA model—a process which is, of course, a modified replication. DNA can also, on occasion, be transcribed from an RNA model. It is equally notable that DNA can sometimes serve, after the manner of RNA, for "translation" (protein synthesis), as found by McCarthy and Holland (1965). In addition, chains whose nucleotides have been modified in various ways, as by the addition of methyl or much larger groups, are capable of guiding replication and transcription. Doubtless the list of nucleotide modifications, including simplifications, which nevertheless allow some kind of replication will become much extended, and the effects of modification will be far better understood, as the functional significance of the various parts of the nucleotide molecule becomes further unravelled. And more primitive forerunners acting like nucleotides may well be found.

The results of recent studies, following up those of Urey and Miller (Urey 1952; Miller 1953; Miller and Urey 1959), of the organic molecules produced by the action of ultraviolet and ionizing radiation, heat, etc. on the constituents of the primitive earth's gaseous and liquid envelopes, are encouraging for an understanding of the physicochemical processes that led to the formation and successful operation of gene material. These constituents, as was realized some years ago— for example, in 1927 by America's then-leading astronomer, Henry Norris Russell—must have been mainly reduced ones prior to the release of abundant free oxygen by the photosynthetic activity of green organisms. Hence the atmospheric compounds consisted mainly of the hydrides of oxygen (i.e., water), of nitrogen (ammonia), and of carbon (methane). But in addition there must have been some cyanides, as well as (at least in the floors underlying the gaseous and liquid envelopes) some phosphates, some inorganic catalysts, and other important substances. The recent studies show that diverse organic molecules of fair complexity, some of them of types resembling those in cells, result from the action of heat, ultraviolet, and ionizing radiations on such mixtures. The products include not only varied carbohydrates and amino acids but also nuclein bases (e.g., adenine). The latter can then become combined, by similar processes, to form nucleosides and even nucleotides (Ponnamperuma, Sagan, and Mariner 1963).

Moreover, these combinations, as well as the amino acids, can under such pseudo-natural primitive conditions become polymerized to some extent. Although the action of the same forces would in time break all these compounds down again, the larger molecules would, as Sagan (1957 *et seq.*) has pointed out, be more resistant owing to the "cage effect" and could sink to shielded regions. There still larger and more varied combinations would tend to be formed and to accumulate up to a much higher equilibrium level, if indeed a permanent level was ever reached.

Thus the outline of "prebiotic synthesis" is no longer so vague or questionable as it was some fifteen years ago, even though it needs far more investigation. Various amino acids and nucleotides (and perhaps simpler compounds that we might term proto-nucleotides), some even as triphosphates, as well as, to a more limited extent, linear polymers of these, must have been present in the waters, already made.

However, it would be absurd to suppose that the nucleic acids, prior to an enormous course of natural selection among them, involving a great multitude of replications, would be able to guide the patterning or shaping of an actual polypeptide (protein) enzyme for replication of the nucleic acids. True, some of the ready-made polypeptides, despite their imprecision and the probable rarity of consistency among them, may have somehow assisted in the replication of nucleic acids, as may also some inorganic adsorbents and catalysts have done; clearly some still unknown conditions or materials must have facilitated this process, for otherwise the replication and selection that led to the nucleic acid's ability to build up or shape a polypeptide enzyme could never have taken place.

Possibly Jehle's (1965) suggestion may have value in this connection. This, following Wilkins' idea of chromosome structure, is to the effect that the two parallel, complementary nucleic acid helices, when they are tending to bind a polypeptide strand in the groove between them, are made into a stabler structure, and one in which the apposed bases chosen are surer to be complementary ones. If there were a tendency for some polypeptides to adhere to nucleic acids in this way, or in any way which afforded the nucleic acids some protection or other advantage, the mutant nucleic acids would (on replication) be selected for better base-choosing, shaping, and, if it were eventually possible, even patterning the synthesis of the adjoining polypeptides. The selection would take place in such wise that the adjoining polypeptides increasingly assisted the survival and replication of these nucleic acids.

That there can be such fairly direct, though doubtless loose, unions is indicated by a number of findings. One is the usual presence of protein strands in chromosomes, some of histone type, others of greater complication, and the attachment of protein envelopes to viruses, even though none of these seems to be built *in situ* or to match the whole chromosome part by part. A second is the temporary joining together of soluble RNA molecules with their appropriate amino acid activating enzymes and with sulfur. A third is the formation of protein antibodies against nucleic acids. A general method is thus suggested by which the first protein attachments, culminating in bit-by-bit linkings of amino acids, might have been achieved. But the attachment process would have been far more direct, and seemingly quite unlike, the present highly involved one. The road from the early process to the present one would be very long, and it is difficult for us at this point to conceive it in concrete terms, for reasons presently to be pointed out.

Evidence has accumulated that denies to proteins in themselves those two critical properties which, taken together, are most characteristic of nucleic acids—namely, that of being able to conduct or guide the formation of more structures built exactly after their own pattern, and that of retaining this ability even after having incurred a pattern change (not to speak of a protracted accumulation of diverse pattern changes). Earlier concepts of "plasma genes" which do not contain material like that in the chromosomes have evaporated as chloroplastids and related plastids, as well as some mitochondria, kinetosomes, etc., have been found to contain DNA. The construction of the great complex of specifically formed and cooperating enzymes and other materials in protoplasm has been increasingly tracked down to its inherited nucleic acids. There remains no valid empirical or theoretical basis for supposing that actual growth or reproduction, of a type allowing even the variants to grow or reproduce *as such,* could occur without a nucleic acid core to guide it.

It is even more unreasonable to suppose that before the operation of Darwinian natural selection any prebiotic processes happened to throw nucleotides together appropriately, along with just the right enzyme or enzymes, giving a combination which allowed these nucleic acids to multiply and *in addition* to guide the formation of more of this specific enzyme. Hence, our previous conclusion is reinforced—that the construction of increasing amounts of such enzymes must have come about through a natural selection among nucleic acid mutants which, in the meantime, could be replicated and which presented some lesser advantages along the road to the synthesis of the actual enzymes.

The Gene-Protein Circularity Puzzle

But an even more difficult group of questions must be faced. What kinds of mutational steps, offering advantages at the time they became established, could have led to the amazingly indirect, complicated, and *circular* method of protein synthesis by which today, in all cellular organisms alike, the specific patterns of the proteins synthesized are determined by those of the nucleic acids? Consider that the present method requires, just for the synthesis of the DNA-replicating enzyme, the prior presence in the DNA constitution of all the following regional patterns, or genes, for transcription into RNA. One is the gene for the messenger RNA by the "translation" of which the protein in question, here the DNA replicase, is synthesized. A second is the gene for the messenger RNA whereby there is synthesized the transcriptase enzyme needed for modeling *any* cellular RNA after a complementary DNA structure. Then there are the sets of ribosomal DNA's which determine the synthesis of the protein *in* the ribosomes. Not least are the DNA regions representing all the soluble RNA's (now some three scores), and finally the DNA regions for the score or more of amino acid activating enzymes. Each sRNA must at one place appropriately fit the triplet in the messenger that codes for the given amino acid, at another place be shaped to attach to just that amino acid, and have a stretch elsewhere appropriately sequenced to latch onto an enzyme of the type which is to carry that amino acid.

Each one of these DNA components, or *genes,* except that for the replicase messenger, must be present and able to function if there is not eventually to be a complete loss of the cell's ability to synthesize any protein whatever. And each of the genes, including that for the replicase messenger, must be present if any more DNA of any kind is to be synthesized. Furthermore, unless each of the proteins mentioned, except the replicase, is present initially, no protein whatever, replicase or any other, can continue to be formed; hence all DNA synthesis also must grind to a halt. Thus, in cells as we know them, including bacteria, the production of all these nucleic acids and proteins is completely interdependent, and intricate cooperation among them all is required for the cells', or cell-lines', continued life and for their further evolution.

This system is circular in various respects, but most basically because not only does the production of protein require the DNA but the production of DNA requires the protein, like the hen and the egg in the riddle of "which came first?" Nevertheless, as in the riddle, an outstanding difference remains: It is the specific sequences in the DNA which determine those in the proteins, and changes in the former result in corresponding changes in the latter, whereas the reverse relation does not hold any more than, in general, do *other* acquired characters become inherited. This circumstance clearly gives the gene material primacy. And although this does not solve the riddles of how this many-linked circular system evolved from one that at first must have been inordinately simpler and more direct, the consideration should here be emphasized that, as I italicized in 1918, ". . . *characters and factors* [i.e., genes] *which, when new, were originally merely an asset finally became necessary* because other necessary characters and factors had subsequently changed so as to be dependent on the former."

That the riddles can be broken is indicated by findings, some mentioned above, showing a greater "flexibility" (as Haruna and Spiegelman 1965 term it) in some features of the system than was earlier suspected. Especially significant among these features are the ability of RNA to serve for transcription into DNA and (on other occasions) that of DNA to serve for translation into proteins.

Other Problems Concerning the Gene Material
as Life's Organizer

Certainly the development of "degeneracy"—or, as I have preferred to put it, "synonymy"—in the messenger "code" and in the sRNA molecules is a secondary acquirement. This development is to be understood, as I pointed out in 1963 in a class lecture at Indiana University March 6 and in a seminar at the California Institute of Technology in June, to result from an insertional duplication ("repeat" formation) of a chromosome section. Such duplications must constitute the usual method, at least in cellular types, of increase in size, and eventually in complexity, of genomes (Bridges 1935; Muller 1935a,b, 1936, 1938; Offermann 1936). In the development of synonymy, the duplication would have included a gene for sRNA. Later, at just one of the two sites of this sRNA gene, a relatively innocuous mutation of a nucleotide would occur in its "coding" triplet. In some descendant carrying this, a complementary mutation must occur in a corresponding triplet that codes for a messenger. The mutant messenger would otherwise have malfunctioned but, finding itself provided with an appropriate mutant sRNA, it could now become "established." In this descendent strain, then, the new, synonymous sRNA would be actually necessary. It would be irreversible in the further evolution of the strain after the first such messenger mutation had been followed up by identical ones at other corresponding messenger sites.

Other geneticists, at nearly the same time or soon afterward, have independently expressed practically identical concepts. One of them, Sonneborn, has made, among other contributions, the critical one that synonymy is actually advantageous. It permits many mutants which otherwise would be "nonsense," or at least of a form not coding an amino acid, and which would therefore be deleterious or lethal, to cause instead the substitution of one amino acid for another in some protein—a natural experiment which would sometimes turn out favorably.

Moreover, it is quite possible that only one or two, or perhaps a few, of the twenty now-primary amino acids were components of the first useful proteins synthesized. And it is even possible that only a pair of base types (corresponding to a purine and a complementary pyrimidine) was present in the earliest replicating gene material. With fewer amino acids among which to choose, the "code" could have been of only one or two kinds of nucleotides. Perhaps the system did not yet discriminate well in regard to which purine was present, or which pyrimidine, or even between ribose and deoxyribose nucleotide or other nucleotide-like structures.

It should be taken into account also that the first enzymatically acting polypeptides must have been far simpler and shorter than those in present cells. The numerous seemingly "excess" parts of the enzymes of today must, to be persistent in evolution, serve as yet unsuspected, perhaps subtler, more sophisticated, and less often utilized functions. So too the genes were much simpler, shorter, and individually far less versatile in their influences, at the earlier stages of evolution of the gene material.

As with proteins but much more so, in the evolution of gene material demarcated into actual genes, an enormous increase in gene size, complexity, and versatility of action, including pleiotropy, has occurred. In the RNA virus which causes satellite tobacco necrosis (STNV), the gene for virus coat protein, which was recently caused to undergo translation *in vitro* by Spiegelman's group (Clark *et al.* 1965) and which constitutes the only gene material of that virus, contains, they calculate, about 1200 nucleotide pairs in line, the coat protein correspondingly having about 400 amino acids. This gene (no doubt degenerate, however, rather than merely primitive) should be contrasted with those of more and more complex forms of life, such as bacteria, *Drosophila,* and mammals. It is much shorter than the bacterial genes for which estimates have been made; these in turn are much shorter than *Drosophila* genes of average size, and the latter than mammalian ones, as discussed below.

My re-estimates of gene number in *Drosophila*—namely, some 10,000, based on several different criteria—when divided into the total number of nucleotides, based on DNA content, make its gene nearly an order of magnitude greater than that of STNV just cited. Mammalian gene-number estimates—those by Muller (1950), those based on more recent data on the frequency of spontaneous mutations at specific loci in relation to the maximum mutational load that could be carried, and those from data on the frequencies of X-ray induced mutations at specific loci as compared with that of total induced lethals—agree on a maximum of not much more than 30,000. This number, divided into the four billion figure for the approximate number of nucleotide pairs per genome, gives about 133,000 pairs for the average-sized gene, over one magnitude above that for *Drosophila* and some two magnitudes above the number for the STNV gene.

What do these vast gene sizes, apparently resulting in polypeptides having, on the average, over 30,000 amino acids and molecular weights of over three million, really signify? Are these genes subdivided into "subgenes," as supposed by Serebrovsky (1929), perhaps by lesser "punctuation marks"? The bacteria in their metabolic processes must already be enormously complicated. But the higher organisms are so much more so, not only in "structure" but also in the biochemical interadjustments and inner workings and development of their multitudes of different parts, as modern studies increasingly emphasize, that a few tens of thousands of proteins, by themselves, might hardly be enough. As shown by Jacob and Monod (1961) in bacteria, there are also parts of the gene material that appear not to synthesize protein, yet to act as regulators of other gene material which does so. There should be far more, and far more varied, processes of this kind, and even systems of processes, as well as gene material underlying them, in higher forms. Moreover, it is ever more evident that, in both *Drosophila* and man, a single gene has many more effects, some very subtle, than its conspicuous ones (see, for example, Muller and Kaplan 1966).

As the genome content increased, natural selection still had to act by choosing between entire individuals. Hence the mutation frequency per nucleotide per number of its replications, and still more so per unit of time as the duration of the generation increased, had to be brought ever lower, to avoid species extinction through the sheer pressure of "spontaneous" mutation. In *Drosophila* the mutation frequency has already attained the low rate *per nucleotide* of only one mutation, including errors in replication, in about thirty billion cell generations or, roughly, sixty million years. The corresponding figure for mammals is something like one in four hundred billion cell generations, or, for man, not far from that number of years. This incredible accuracy in matching complements, and in stability in general, bespeaks the existence of extraordinary biological mechanisms, based on the gene material. These mechanisms are among the usually ignored processes that higher forms had to evolve. The earliest gene material only had to be accurate and stable enough to show a net increase, per replication, of the minuscule parental type (the rest of the progeny being mutants or fatalities), and it probably did not succeed for some time in doing better than that.

Well recognized, of course, is the need for chemogenetic investigation of the more obvious of the later accomplishments of the gene material. However, these matters are more available for study than are the early mechanisms and are being actively pursued. A discussion of them is outside the province of this chapter.

Life Has Meant Evolution the Hard Way

A personal objective of this chapter has been to put together a connected account of my own ventures in the quest concerning gene material, before the great chemogenetic breakthrough. These ideas have in the main been presented in the form of scattered papers and seminar or conference lectures, even scattered individual remarks, of a seemingly "speculative" nature. However, although never gathered together in a book, and now very rightly submerged in the new knowledge, they have ever since their inception been taught in a connected form to my students, and through this route, as well as through the papers and the non-class lectures, they may have had some influence on the course of further developments in the subject made by others. At any rate, the main ideas seem to me to be still valid, as far (or for as short a way) as they went.

Meanwhile, there has been a marked change in the attitude taken by geneticists and other biologists in regard to these matters. This change may be illustrated by the following personal incidents of long ago. As I was leaving the podium after my 1921 talk at the Naturalists' symposium, the chairman, the noted paleontologist Henry Fairfield Osborn, commented to me ironically, "I'm glad you have a sense of humor, Muller." As for my 1926 talk, the organizer of the First International Congress of Plant Sciences, B. M. Duggar, had tried to induce me to change the wording "the basis" to "a basis" in my title, "The gene as the basis of life." Later, at the symposium itself, in the talk given just before mine by the noted geneticist E. M. East, a main theme was that the so-called gene should only be regarded as a mental construction—one which has, however, proved to have its use in predicting the results of crosses. Yet, in self-accusation, I must add that, despite my own convictions concerning the gene *material*, I had never suspected that its actual structure, and even the connection between this and its remarkable faculties, would be worked out within my own day.

In closing, let us briefly review the main thesis—that life as we know it, if stripped of all its superstructures, lies in the three faculties possessed by the gene material. These may be defined as, firstly, the faculty of self-specification, after its own pattern, of new material produced by it or under its guidance; secondly, that of performing this operation even when it has itself undergone a great succession of permanent pattern changes which, taken in their totality, can be of a practically unlimited diversity; thirdly, that of significantly and (for different cases) diversely affecting, through these changes, other materials and, therewith, its own success in producing further life.

These three faculties are, it will be noticed, just the same, in essence, as were subsumed under the mechanism of evolution by natural selection as originally understood by Darwin (1859). In past expositions of this evolution the first of these faculties was represented by multiplication, the second by heritable variations, and the third by the resulting differences in the type and degree of adaptation, that is, of fitness for multiplication in one or another environment. Thus, the "stripped down" definition of a living thing here offered may be paraphrased: that which possesses the potentiality of evolving by natural selection. For evolution to occur or, indeed, for life itself to exist, nothing else is needed than these three faculties in combination and, eventually, facilties and conditions for exercising them. The gene material alone, of natural materials, possesses these faculties, and it is therefore legitimate to call it living material, the present-day representative of the first life.

Conceivably, under the different conditions of other worlds, at other temperatures, other substances than nucleic acids, perhaps in other solvents than water, could form a different kind of gene material which, finding the facilities needed, would undergo its own "biological" evolution. Yet even that paralife would be based on the possession, by the material which initiated and organized it, of the same three faculties, made possible by two analogous kinds of arrangement in its structure, and on natural selection.

Summary

Outstanding nineteenth and twentieth century developments in the evidence, conceptions, and speculations concerning the origin and basis of life have been considered, with special reference to whether primacy in these respects should be attributed to some form of "protoplasm" in general, or of "gene material," or whether neither of these should be considered to have primacy over the other.

The author's view of the gene material's having primacy (first expressed definitively in 1926) has been defended. According to this view (as it may today be stated), any living thing, stripped of all its nonessentials, must only have (or have in its forebears had) the following three faculties: the faculty whereby it can form more bodies after its own pattern; that whereby, in this process, changes, even indefinitely cumulative ones, can occur, which nevertheless allow the changed successors to form more bodies of these still newer types; that whereby these different kinds of successors can differently and significantly affect (or be affected by) materials or conditions other than their own and can thus (when in given surroundings) possess different possibilities for the continuance and extension of their own or still later successor types. Anything having the above three faculties and the external facilities and conditions for exercising them will possess the potentiality of unlimited evolution by natural selection.

The gene material, it is argued, has these faculties, and primitive conditions afforded it enough means of exercising them to allow it to evolve protoplasm that served it. That is, those descendants of it must have prevailed that altered other materials so as to form them into a surrounding, accessory system, which with increasing effectiveness fostered the self-reproduction of that gene material. In so doing, the accessory system would also be led to foster, under the control of the gene material, the formation, through metabolic processes, of correspondingly more of its own organization.

Thus the gene material itself has the properties of life. This may be epitomized by a statement that *the criterion for* any material's having *life is* whether or not it has the potentiality, at least under some circumstances, of *evolution by* Darwinian *natural selection.* (The words in italics, alone, form a simpler statement.)

The great modern findings concerning the chemical structure and workings of the nucleic acids and of other material of organisms, as well as findings concerning prebiotic possibilities of synthesis of organic materials, have been held to substantiate strongly the above concepts. Included here is the concept of the uniqueness of structure of gene material, since even in diverse cytoplasmic structures (including invaders) having the three faculties nucleic acid has been found to be present.

It has been pointed out, however, that these modern findings also raise certain new, great, and difficult problems (as yet not widely enough recognized as problems). Two of these have been herein discussed at some length. One is concerned with how the protoplasmic organization common to all cellular organisms, with its complicated circularity of gene-protein production, evolved. The other deals with how the primitive gene material itself became further organized and stabilized, until the enormous genes of higher forms were produced. Research directed toward the solution of these two questions is urgently needed.

Addendum

In 1965 two books, both based on symposia relevant to the foregoing discussions, the first held in 1963 and the second in 1964, were published by the Academic Press, New York. Because of a lengthy illness, I learned about these books only after the present article had been sent to press.

The first book, sponsored by the National Aeronautics and Space Administration and edited by S. W. Fox, *The Origins of Prebiological Systems,* contains much chemical information on reactions that may have supplied materials for the formation and maintenance of the first life. Insofar as the 34 participants were concerned with life's nature, however, only a handful of them—including among the most notable of these exceptions Haldane and Schramm—took a position essentially like that herein expressed. Many of the others espoused the proto-plasmic-primacy view still advocated (although with some recent concessions concerning the role of gene material) by Oparin, himself a participant, who received much acclamation.

The second book, *Evolving Genes and Proteins,* records a symposium sponsored by the National Science Foundation; it is edited by V. Bryson and H. J. Vogel. It presents a wealth of important biochemical researches which, with some outstanding exceptions, deal with the biological stages that followed the adoption of the main features of the cycle of nucleic acid-protein synthesis now in use. Among these exceptions is a chapter by Alexander Rich, who makes suggestions similar to those of the present article concerning the genesis of replicating nucleic acids and of the evolution of their present method of synthesizing proteins and themselves. The chapter by the late David Bonner and his colleagues shows one way in which genes of higher organisms have become more highly organized and versatile, by an advantageous coalescence that has nevertheless been sparing of material. Among the nearly 200 participants, there were few who expressly challenged the position that the gene material is primary in life, but this subject was seldom discussed except by implication.

Literature Cited

AVERY, O. T., C. M. MacLEOD, AND M. McCARTY, 1944. Studies on the chemical nature of the substance inducing transformation of pneumococcal types. J. Exp. Med. **79:** 137–158.

BONNEVIE, CHRISTINA, 1908. Chromosomen von *Ascaris, Allium,* und *Amphiuma,* etc. Arch. Zellforsch. **1:** 450–514.

BRIDGES, C. B., 1935. Salivary chromosome maps. J. Hered. **26:** 60–64.

CLARK, J. M., JR., A. Y. CHANG, S. SPIEGELMAN, AND M. E. REICHMANN, 1965. The *in vitro* translation of a monocistronic message. Proc. Nat. Acad. Sci. U.S. **54:** 1193–1197.

DARWIN, C., 1859. *On the Origin of Species by Natural Selection; or The Preservation of Favoured Races in the Struggle for Life.* J. Murray, London.

DRIESCH, H., 1894. *Analytische Theorie der Organischen Entwicklung.* Engelmann, Leipzig.

ENGELHARDT, W. A., AND M. N. LJUBIMOVA, 1939. Myosin and adenosine-triphosphatase. Nature 144: 668–669.

FRANKLIN, R. E., AND R. G. GOSLING, 1953. Molecular configuration in sodium thymonucleate. Nature 171: 740–741.

GRIFFITH, F., 1928. The significance of pneumococcal types. J. Hyg. 27: 113–159.

HAECKEL, E., 1866. Entstehung der ersten Organismen. *Generelle Morphologie der Organismen,* vol. I, pp. 167–190. George Reimer, Berlin.

HAGEDOORN, A. L., 1911. Autokatalytical substances the determinants for the inheritable characters: A biochemical theory of inheritance and evolution. Vorträge Aufsätze Entwicklungsmech. Organismen 12: 1–35.

HARUNA, I., AND S. SPIEGELMAN, 1965. Recognition of size and sequence by an RNA replicase. Proc. Nat. Acad. Sci. U.S. 54: 1189–1193.

HERSHEY, A. D., AND M. CHASE, 1952. Independent functions of viral protein and nucleic acid in growth of bacteriophage. J. Gen. Physiol. 36: 39–56.

HERTWIG, O., 1884. Das Problem der Befruchtung und der Isotropie des Eies, eine Theorie der Vererbung. Jena. Z. Naturwiss. 18: 21–23.

HOROWITZ, N. H., 1945. On the evolution of biochemical synthesis. Proc. Nat. Acad. Sci. U.S. 31: 153–157.

JACOB, F., AND J. MONOD, 1961. Genetic regulatory mechanisms in the synthesis of proteins. J. Mol. Biol. 3: 318–356.

JEHLE, H., 1950. Specificity of interaction between identical molecules. Proc. Nat. Acad. Sci. U.S. 36: 238–246.

———, 1965. Replication of double-strand nucleic acids. Proc. Nat. Acad. Sci. U.S. 53: 1451–1455.

KÖLLIKER, A. VON, 1885. Die Bedeutung der Zellkerne für die Vorgänge der Vererbung. Z. wiss. Zool. 42: 1–46.

LEDERBERG, J., 1947. Gene recombination and linked segregations in *Escherichia coli.* Genetics 32: 505–525.

LIPMANN, F., 1941. Metabolic generation and utilization of phosphate bond energy. Advance. Enzymol. 1: 99–162.

LOEB, J., 1906. *The Dynamics of Living Matter.* Columbia Univ. Press, New York.

McCARTHY, B. J., AND J. J. HOLLAND, 1965. Protein synthesis with single-stranded DNA as a template. Science 150: 378.

MILLER, S. L., 1953. A production of amino acids under possible primitive earth conditions. Science 117: 528–529.

MILLER, S. L., AND H. C. UREY, 1959. Organic compound synthesis on the primitive earth. Science 130: 245–251.

MULLER, H. J., 1917. An *Oenothera*-like case in *Drosophila.* Proc. Nat. Acad. Sci. U.S. 3: 619-626.

———, 1918. Genetic variability, twin hybrids and constant hybrids, in a case of balanced lethal factors. Genetics 3: 422–499.

———, 1920. Further changes in the white-eye series of *Drosophila* and their bearing on the manner of occurrence of mutation. J. Exp. Zool. **31**: 443–473.

——, 1922. Variation due to change in the individual gene. Amer. Natur. **56**: 32–50.

——, 1923. Mutation. *Eugenics, Genetics and the Family,* vol. I, pp. 106–112. Proc. 3rd Int. Eugen. Congr. (New York, 1921). Williams and Wilkins, Inc., Baltimore.

——, 1928. The measurement of gene mutation rate in *Drosophila,* its high variability, and its dependence upon temperature. Genetics **13**: 279-357.

——, 1929. The gene as the basis of life. Proc. Int. Congr. Plant Sci. (Ithaca, 1926) **1**: 897–921.

——, 1935a. A viable two-gene deficiency phaenotypically resembling the corresponding hypomorphic mutations. J. Hered. **26**: 469–478.

——, 1935b. The origination of chromatin deficiencies as minute deletions subject to insertion elsewhere. Genetica **17**: 237–252.

——, 1936. Bar duplication. Science **83**: 528–530.

——, 1938. The remaking of chromosomes. Collecting Net, Woods Hole **8**: 183–195.

——, 1940. An analysis of the process of structural change in chromosomes of *Drosophila.* J. Genet. **40**: 1–66.

——, 1941. The threads that weave evolution. Trans. New York Acad. Sci. Ser. II **3**: 117–125.

——, 1947. The gene. Proc. Roy. Soc. B **134**: 1–37.

——, 1950. Our load of mutations. Amer. J. Hum. Genet. **2**: 111–176.

——, 1962. *Studies in Genetics.* Indiana Univ. Press, Bloomington.

MULLER, H. J., AND W. D. KAPLAN, 1966. Dosage compensation of *Drosophila* and mammals as showing the accuracy of the normal type. Genet. Res. **7** (in press).

OFFERMANN, C. A., 1936. Branched chromosomes as symmetrical duplications. J. Genet. **32**: 103–116.

OPARIN, A. I., 1938. *The Origin of Life.* The Macmillan Co., New York (1957 ed., Academic Press, New York).

PAULING, L., AND M. DELBRÜCK, 1940. The nature of the intermolecular forces operative in biological processes. Science **92**: 77–79.

PONNAMPERUMA, C., C. SAGAN, AND R. MARINER, 1963. Synthesis of adenosine triphosphate under possible primitive earth conditions. Nature **199**: 222–226.

ROUX, W., 1883. *Über die Bedeutung der Kernteilungsfiguren.* Engelmann, Leipzig.

RUSSELL, H. N., R. S. DUGAN, AND J. Q. STEWART, 1927. *Astronomy.* Ginn and Co., Boston.

SAGAN, C., 1957. Radiation and the origin of the gene. Evolution **11**: 40–55.

SEREBROVSKY, A. S., 1929. A general scheme for the origin of mutations. Amer. Natur. **63**: 374–378.

SPIEGELMAN, S., 1945. The physiology and genetic significance of enzymatic adaptation. Ann. Missouri Bot. Garden **32**: 139–163.

STANLEY, W. M., 1935. Isolation of a crystalline protein possessing the properties of tobacco-mosaic virus. Science **81**: 644–645.

STRASBURGER, E., 1884. *Neue Untersuchungen über den Befruchtungsvorgang bei den Phanerogamen, als Grundlage für eine Theorie der Zeugung.* Gustav Fischer, Jena.

TROLAND, L. T., 1914. The chemical origin and regulation of life. Monist **22**: 92–134.

——, 1916. The enzyme theory of life. Cleveland Med. J. **15**: 377–387.

——, 1917. Biological enigmas and the theory of enzyme action. Amer. Natur. **51**: 321–350.

UREY, H. C., 1952. *The Planets.* Yale Univ. Press, New Haven.

WATSON, J. D., AND F. H. C. CRICK, 1953a. A structure for deoxyribose nucleic acid. Nature **171**: 737–738.

WATSON, J. D., AND F. H. C. CRICK, 1953b. Genetical implications of the structure of deoxyribonucleic acid. Nature **171**: 964–967.

WEISMANN, A., 1883. *Über die Vererbung.* Gustav Fischer, Jena.

WILKINS, H. F., A. R. STOKES, AND H. R. WILSON, 1953. Molecular structure of deoxypentose nucleic acids. Nature **171**: 738–740.

WILSON, E. B., 1896. *The Cell in Development and Inheritance.* Columbia Univ. Press, New York. (1966 reprinting, with 30-page Introduction by H. J. Muller, Johnson Reprint Corp., New York.)

Index